D1179881

The Inorganic Raw Materials of Antiquity

The Inorganic Raw Materials of Antiquity

Andrée Rosenfeld

FREDERICK A. PRAEGER, *Publishers*
NEW YORK · WASHINGTON

BOOKS THAT MATTER
Published in the United States of America in 1965
by Frederick A. Praeger, Inc., Publishers
111 Fourth Avenue, New York 3, N.Y.

Library of Congress Catalog Card Number: 65–24572

Printed in Great Britain

Contents

PREFACE xi

INTRODUCTION 1

1 ROCKS AND MINERALS 5

Abundance of Elements and Minerals – Igneous, Sedimentary and Metamorphic Rocks – The Classification of Minerals – Tests for the Identification of Minerals in Hand Specimens

2 THE ROCK FORMING MINERALS 42

Quartz – Silicates – Hydrous Silicates – Non-Silicates

3 THE IGNEOUS AND METAMORPHIC ROCKS 70

Igneous Rocks – Metamorphic Rocks

4 THE PRODUCTS OF WEATHERING 97

The Insoluble Products of Weathering – The Alteration of Sediments – The Soluble Products of Weathering – Deposits of Organic Origin

5 THE METALS OF ANTIQUITY 129

Ore Deposits – The Extraction of Metals from their Ores – Some Metalliferous Minerals not Used as Ores

6 THE MANUFACTURE OF TOOLS, WEAPONS AND ORNAMENTS 157

Tools – Weapons – Vessels – Beads, Amulets, Jewellery and Other Small Objects – Pigments

7 BUILDING MATERIALS, MINING AND QUARRYING 186

Building Materials – Mining and Quarrying – Conclusions

8 THE IDENTIFICATION AND DATING OF ROCKS AND MINERALS 207

Patination and Corrosion – Rocks and Minerals as Evidence for Trade and Exploration – Dating Methods

APPENDIX 235

BIBLIOGRAPHY 239

INDEX 241

List of Illustrations

between pages 114–115

1 Microphotographs of thin sections of igneous, sedimentary and metamorphic rocks. (*By permission of Birkbeck College, University of London*)

2 Granite showing equigranular texture of a coarse grained rock. (*By permission of Birkbeck College, University of London*)

3 Quartz Porphyry. (*By permission of Birkbeck College, University of London*)

4 Porphyritic Granite. (*By permission of Birkbeck College, University of London*)

5 Pebble conglomerate. (*By permission of Birkbeck College, University of London*)

6 Predynastic Egyptian (Amratian) disc mace-head of diorite. (*By permission of Petrie Collection, University College London*)

7 Blade of spherulitic obsidian

8 Vesicular basalt. (*By permission of Birkbeck College, University of London*)

9 Gneisses. (*By permission of Birkbeck College, University of London*)

10 Predynastic Egyptian (Gerzean) vase of breccia. (*By permission of Petrie Collection, University College London*)

11 Predynastic Egyptian palette of slate in the form of an hippopotamus. (*By permission of Petrie Collection, University College London*)

12 Archaic Egyptian (Dynasty I–II) dish of banded calcite known as 'Egyptian alabaster' (*By permission of Petrie Collection, University College London*)

13 Archaic Egyptian (Dynasty I–II) cup of felspar porphyry. (*By permission of Petrie Collection, University College London*)

14 Prehistoric Sickles. (*By permission of the Trustees of the British Museum London*)

15 Axes. (*By permission of the Trustees of the British Museum London*)

16 Bronze dagger and sword and imitations in flint from the Early Bronze Age in Denmark. (*By permission of The Danish National Museum*)

17 Oval pedestal dish of clear Glass from the Roman period in Egypt. (*By permission of Petrie Collection, University College London*)

18 Miniature bottle of variegated black and white Glass with appliqué handles, probably of Saitic date. (*By permission of Petrie Collection, University College London*)

19 Blue faience Ushabti figure of Queen Henūt-tawy of Dynasty XXI. (*By permission of Petrie Collection, University College London*)

20 Pink granite statue of Rameses II, the high state official, from Memphis in Egypt (XIXth Dynasty). (*By permission of the Trustees of the British Museum London*)

21 Marble statue of 'crouching Aphrodite' from Rhodes. (*Hirmer Fotoarchiv*)

22 The unfinished obelisk at Aswan. (*By permission of Paul Popper*)

23 Flint handaxes. (*By permission of the Trustees of the British Museum London*)

24 Fragment of coarse sandstone (millstone grit) weathered under acid, humid soil conditions. (*By permission of Dr I. W. Cornwall*)

25 The effects of salt infestation on a Palestinian pot. (*By permission of H. W. M. Hodges*)

26 Thin sections of Windmill Hill pottery. (*By permission of H. W. M. Hodges*)

Figures

1 Diagram to show igneous intrusions and volcanic rocks 10
2 Structures of chemically inactive and active substances 15
3 Ionic bonding of chlorine and sodium atoms 16
4 Homopolar bonding of hydrogen atoms 18
5 SiO_4 tetrahedron 21
6 Single chain structure of silicate tetrahedra 22
7 Double chain structure of silicate tetrahedra 22
8 Sheet structure of silicate tetrahedra 24
9 Crystals of the cubic system 27
10 Crystal of the tetragonal system 28
11 Crystals of the orthorhombic system 29
12 Crystals of the monoclinic system 30
13 Crystal of the hexagonal system 31
14 Palaeolithic flint flake showing conchoidal fracture 33
15 Specimen of galena showing cubic crystals with cleavage parallel to the cube face 34
16 Specimen of fluorspar showing cubic crystals with cleavage planes along the diagonals of the cube faces 34
17 Specimen of barytes showing tabular habit 35
18 Specimen of fibrous gypsum 36
19 Specimen of hematite showing reniform habit 37
20 Crystals of quartz 44
21 Crystal of orthoclase 46
22 Twinning of felspar crystals 47
23 Tourmaline crystal 57
24 Calcite crystal: dog-tooth spar 107
25 Calcite crystal: nail-head spar 108
26 Specimen of gypsum 115
27 Diagrammatic section across a copper lode 134
28 Oxidation curves for carbon and some metals smelted in antiquity 150
29 Oxidation curves for carbon and some metals not known in antiquity 152
30 Diagrammatic section through the ore deposit at Laurium 200

Tables

1 Abundance of elements 7

2 Composition of sea water 8

3 Ionic sizes of the common elements 19

4 The rock forming minerals 73

5 Classification of igneous rocks, 1 74

6 Classification of igneous rocks, 2 75

7 Grain size of sediments 99

Preface

THE NEED for this book was felt as a result of teaching a course on 'the raw materials of ancient man' to postgraduate archaeology students. While teaching this course it was found that books to which the students can be referred treated the subject of petrology, either from a purely academic standpoint or, if written with a practical bias, were aimed at students of modern economic geology. The subject of ancient economic geology has never been clearly outlined. Although there are some excellent studies of ancient materials, these are either concerned with a single region or with only a few particular materials. There is no book which adequately serves as an introduction to the subject of identifying and understanding the mineral resources of antiquity.

It also became clear as a result of experience in dealing with samples sent in for identification from excavations, that there is a real need for archaeologists in the field to be able to identify adequately the type of materials uncovered and to assess their possible significance before enlisting specialist examination. Not only the specialist's sanity, but also the accuracy of his analysis can only benefit from questions such as, 'I have a piece of igneous rock from the middle of Wiltshire; this must be a foreigner, where does it come from?', or, 'Are the green stains on these bones from copper? I enclose known copper-stained bones for comparison', rather than 'This is a red clay from my site, what is it?'

In a sense, therefore, this book is the result of two different needs: those of the trainee archaeologist, and those of the archaeologist in the field. There is, however, a further important application for the subject of this book, in connection with the academic study of ancient technologies.

The first part of this book is devoted to a description of the minerals and rocks which archaeologists are likely to encounter. The theoretical basis of rock and mineral identification is only briefly outlined, and the emphasis throughout the first part of the book is on the macroscopic description of rocks and minerals. Microscopic and chemical techniques of investigation are not dealt with. The detailed descriptions of individual minerals and rocks are intended as a useful reference work which should be helpful, also, in the more practical aspect of actual macroscopic rock identification. For macroscopic analysis, however, which is based largely on description rather than on quantitative measurement, no amount of text can fully replace the knowledge gained from the practical experience of handling rock and mineral samples. In the second part of the book, where the applications of petrology to archaeology are discussed, a knowledge of the concepts and terms discussed in chapters 1 to 5 is assumed.

The discussion in chapter 6 of the uses of rocks and minerals in antiquity is general, but numerous examples from antiquity have been drawn to illustrate the theoretical points made. This chapter is, however, not intended as a work of reference, and it is not a comprehensive summary of the materials used in antiquity.

Finally, the last chapter illustrates the extent to which the more specialist analyses of inorganic materials may benefit various aspects of archaeological studies.

I should like to record my gratitude to colleagues who have helped me in the preparation of this book: to Professor A. Knopf who has given his permission to reproduce in an abbreviated form (in Appendix 1) his table of mineral identification; to the late Professor F. E. Zeuner and Dr I. W. Cornwall who persuaded me to undertake the task of writing this book; and to Mr H. W. M. Hodges and Dr B. Roberts who have given so much of their time and thought to discussions about various sections of the book.

I am deeply indebted to Dr B. Roberts for his invaluable assistance in selecting for photography rock specimens from the geological collection of Birkbeck College, London, and to Mr H. S. Smith in selecting objects from the Petrie Collection,

University College, London. The excellent drawings in this book are the careful work of Messrs Peter Pratt and Martin Weaver.

Finally, I also want to express my gratitude to Dr Peter J. Ucko for his reading and invaluable criticism of an amorphous manuscript. Without his help and logic the book would not have crystallized into its present form.

British Museum
October, 1964

ANDRÉE ROSENFELD

Introduction

THE artefacts most commonly recovered from any archaeological excavation are made of inorganic materials: rocks, baked clay, metals, glass, etc. Only where special conditions of preservation prevail are a wide variety of organic materials recovered but, in most regions, the preservation of organic materials other than bone or ivory is exceptional. Much archaeological research has of necessity, therefore, concentrated on the study of the inorganic artefacts manufactured in ancient cultures.[1]

That this book is solely devoted to a discussion of ancient materials of mineral origin should not be interpreted as a denial of the importance of organic materials to ancient peoples. In fact there is no doubt that both animal and vegetable substances were, at all times, extremely important raw material sources to ancient communities. In many cases these organic materials were used for more varied and equally important purposes as the inorganic materials. In the absence of direct evidence for the use of such organic materials, however, their use has had to be inferred from studies of the inorganic artefacts used to shape them. This archaeological fact is the justification of the limited coverage of this book which does not in itself seek to exaggerate the importance in antiquity of inorganic over organic materials.

All too often archaeologists are content to classify the inorganic materials which they uncover as 'stone', 'metal', or 'pottery', etc. There are, however, at least three good reasons for the archaeologist to study and identify his inorganic materials in more detail. The complexity of classification and detail of identification

[1] Throughout this book *prehistory* has been used to refer to the preliterate societies of the ancient world, and *antiquity* to refer to any society of the ancient world whether non-literate or literate.

needed at any particular time depend largely on which of the three reasons is under consideration. It is the properties of materials worked which have to be considered when dealing with technological problems. In this context, therefore, identification and classification of various rocks or metals need only be taken so far as to distinguish materials of different physical properties. In considering problems of ancient trade or travel it is the recognition of ancient sources of materials which is the aim. The solution of these archaeological problems depends on accurate and detailed identification of the composition and texture of inorganic materials. The third archaeological problem which can be influenced by petrological studies, is that of dating. Several archaeological dating techniques depend on the availability of suitable samples of inorganic materials. To be reliable, the samples submitted for dating must be identified and examined with sufficient accuracy to ascertain the extent of any alteration or contamination.

A wide variety of inorganic materials were known in antiquity and used for many purposes, and these materials were often carefully selected to take advantage of their physical properties. A knowledge of the physical properties of rocks, metals, and other materials, together with an understanding of the technological processes involved, is not only essential to the archaeologist's understanding of how artefacts were made, but is also invaluable for his appreciation of their effectiveness as tools and weapons, etc. The recognition of the properties of a material from which an artefact is made is, however, not only important in the context of function but in the context of form. The properties of materials often strongly influenced the final shape of an artefact so that they are an essential factor in the archaeologist's study of typology.

In antiquity the choice of materials used for any one purpose was limited by the technological capabilities of the people concerned; thus, during the Palaeolithic period the rocks used were those which could be worked by flaking, whereas in the Neolithic period, with the development of grinding and polishing techniques for working stone, a wider range of rocks became available. Later still, with the techniques of smelting, the use of metals led to widespread and fundamental cultural changes.

Of course, throughout antiquity technological limitations were such that only surface rocks could be exploited, for it is only with the development of advanced geological techniques that deep-seated mineral resources can be detected and exploited. Thus, even when minerals or rocks were mined in antiquity, such mines were restricted to localities where there were surface indications of the occurrence of the materials required. Very early in prehistory, however, the restrictions on available raw materials imposed by local geology were overcome in part, at least, by trade or travel.

Using techniques of stylistic and typological analysis, the archaeologist also requires a knowledge of rock identification to recognize imported materials. To trace the source of imports may require detailed petrological identification and analysis beyond the scope of the non-specialist. It is, however, important that the archaeologist should be able both to recognize for himself which materials to submit for specialist analysis and to assess for himself the significance of the petrological problems involved in specialist analysis.

In the context of dating problems, the archaeologist should also be able to assess the suitability of samples for any given dating technique, and be able to assess the reliability of the dates obtained by such dating methods. In view of the fact that both the techniques of dating obsidian artefacts and of radioactive dating of recent rocks need further refinement before they can be considered really reliable, this is an important consideration.

CHAPTER ONE

Rocks and Minerals

IN COMMON parlance, the words stone, rock, and mineral are frequently used, rather loosely, to refer to the various solid constituents of the earth's surface. In the strict sense of petrology, however, these terms are well defined, for rocks and minerals refer to quite distinct aspects of the earth's crust. The word stone is never used in a petrological sense, for all the solid inorganic parts of the earth's crust are classed either as rocks or as minerals. A stone is simply a piece of rock, and used as an adjective the word is useful to designate certain materials. Thus in the manufacture of artefacts, for instance, 'stone tools' can be contrasted with 'metal tools'.

Rocks are the more or less homogeneous solid units making up the earth's surface. The term rock, therefore, covers not only consolidated materials such as granite, basalt, or limestone, but also the unconsolidated sediments such as the vast expanses of desert sand, and the thick deposits of clay in wide river valleys. The composition of different rocks varies considerably, and a closer examination of any rock will show that it consists of a close aggregate of fragments of distinct chemical composition and structure. The same chemical substances occur in rocks of quite different types in varying proportions and combinations; they are the *minerals* or *mineral species*. Hence a rock is made up of an aggregate of minerals. The majority of rocks are made up of a number of different minerals, but exceptionally, the rock may consist of a single mineral species – for instance, a pure white marble consists of calcite only.

Minerals are clearly defined substances, which have a constant chemical *structure*. The chemical composition of the mineral may vary somewhat within a given structure (this will be discussed more fully below). The atoms of a mineral are stacked according to a regular pattern, and under suitable conditions this results in the formation of a regular crystal form. The regular atomic structure of minerals is a primary characteristic, on which a number of other properties of the minerals depend, such as the hardness, the specific gravity and a number of optical properties.

The same chemical composition may occur with two or more different atomic structures, and this gives rise to distinct minerals. Good examples are the minerals diamond and graphite. Both are chemically composed of pure carbon. The internal packing of the carbon atoms is different in the two minerals. In graphite the atoms are arranged in sheets, whereas in diamond they are arranged in a three-dimensional network, and this is reflected in their various properties: the hardness and brilliance of diamond and the dull black lustre and softness of graphite.

From the above discussion it is clear that before the identification of rocks can be attempted, it is necessary to identify their constituent minerals. To identify the minerals should, theoretically, involve an examination of their chemical composition and atomic structure. This can be done, the first by normal chemical analysis, and the latter by X-ray diffraction. In practice however, this is rarely necessary since the essential properties of minerals, chemical composition, and atomic structure, result in a large number of other 'secondary' properties which can usually be determined without any special skills or apparatus; for instance, colour, lustre, hardness, crystal shape, fracture, etc. (there are also optical properties which can only be determined with a petrological microscope, and are essential for very small grains or for very detailed work; these will not be dealt with). The identification of minerals in hand specimens (i.e. without use of a microscope, but with a lens – magnification ×10) relies on the observation and measurement of these unrelated 'secondary' properties, and is not easily systematized. A systematic classification of minerals could be based on crystal shapes, since the crystal form of a mineral is a direct consequence of its atomic structure, but crystal shapes are often difficult to determine and in practice an identification must be based on a combination of all properties observed. The presentation of minerals in chapters 1, 4, and 5 is therefore largely descriptive although the chemical composition and crystallographic systems are also given. These sections are intended primarily for reference; a useful, but by no means exhaustive, identification table is included in Appendix 1.

Abundance of Elements and Minerals

The number of possible stable chemical combinations is very large, and occasionally, as in the case of graphite and diamond, the same chemical substance will give rise to different minerals. So it is not surprising that the number of mineral species is extremely large. Yet, among the thousands of minerals which have been described, there are only about twenty abundant minerals which constitute some 99 per cent of the earth's crust. Most of these minerals are *silicates*, i.e. minerals which contain the two elements silicon and oxygen in combination with one or more metallic elements. Other minerals, including the economically important group of metal ores, are much rarer. Only those minerals which are significant to the identification of rocks, or which were used in antiquity will be considered here.

TABLE 1*

Common Elements	Chemical Symbol	% by weight	*Rarer Elements*	Chemical Symbol	% by weight
Oxygen	O	49·13	Titanium	Ti	0·61
Silicon	Si	26·00	Hydrogen	H	1·00
Aluminium	Al	7·45	Manganese	Mn	0·10
Iron	Fe	4·20	Phosphorus	P	0·12
Calcium	Ca	3·25	Sulphur	S	0·10
Sodium	Na	2.40	Carbon	C	0·35
Potassium	K	2·35	Chlorine	Cl	0·20
Magnesium	Mg	2·35	All others		0·39
		97·13%			2·87%

* Figures from L. V. Pirsson; revised by A. Knopf, *Rocks and Rock Minerals*, (New York, 1958), p. 13; based on R. C. Wells, (1937), U.S. Geol. Survey Bull. **878**, pp. 3–5.

An estimation of the abundance on the earth's surface (the outer 10 mile crust) of the elements silicon, oxygen, and the common metals iron, magnesium, aluminium, calcium, sodium, and potassium is given in Table 1.

The figures do not refer to the abundance of the elements on the whole planet, but to the hard outer crust of the earth only, known as the *lithosphere.*

The composition of the earth as a whole is vastly different, for the core of the earth consists almost entirely of iron and nickel. This dense core is separated from the lithosphere by a layer of very dense rock, much richer in iron and poorer in silica than the composition of the surface rocks listed in Table 1. In a survey of the materials available to man, only the outer crust of the Earth need be considered. This includes all surface rocks of the lithosphere, and, strictly speaking, also the hydrosphere and the atmosphere.

TABLE 2*

Sea Water	% by weight	*Salts in Sea Water*	Chemical formula	% by weight
Water	96·5	Sodium chloride	$NaCl$	77·76
Dissolved salts	3·5	Magnesium chloride	$MgCl_2$	10·88
Dissolved gases:		Magnesium sulphate	$MgSO_4$	4·74
Oxygen	trace	Calcium sulphate	$CaSO_4$	3·60
Carbon dioxide	trace	Potassium sulphate	K_2SO_4	2·46
Nitrogen	trace	Magnesium bromide	$MgBr_2$	0·22
		Calcium carbonate	$CaCO_3$	0·34
				100·00%

* Figures from H. H. Read and J. Watson, *Introduction to Geology*, Vol. I, Principles. (London, 1962), p. 201.

Table 2 shows the composition of the hydrosphere, which consists of the oceans and seas, and also lakes and rivers. An important feature of the hydrosphere is the continuous circulation of the water: evaporation from the large ocean surfaces to cloud formation, precipitation as rain or snow and drainage of rivers back to the oceans. This circulation is as essential to terrestrial life forms as the atmosphere. The circulation of water is also the most important agent of erosion and sedimentation. It is responsible for the breaking up and removal of surface rock and consequent exposure of rocks which have formed deep below the surface of the earth. It also results in the formation of new minerals and rocks.

Igneous, Sedimentary and Metamorphic Rocks

Igneous rocks: The thickness of the earth's crust varies. It is thickest beneath the continents where it has an average depth of 35 kilometres; beneath the oceans it averages only about 5 kilometres. The temperature of the rock increases fairly rapidly with depth. This temperature gradient varies considerably from region to region, and is noticeably greater near regions of volcanic instability. It ranges from 30°C per kilometre in Britain to 9–10°C per kilometre in South Africa. South Africa is a particularly stable land mass, whereas Britain is prone to low intensity earth tremors. In regions such as Iceland or Japan, the gradient is higher still. In most regions of the earth this is not sufficient to cause the rock to be molten even at the base of the lithosphere, for pressure also increases rapidly with depth. In certain regions, however, large masses of molten rock have occured at varying depth and at different times in the earth's history. Such molten rock is known as *magma*. When the magma cools, it solidifies and forms rocks known as *igneous rocks*.

Under certain conditions molten magma is forced up into the earth's solid crust and invades the existing rocks, often loosely termed *country rock*. The magma is either forced up in a large mass which displaces and partly destroys the original country rock, or it is pushed up through cracks and fissures in the country rock and crystallises to form the various igneous rocks (Figure 1).

The large masses of such intrusive igneous rock are known as *batholiths*. They are large dome-shaped structures which may be as much as 100,000 square miles in area. Batholith structures are characteristically surrounded by country rock which has been

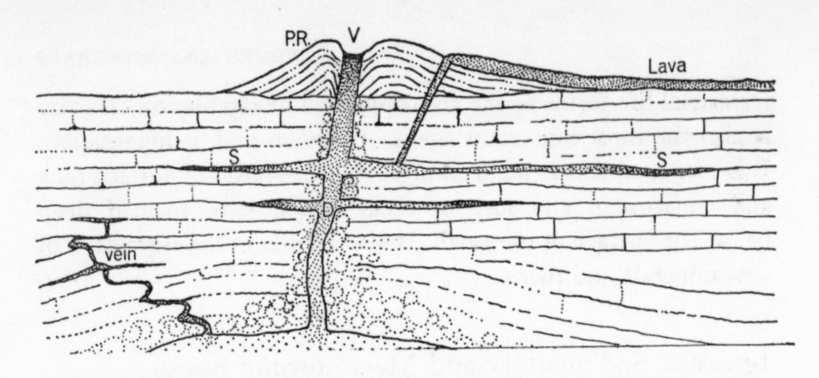

Figure 1 Diagram to show igneous intrusions and volcanic rocks. S = sill; D = dyke; V = volcanic neck; P.R. = pyroclastic rocks.

much altered by heat. These altered rocks are a form of *metamorphic rock*, and the surrounding structure is known as the *contact metamorphic aureole* (see p. 90). The granite mass of Dartmoor in south-west England is an example of a batholithic structure surrounded by a metamorphic aureole rich in metal ores. Larger examples are found as the cores of the mountain ranges of British Columbia, Alaska, and many others.

The magma which is forced along fissures forms *dykes* in vertical fissures and *sills* in horizontal fissures. Dykes and sills vary considerably in size, ranging from a centimetre to half a mile in width, and extending for tens of kilometres in length. The distinction between dykes and sills does not affect the type of rock formed. When a dyke reaches up to the surface of the earth, magma flows out as lava and forms sheets of rock known as *volcanic rock*.

Joints are cracks and fissures which result from the stresses set up in the rock as it cools. Joints are normally developed according to a fairly regular system in igneous rocks.

When cooling is regular in a mass of magma, centres of contraction tend to be set up at fairly regular intervals. A system of cracks radiates outwards from these centres. In granites, the joints tend to develop in three roughly perpendicular directions, so that joint blocks are rhomboidal in shape. In many lava flows and dykes and sills, a columnar joint system is developed. They are formed when cracks at roughly 120° radiate from centres of cooling on the surface of the rock mass (or on contact with the country rock). The intersection of these fissures produces six-sided prisms. This type of jointing is particularly well developed in basalts, strikingly exposed in the well known Giant's Causeway of Northern Ireland.

Sedimentary rocks: Rocks which are exposed at the earth's surface are continually being broken up by weathering. Changes in temperature result in the physical breaking up of the rock into 'scree'. Rivers abrade the scree into pebbles, sand, and silt. Rain and the acid humus of vegetation cause the chemical disintegration of the rock minerals, and the formation of new minerals, clays, salts, and iron oxides. The breakdown products of the rock are carried downhill by streams and by gravity. Wind and ice are also important transporting agents of rock debris, but they do not necessarily move materials down from high to low ground. There is a general tendency for high ground to be eroded, and for the land to be levelled. The rock debris which is carried from the mountains is redeposited in the lowlands and in the sea. The accumulations of rock debris are known as *sedimentary rock*. Unconsolidated debris is also rock in the strict sense of the word. Under the pressure of thick sediments, the sedimentary rocks become consolidated.

Sedimentary rocks form only a thin veneer on the surface of the earth's crust which consists very largely of igneous rocks, and the minerals of sedimentary rock are derived from the igneous rocks in the first instance. The more resistant minerals of igneous rocks, especially quartz, become incorporated in the new sediment. Many other minerals of igneous rocks, however, are rare in sediments because they weather easily, and are changed by chemical processes to clay minerals which are important in the formation of sediments.

Distinction between Igneous and Sedimentary Rocks: Sedimentary rocks can normally be distinguished from igneous rocks fairly easily. Sediments often show a stratified structure known as bedding; this is never found in igneous rocks, although the latter may occasionally develop a system of joints and fissures which may superficially resemble bedding.

The separate grains in sedimentary rocks show traces of their mode of transport, for instance, the surface of water-transported sand grains are shiny, whereas wind-transported sand grains have a frosty surface. The grains of a sedimentary rock may be very closely compressed but remain separate and they may be cemented together with substances such as calcite, silica, or iron oxide. In an igneous rock, the grains are closely interlocked crystals (Pl. 1). Sedimentary rocks frequently contain fossils, igneous rocks cannot contain any fossils.

Metamorphic rocks: Under certain conditions surface rocks (sedimentary or igneous) may become buried deep down in the earth's crust, and become subjected to conditions of pressure and heat. This causes alterations of the rock structure known as *metamorphism*. In general, metamorphic processes cause more important changes in sedimentary rocks than in igneous rocks. The resultant rocks are the *metamorphic rocks*. Metamorphism causes the recrystallization of the rock components and frequently results in the formation of new minerals (for instance chlorite, white mica, garnet) many of which are characteristically associated with metamorphism.

Metamorphic processes also modify or obliterate the original rock structures. In sedimentary rocks, the bedding may be completely destroyed and a new alignment of minerals is obtained perpendicular to the direction of pressure (Pl. 1). The foliated structure of slates for instance is not bedding, but results from the alignment of platy crystals under stress. It is not always easy to distinguish between a highly consolidated sedimentary rock and a slightly metamorphosed rock. For instance, the series from mudstone or shale to slate is a gradual one with many intermediate forms.

In metamorphic aureoles there is generally a permeation of the country rock by the volatile part of the magma, mostly water vapour with gases and other substances in solution, including metals. This results in the formation of new minerals rich in volatile substances such as chlorine, fluorine, and water, and of metal ores.

It has been suggested that when metamorphism proceeds so far that the rock is entirely remelted, it returns to magma and forms igneous rocks; the process may therefore be cyclical.

The most important rocks of the lithosphere are therefore the igneous rocks, of which granite and basalt are characteristic examples. Sedimentary rocks and metamorphic rocks are much less abundant, but the sediments may cover large areas, and completely cover the underlying igneous and metamorphic rocks.

The recognition of the rocks, therefore, depends in the first instance on their mode of formation. The classification of sedimentary rocks is based to a large extent on their grain size. For igneous and metamorphic rocks, a further classification depends on their mineral constituents. It is therefore essential, before considering the rocks themselves, to discuss in some detail the identification of rock-forming minerals.

The Classification of Minerals

Several systems for the classification of minerals have been devised, based on either the crystal symmetry or the chemical composition of the minerals. In considering the raw materials of antiquity, neither of the above criteria are of especial significance, and the mineral groupings adopted here are dictated by their most common occurrences in prehistoric contexts. The principal rock-forming minerals are described from the point of view of their use in the identification of rocks in hand specimens, and some less common minerals are described where they are relevant as raw materials in antiquity. Other groups of minerals are the metal ores, primarily oxides, sulphides, and carbonates of metals, and the minerals of chemical sediments, among which calcite, gypsum, common salt, and various forms of silica are most common.

Many of the common rock-forming minerals are *silicates*, that is minerals based on the combination of metallic elements with silicon and oxygen. In order to appreciate the significance of the silicate minerals and their properties, it is necessary to outline their atomic structure, and this entails a brief digression into mineral chemistry.

Mineral chemistry: There are a number of ways in which atoms combine together to form chemical compounds. Some forms of chemical bonding are much stronger than others, and the nature of the bonding involved in crystal structures has a direct influence on the properties of the minerals. For instance, breakage or cleavage, occurs most distinctly along planes of weak chemical bonding. The strongest forms of chemical bonding are those which involve the structure of the atoms, that is those in which the electrons are involved.

Atoms may be described as miniature solar systems, consisting of a heavy central nucleus, surrounded by a number of electrons in orbit. Each electron carries one negative charge. The central nucleus carries positive charges which balance the total negative charges of the electrons in orbit. Thus, if the atom loses one electron it is left with a positive charge, similarly if it gains an extra electron it acquires an extra negative charge.

The orbits in which the electrons move around the nucleus may conveniently be represented as a series of well defined concentric *shells*. The number of electrons which can be accommodated in any one orbit, or shell, is strictly limited. The inner shell cannot carry more than two electrons. If an atom has three or more electrons, the inner shell is filled and the other electrons move in the second orbit, which can hold as many as eight electrons. If there are more than ten electrons in all, a third electron shell forms around the second shell. The shells are usually numbered or referred to by letter, from the inner shell outwards: 1 to 7, or – K, L. M, N, O, P, Q. No atoms are known to have more than seven electron shells. The number of electrons which can be accommodated within any one shell varies, but in all except the K shell, 8 electrons form a particularly stable system. The K shell cannot accommodate more than 2 electrons and forms a stable system with 2 (Figure 2a). When an atom has a full outer shell (i.e. 2 in K, or 8 in the others) it is chemically inactive. Chemical substances consist of combinations of atoms which mutually 'lend' or 'share' electrons so that they each form stable systems of electron shells. The individual atoms of a chemical compound are electrically unstable, i.e. they loose or acquire electrons from the others, but the compound as a whole is quite stable.

Ionic bonding: The stable configuration of the outer shell is achieved either by the loss of, or by the acquisition of, electrons. For instance, the element chlorine has 17 electrons: two electrons in the K shell, a further 8 in the L shell, and the remaining 7 in the M shell. This leaves space for one electron in the M shell to complete the stable 8 electron configuration (Figure 2b). A

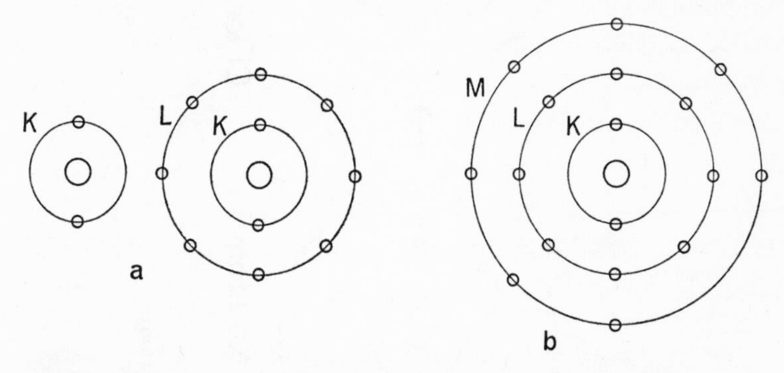

Figure 2 (a) Structure of chemically inactive substance with complete outer shells: helium with two electrons in the K shell; neon with eight electrons in the L shell. (b) Structure of chemically active substance with incomplete outer shell: chlorine with only seven electrons in the M shell.

sodium atom has 11 electrons: 2 in the K shell, 8 in the L shell, and only one in the M shell. It can lose the one M shell electron to form a stable 8 electron configuration. When sodium and chlorine combine to form sodium chloride (common salt), the single electron from the outer shell of sodium is taken up by chlorine. This results in the formation of a negative electrical charge on the chlorine, and a positive charge on the sodium atoms (Figure 3). Atoms which are electrically charged in this

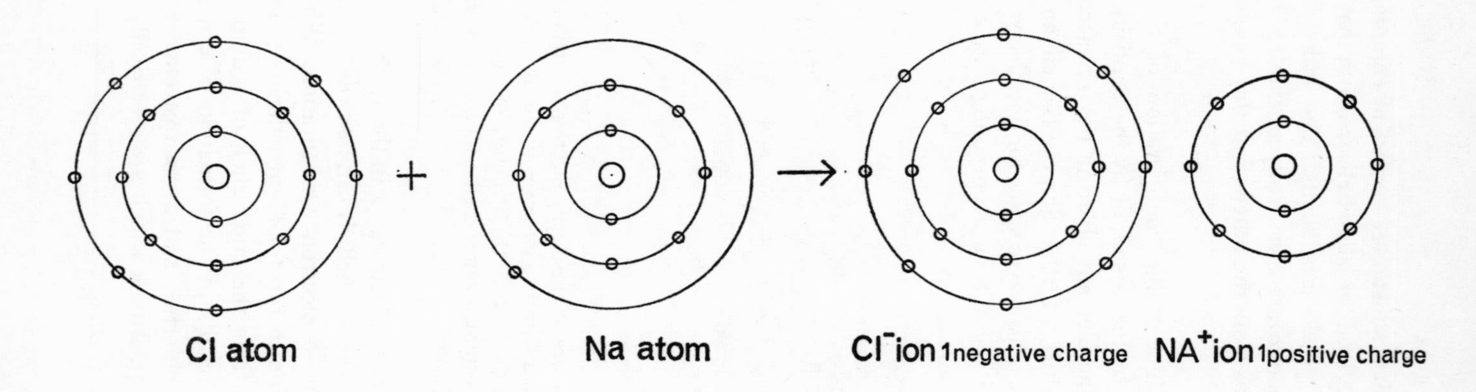

Figure 3 Ionic bonding of chlorine and sodium atoms

way are called *ions*. A positively charged ion, which has lost one or more electrons is a *cation*; a negatively charged ion, which has gained one or more electrons is an *anion*. Thus ionic bonding is the attraction between oppositely charged ions. The charge on an ion depends on the number of electrons which are gained or lost. Chlorine and sodium both gain or lose one electron. They are said to have a valency of 1. Calcium, which has an outer shell of 2 electrons (total number of electrons 12) loses two electrons to form a cation with two positive charges, and requires two chlorine atoms, each taking one of the spare electrons, to form calcium chloride. Calcium is said to have a valency of 2 and the formula for calcium chloride is written $CaCl_2$, (Ca=calcium, Cl= chlorine).

Some elements have slightly more complex atomic structures with up to 18 electrons in shell 3 (=M) and up to 32 electrons in shell 4 (=N). With configurations of this type, an element may have more than one valency. The only multivalent element to be considered here is iron. Iron may be divalent (Fe^{2+}) or it may be trivalent (Fe^{3+}). Divale ntiron is known as *ferrous* iron, and trivalent as *ferric* iron. The salts of ferrous and ferric iron differ in both chemical and physical properties, for instance the red-brown colour of many soils is due to the presence of ferric oxide, whereas the greenish grey colour of permanently waterlogged soils results from the presence of ferrous oxide.

Homopolar or Covalent bonding: Another way in which strong chemical bonding between atoms can be maintained is by the 'sharing' of electrons from the outer shell to obtain the stable 8 electron configuration (2 electrons in the K shell). For example, the gas 'hydrogen' consists of molecules, each made up of two hydrogen atoms linked together by a homopolar bond. Hydrogen is the simplest atomic substance or element, having only one electron around the nucleus. It requires a second electron to complete its K shell. This is achieved by the combination of two atoms, each 'sharing' an extra electron from the other (Figure 4). The chemical formula for the gas 'hydrogen' is written H_2. The gas 'oxygen' also consists of molecules of two oxygen

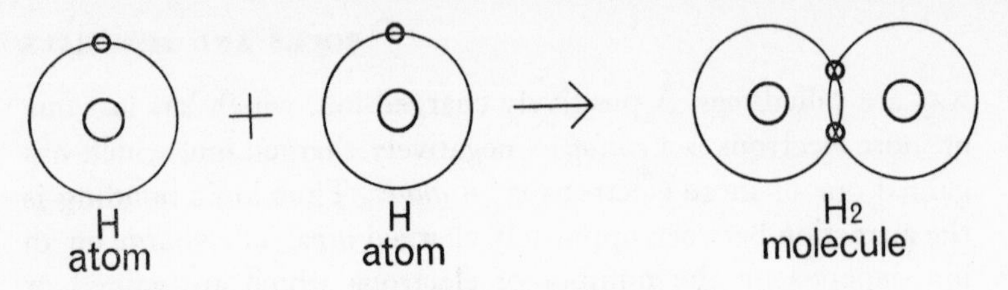

Figure 4 Homopolar bonding of hydrogen atoms

atoms. An oxygen atom has two spaces in its outer shell. The molecule of oxygen consists of two atoms closely bound by the mutual 'sharing' of two electrons. The formula for oxygen is therefore O_2.

In some substances both ionic and homopolar bonding are combined. Calcium carbonate for instance, the chemical formula for which is $CaCO_3$, has homopolar bonds between the carbon (C) and the three oxygen (O_3) atoms leaving two spaces unfilled. The bond between the calcium (Ca) and the carbonate (CO_3) is ionic. Thus two ions of valency 2 are involved: calcium which forms the cation (Ca^{2+}) and the carbon and oxygen group which forms the anion ($(CO_3)^{2-}$). An ion may therefore consist of a closely bound group of atoms known as a *radicle* which has an electrical charge.

The concept of valency can equally be applied to homopolar bonding. In the above examples hydrogen is seen to have a valency 1, and oxygen a valency 2. The concept of valency is important since it is an expression of the relative proportions of atoms of different kinds which combine to form a chemical substance. The valency of an atom is sometimes likened to the number of 'hooks' which must be attached to other valency 'hooks' to form a chemical compound.

Other, weaker types of chemical bonding are rather complex, and result from residual electric charges on the molecules. They are important in mineralogy for their effect on the properties of crystal structures. A striking example is the excellent cleavage properties of mica. Mica consists of a complex molecule of silica with aluminium and other metals. The molecules form a regular sheet structure bound by both homopolar and ionic bonding. There are also bonds between the atoms from one sheet to the next, but these are much weaker than the ionic and homopolar bonds within the sheet structure so that the mica crystals easily break into thin sheets, parallel to the sheets of the molecular structure.

Ionic replacement and mineral series: It has already been stressed that minerals grow into regular crystal forms because of their internal atomic (or molecular) structure. The manner in which the atoms are grouped or stacked together will depend not only on their valencies and the type of chemical bonding involved, but also on the relative sizes of the atoms or ions involved. The size of an atom depends partly on the number of electron shells, but in some elements the shells have smaller radii than in others, so that its size also depends on the density of the structure of the atom. The size of the ion differs slightly from that of the atom; cations which have lost one or more electrons are slightly smaller than the corresponding atom, anions are somewhat larger. Examples of comparative ionic sizes are shown in Table 3.

TABLE 3*

Ionic sizes in Ångstrom Units of the common elements

Silicon	0·42	Magnesium	0·66	Potassium	1·33
Aluminium	0·51	Ferrous iron	0·74	Sodium	0·97
Oxygen	1·32	Ferric iron	0·64	Calcium	0·99

* Figures from H. H. Read and J. Watson, *Introduction to Geology*, Vol. I. Principles. (London, 1962), p. 92.

Oxygen, chlorine, and sulphur are seen to have large ions, some metals, such as iron, nickel, and magnesium are much smaller. It is important to note the close similarity in size between silicon (0·42Å)[1] and aluminium (0·51Å). When two ions have closely similar sizes, the replacement of the one by the other does not affect the structure of the mineral. Such replacements occur very frequently in the silicate minerals, where some of the silicon is replaced by aluminium; other replacements which frequently occur are iron by magnesium, and calcium by sodium. Thus

[1] Å = Ångstrom unit, a unit length equivalent to 10^{-8} cm.

chemical composition of a mineral may vary without affecting its crystallographic structure. This gives rise to series of minerals of closely related physical properties, but with varying chemical composition. An example may be found among the olivines. They are a group of minerals, the extremes of which are a pure magnesium silicate and a pure iron silicate. An intermediate mineral exists which is a silicate of iron and magnesium. In this case the interchange of ions is between ions of the same valency, ferrous iron and magnesium (Fe^{2+} and Mg^{2+}). Where the replacement of silicon by aluminium occurs, silicon of valency 4 is replaced by aluminium of valency 3. This disturbs the electrical neutrality of the mineral, and an extra cation is required to re-establish a stable molecule. This is achieved either by replacing a cation of valency 1 by one of valency 2 (for example – calcium for sodium), or by the addition of extra univalent cations such as K or Na. This results in minor changes in the structure and hence in the properties of the minerals. The felspars (see below) form such a series.

Structure of the silicate minerals

The basic unit of silicate minerals is a tetrahedron (four-sided solid figure) in which each corner is occupied by an oxygen ion, and the centre by a silicon ion (Figure 5). This is the SiO_4 tetrahedron, which is itself not electrically neutral, and has a valency of 4. The SiO_4 units may occur separately, with metallic ions, or they may be linked into chains, rings, sheets, or three-dimensional structures, by sharing oxygen atoms. The metallic ions can then be accommodated within these different silicate structures according to valency and ionic size. In this way a large number of silicate minerals is produced, and these fall into distinct structural types: the chain structures, the sheet structures, etc. Since the classification of silicate minerals (the rock-forming minerals) is based to a greater extent on their structure and only secondarily on their chemical properties, it is necessary to consider the main types of silicate structures in more detail.

Separate SiO_4 groups: The silicate tetrahedra are linked by metal-

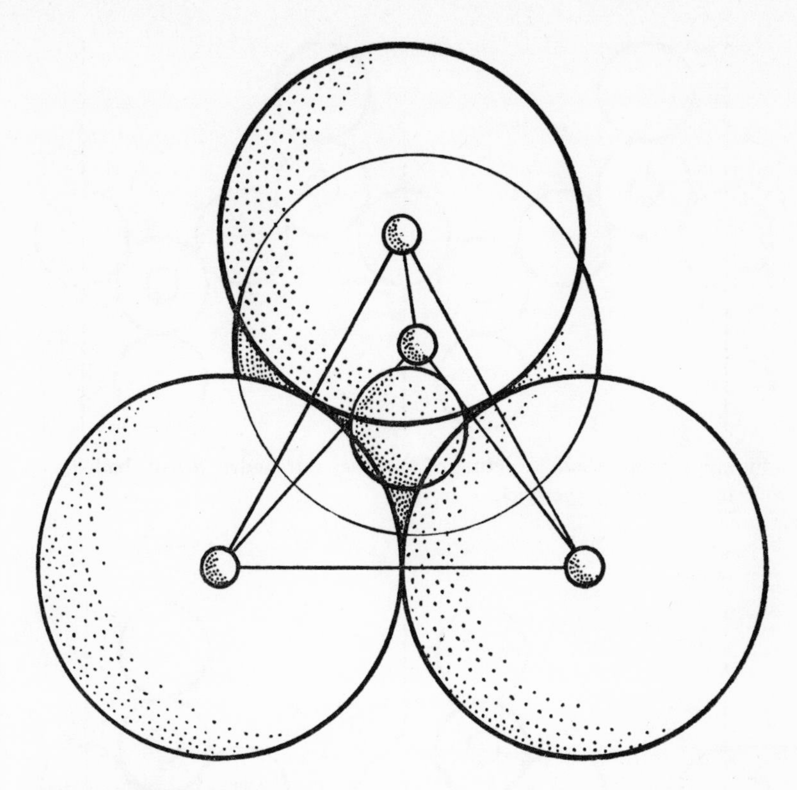

Figure 5 SiO_4 tetrahedron

lic cations, and stacked in a regular manner. This gives three-dimensional structures which can be densely packed. Minerals which have this structure generally have a relatively high specific gravity. Olivine is an example of the separate SiO_4 structure, in which the metal cations are magnesium and iron.

Chain structures: The SiO_4 tetrahedra are linked in a chain through the sharing of an oxygen atom between any two neighbouring tetrahedra (Figure 6). The resulting structure has only three oxygen ions to each ion of silicon and the chemical formula is $n(Si_2O_6)$ (where n is any whole number defining the length of the chain). In these structures some of the silicon may be replaced by aluminium without affecting the structure of the chain. A very important group of rock-forming minerals known as the pyroxenes have this type of silicate structure. The metal

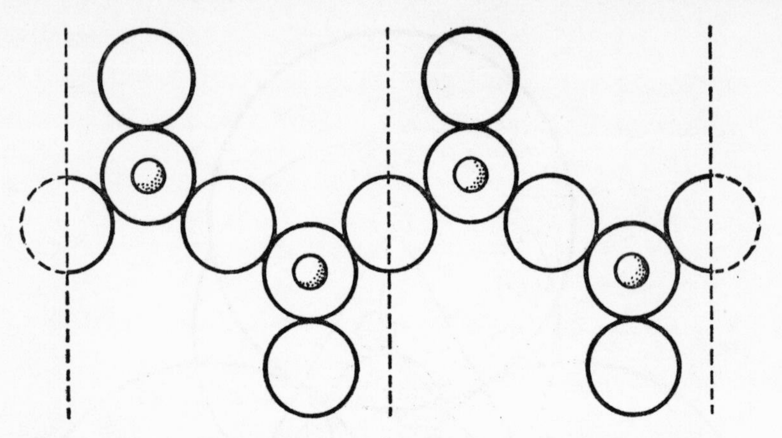

Figure 6 Single chain structure of the silica tetrahedra. Small shaded circle = silicon; large circle = oxygen

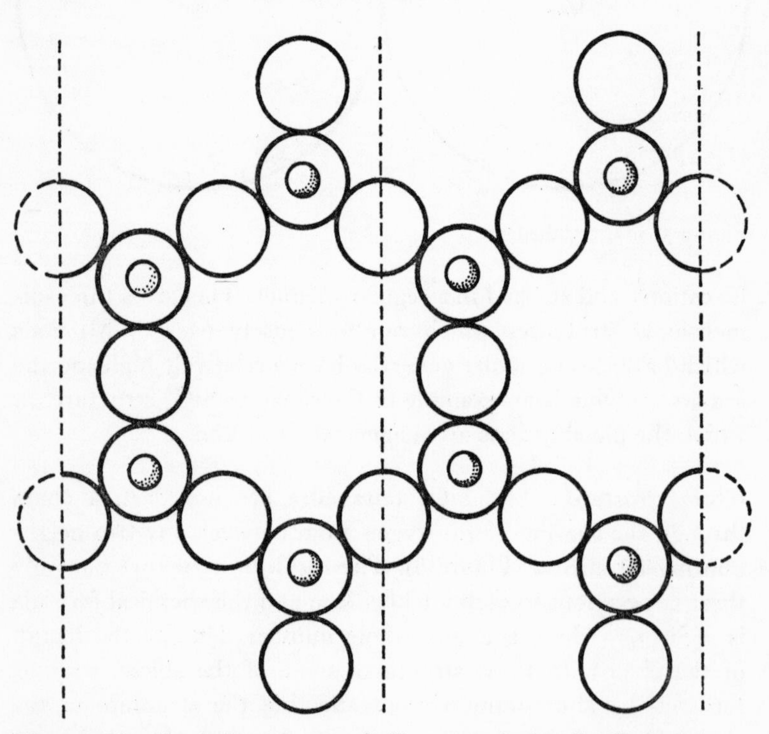

Figure 7 Double chain structure of silicate tetrahedra. Small shaded circle = silicon; large circle = oxygen

ions most frequently associated with the chain structures are magnesium, iron, calcium, and sodium.

Double chain structure: A somewhat more complex structure occurs when two silicate chain structures, placed side by side, are linked through the sharing of further oxygen atoms at regular intervals (Figure 7). The ratio of oxygen to silica is further reduced and the chemical formula is $n(Si_4O_{11})$. The important rock-forming minerals in this group include the hornblendes, a series of minerals with Si_8O_{22} as the basic silicate unit, (i.e. twice Si_4O_{11}). Some replacement of silicon by aluminium frequently takes place. The metal cations in hornblende are iron, aluminium, magnesium, calcium, and sodium, so that a great variety of hornblendes exists, depending on which metal cations are present. They all have very closely related properties.

In a crystal, a number of chain or double-chain structures are held together only by occasional cation bondings, so that the structure has distinct planes of weakness between the chains. These planes of weaker chemical bonding are the cleavage of the minerals, and minerals with the single or double chain structure tend to break into long narrow fragments.

Sheet structures: When the silicate tetrahedra are joined at three of their corners by sharing oxygen atoms, a two-dimensional sheet is formed (Figure 8) in which the oxygen to silicon ratio is further reduced to five oxygen ions to two silicon ions. The chemical formula is Si_4O_{10}. Such silicate structure gives rise to the flaky properties of minerals such as the micas. In the micas, one in four of the silicon ions in the sheet structure is replaced by aluminium. The replacements of the cation Si^{4+} by the cation Al^{3+} leaves an additional negative charge on the structure. This is balanced by potassium cations, (K^+), which form a distinct layer between the adjoining sheets of the metal silicate. The potassium bonds are weak and micas have a well-developed cleavage, parallel to the silicate sheets. In other sheet silicates, such as talc, there is no replacement of silicon by aluminium, and the bonding between the sheets is left weaker still. This accounts for the extreme softness of minerals such as talc and steatite.

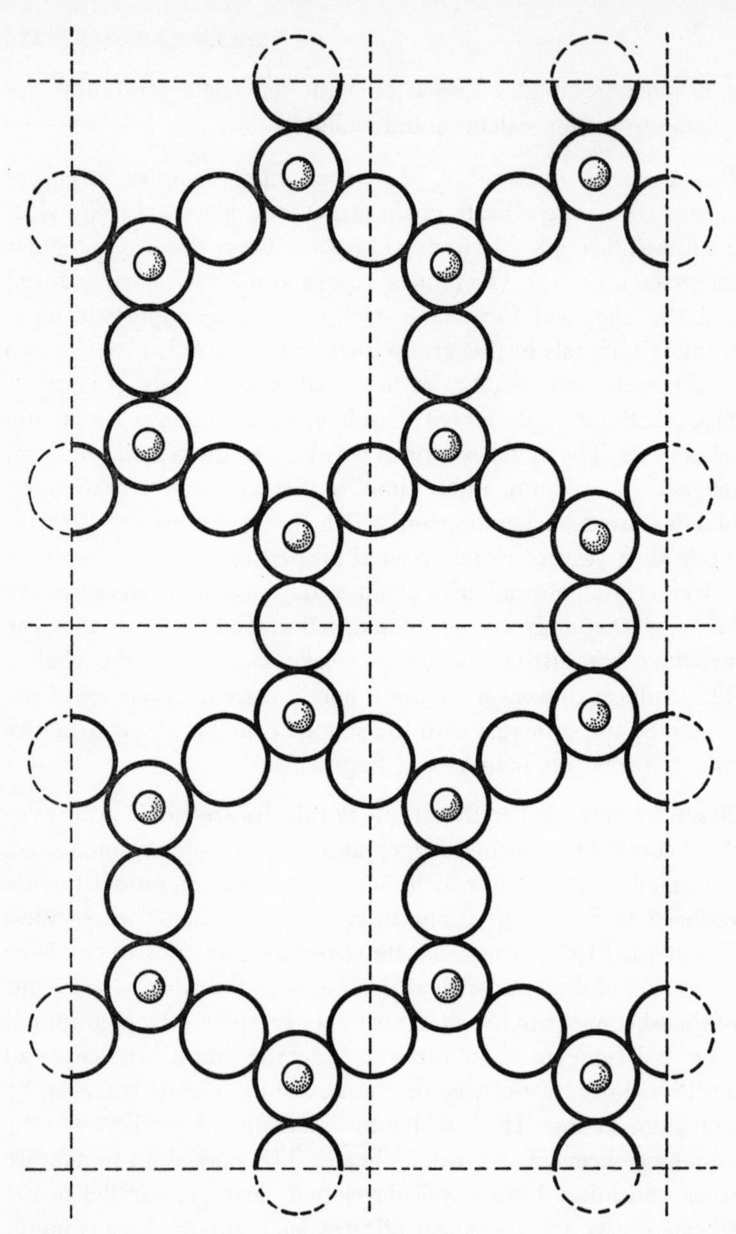

Figure 8 Sheet structure of silicate tetrahedra. Small shaded circle = silicon; large circle = oxygen

Three-dimensional structures: When each silicate tetrahedron is joined by all four corners to adjoining tetrahedra, a three-dimensional network is formed, with the proportion of silicon to oxygen reduced to 1:2 (SiO_2). Since the charges of SiO_2 are balanced, a framework of silicon and oxygen forms a stable mineral of pure silica, which is quartz (or rock crystal). Such an unbroken three-dimensional structure accounts for the hardness of quartz and the absence of any defined planes of weakness. Another group of minerals with this structure are the felspars. In the felspars, the replacement of some of the silicon ions by aluminium leaves the structure electrically charged, and this is balanced by the addition of cations of potassium, sodium, or calcium, thus again giving rise to a series of minerals of closely-related properties. The addition of cations in a three-dimensional SiO_2 framework makes these minerals slightly less hard than quartz, and allows planes of weakness to form along which cleavage takes place.

Properties of silicates: The silicate minerals can thus be grouped in terms of increasing complexity of silicate structure, from the simple silicate tetrahedron to a three-dimensional framework of tetrahedra linked by the mutual sharing of all the oxygen ions at the corners of the tetrahedron configuration.

Since the valency of oxygen is 2, the simple SiO_4 tetrahedron has a resultant valency of 4; each oxygen ion uses one of its valency bonds to join the silicon ion and the other is left free to join with metal cations iron and magnesium, as in the case of olivine. In the more complex silicate structures, the tetrahedra are joined by mutually sharing one or more oxygen ions which thus use up both valency bonds in the formation of the silicate structure. There are therefore fewer valency bonds left free for the metallic cations. A consequence of this is the reduction in the ratio of metallic ions. This ratio of metal to silicon is more frequently expressed in terms of their oxides, i.e. of metal oxide to silica (SiO_2). It follows that the more complex the silicate structure, the richer in silica will be the corresponding mineral; the extreme form is quartz, which consists of pure silica. The complexity of the silicate also has a direct result on a number of physical properties of the minerals, some of which have already been mentioned. The density of minerals is found to decrease with the complexity of structure, for the atoms can be more closely packed in the simpler structures. The heavy metal ions, such as iron and magnesium, are more generally associated with the simple silicate structures, hence the general term ferro-magnesium minerals for this group. The more complex silica-rich structures are generally found with the lighter metals such as sodium, potassium and calcium (also known as the alkali metals).

Tests for the Identification of Minerals in Hand Specimens

The assignment of rocks and minerals to their respective classes can be carried out by a number of simple tests and observations and some general knowledge of the more important groups of minerals and rocks. This section deals with the techniques and methods used for the identification of minerals in hand specimens, using only simple apparatus such as a hand lens, penknife, streak plate, and specific gravity bottle. A few chemical tests have been included in the description of minerals, where these are useful to distinguish between minerals of similar properties.

Crystal shapes: When allowed to grow freely, the atomic structure of minerals will result in the formation of regular crystal forms. The shapes of crystals can be defined in geometrical terms. It has been found that all crystal shapes can be expressed as variants of six crystallographic systems.

Each mineral crystallizes according to its chemical composition and structure in one of these systems; whereas it may exhibit more than one crystal habit, certain habits will be much more common, and each falls within the same crystallographic system. For instance, iron pyrites, which belongs to the cubic system generally crystallizes into regular cubes. It may however also crystallize into other forms, derived from the cube: the octahedron (consisting of two four-sided pyramids Figure 9b) or a complex form such as the pyritohedron (Figure 9c) with 12

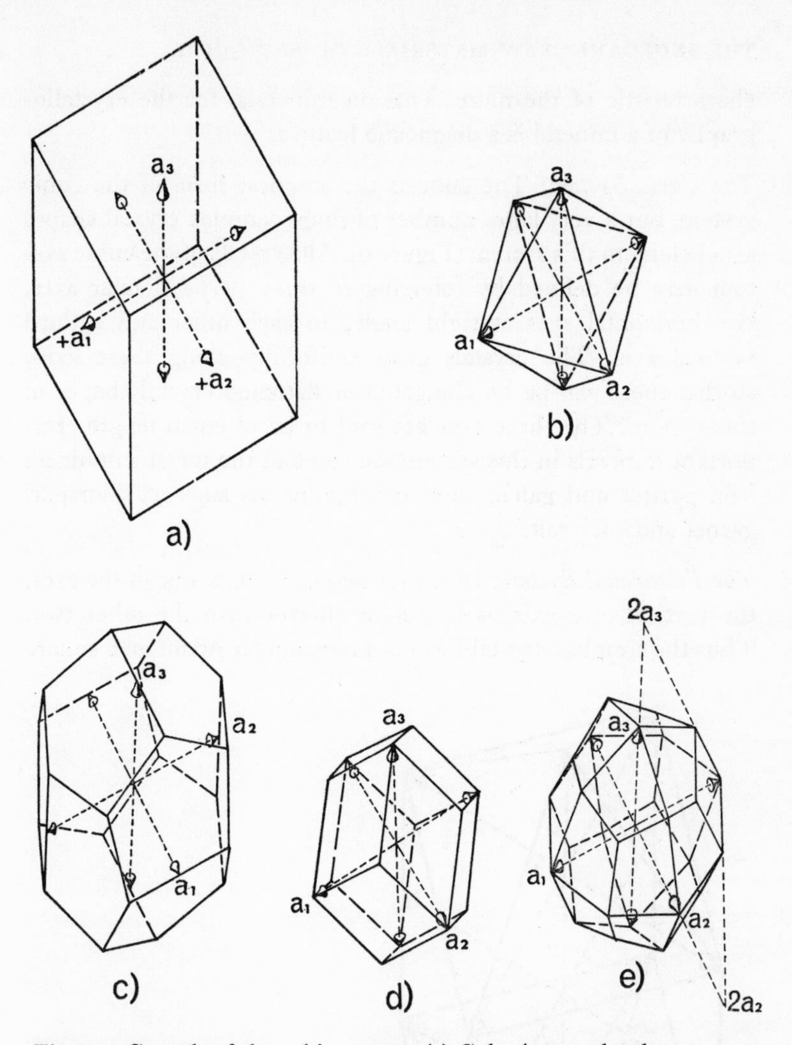

Figure 9 Crystals of the cubic system. (a) Cube (e.g. rock salt, fluorspar) (b) Octahedron (e.g. iron pyrites) (c) Pyritohedron (e.g. iron pyrites) (d) Rhombododecahedron (e.g. garnet) (e) Trapezohedron (e.g. garnet)

crystal facets. The possible crystal forms and their nomenclature are rather complicated when dealing with figures such as the pyritohedron and others with more facets. It is worth while, however, to consider some of the simpler crystal forms, which are characteristic of the more common minerals, for the crystallography of a mineral is a diagnostic feature.

The Cubic System: The cube is the simplest form of the cubic system, but a very large number of more complex crystal shapes also belong to this system (Figure 9). All crystals of the cubic system may be defined by referring to three perpendicular axes, two horizontal axes at right angles to each other and a third vertical axis. The crystals grow uniformly along these axes, so that there can be no elongated or flattened crystal shapes in this system. The three axes are said to be of equal length. Important minerals in this system are some of the metal sulphides: iron pyrites and galena, and other minerals such as fluorspar, garnet and rock salt.

The Tetragonal System: In the tetragonal system, one of the axes, the vertical or c-axis, is longer or shorter than the other two. Thus the simplest crystal form is a rectangular prism on a square

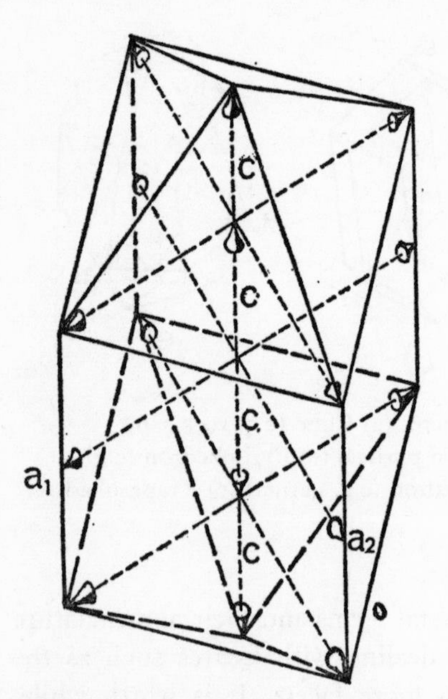

Figure 10 Crystal of the tetragonal system. Prism and pyramid (e.g. zircon)

base. The crystal forms in this system tend to be elongated four-sided or eight-sided prisms with or without pyramidal ends (Figure 10). A figure resembling the octahedron also occurs.

The principal minerals in this system of interest to archaeologists are zircon, cassiterite (tin ore) and copper pyrites.

The Orthorhombic System: The three perpendicular axes are all of unequal lengths. The horizontal axis from left to right is called the b-axis, the second horizontal axis at right angles to b is the a-axis, and the vertical axis is the c-axis. Crystals of the orthorhombic system are frequently rectangular and *tabular* such as barytes (heavy spar) (Figure 11) or they are *prismatic* as in olivine and topaz.

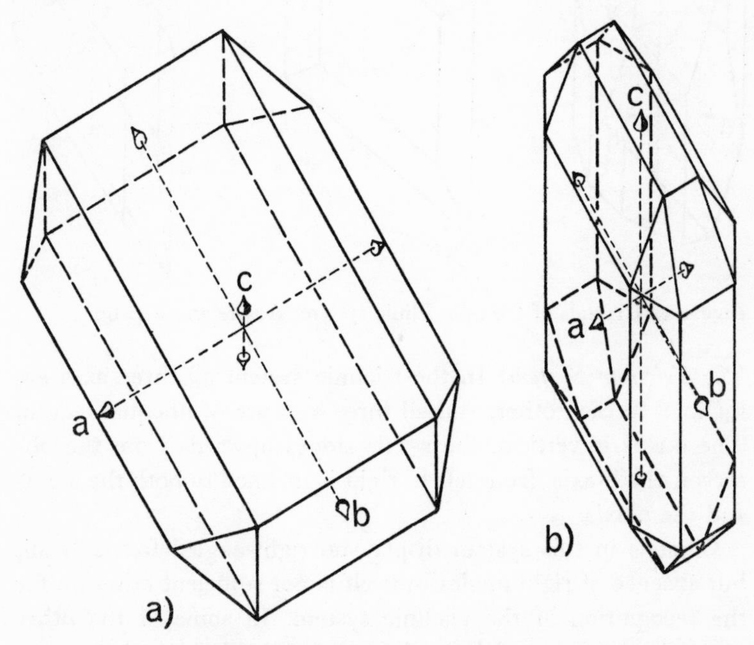

Figure 11 Crystals of the orthorhombic system. (a) Tabular (e.g. barytes) (b) Prismatic (e.g. olivine)

The Monoclinic System: In this system the crystal shapes are still referred to three axes of unequal lengths, but one of the axes (the a-axis) is not perpendicular to the other two. The vertical c-axis and the horizontal b-axis are at right angles to each other, and the a-axis is inclined from the horizontal. Crystals of the monoclinic system have a much lower degree of symmetry than those of previous systems. Important minerals which crystallize in the monoclinic system are gypsum, orthoclase felspars, and most pyroxenes (Figure 12).

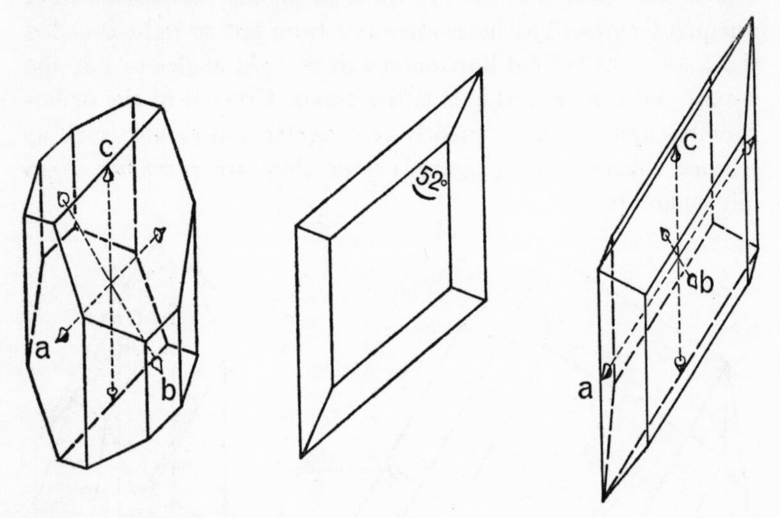

Figure 12 Crystals of the monoclinic system. Augite and gypsum

The Triclinic System: In the triclinic system all three axes are inclined to each other, and all three axes are of unequal length. The c-axis is vertical, the a-axis slopes upwards from the observer, the b-axis, from left to right is inclined to both the a-axis and the c-axis.

Crystals in this system display no right-angled forms at all, but absence of right angles in itself is not sufficient criterion for the recognition of the triclinic system. In some of the other systems the faces at right angles may not be developed, particularly in the monoclinic system, and in some of the cubic forms, such as the garnet type (Figure 9). There are fewer minerals which crystallize in the triclinic system than in any other system, and plagioclase felspar is the only triclinic mineral which will be dealt with here. In plagioclase felspar, the angle between the b- and c-axes is only 3° to 4° greater or smaller than a right angle, so that crystals are difficult to distinguish from monoclinic felspar without accurate measurement.

The Hexagonal System: Lastly, a number of minerals crystallize in six-sided prisms, with or without a pyramidal end. Such crystals can be referred to four axes: one vertical axis, the c-axis, and in the horizontal plane three axes inclined at 120° to each other, the a_1, a_2, and a_3, axes. Two of the most important minerals in this system are quartz (rock crystal) and calcite (calcspar). The common crystals of these minerals are different, though both belong to the same system (see Figures 13 and 24).

The crystal systems have been only briefly outlined. The study of crystallography and the measurement of crystal forms

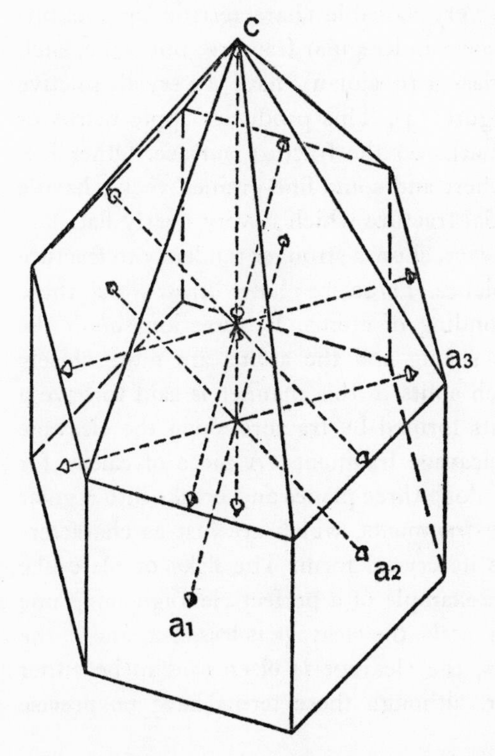

Figure 13 Crystal of the hexagonal system. Prism and pyramid (quartz)

in terms of their axes of reference requires a great deal of practice, and a good eye for three-dimensional figures. In rocks the minerals can rarely grow into large well formed crystals and without microscopic analysis, crystallography is of limited use in the identification of rock forming minerals. Some common minerals are frequently encountered as fully developed crystals and these can be identified from their crystallography: crystals of calcite, gypsum, and fluorspar, which bear certain superficial resemblances to each other and to quartz, can be distinguished by their crystal shapes. There are however, also several other properties which distinguish these and other minerals from each other.

Fracture and cleavage: The manner in which a mineral or rock breaks is sometimes a very valuable characteristic for identification. Most minerals have an irregular fracture; but some, such as quartz, flint, and glasses (obsidian), have a very distinctive *conchoidal* fracture (Figure 14). This produces ripple marks or concentric wave-like marks on the fracture surface. Other less glassy rocks, such as chert and some fine-grained rocks, have a very subdued conchoidal fracture which is very nearly flat.

Many minerals, however, show a stronger tendency to fracture along certain smooth planes. These are planes *across* which there is a relatively weak bonding of atoms. In directions *along* the planes the bonding is strong and the atoms are more closely packed. A crystal which splits in this manner is said to have a *cleavage*. The fragments formed by fracture along the cleavage planes are known as cleavage fragments. A piece of calcite for instance, has cleavages along three planes and breaks into regular rhombohedral cleavage fragments, which are just as characteristic of this mineral as its crystal form. The flaky or plate-like character of mica is an example of a perfect cleavage along one plane only. In other minerals, the cleavage is less clear and in the description of minerals, the cleavage is often said to be either perfect, good, or poor, although these terms have no precise meaning.

Since the direction of the cleavage planes depends on the

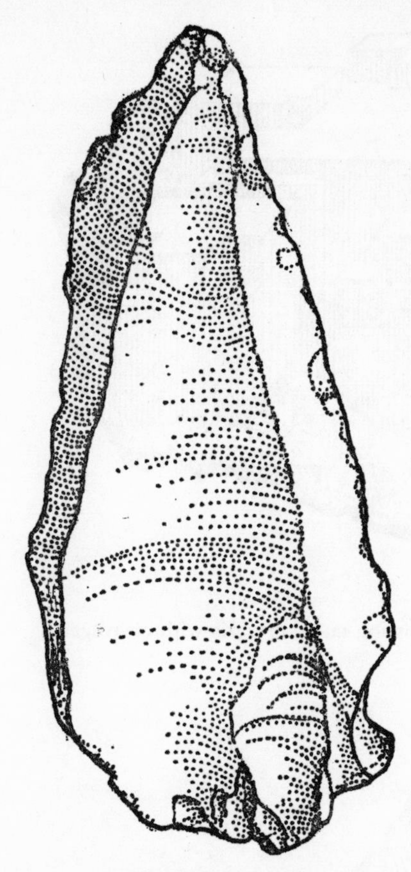

Figure 14 Palaeolithic flint flake showing conchoidal fracture

atomic structure (as do many of the mineral properties) the cleavage directions of any mineral are along well defined planes, which are diagnostic of the mineral. Cleavage planes are also closely related to the crystal form. They are always parallel to *possible* crystal facets, but these crystal facets may not be the ones most commonly developed so that the relationship is often not immediately apparent. For instance, galena (lead sulphide) which forms cubic crystals also has cleavages parallel to the cube faces (Figure 15). Fluorspar also forms cubic crystals, but has its cleavage planes along the diagonals of the cube facets (Figure 16). A cleavage fragment of fluorspar therefore is a cube with the corners cut off.

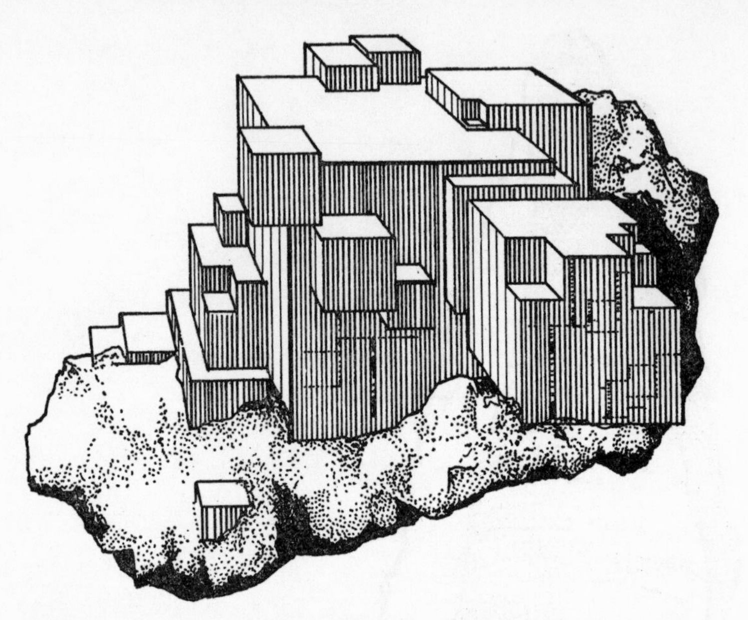

Figure 15 Specimen of galena showing cubic crystals with cleavage parallel to the cube face

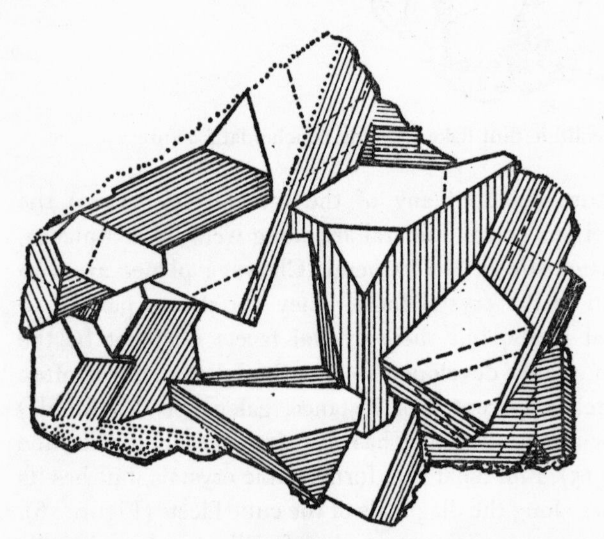

Figure 16 Specimen of fluorspar showing cubic crystals with cleavage planes along the diagonals of the cube faces

It is important to recognize cleavage planes and the hair lines or incipient cracks along the planes of weakness on a crystal which mark the cleavage planes. Some minerals such as quartz have no cleavage planes and always break in an irregular fashion or a conchoidal fashion.

Habit: The habit of a mineral describes the form in which it occurs. Minerals may occur as a mass of crystals, i.e. a *crystalline* habit, as a powdery or *earthy* mass, or as a dense structureless mass, i.e. *massive*.

Some common crystalline habits are said to be *prismatic* for elongated forms (Figures 24 and 25), *tabular* (Figure 17) for flat

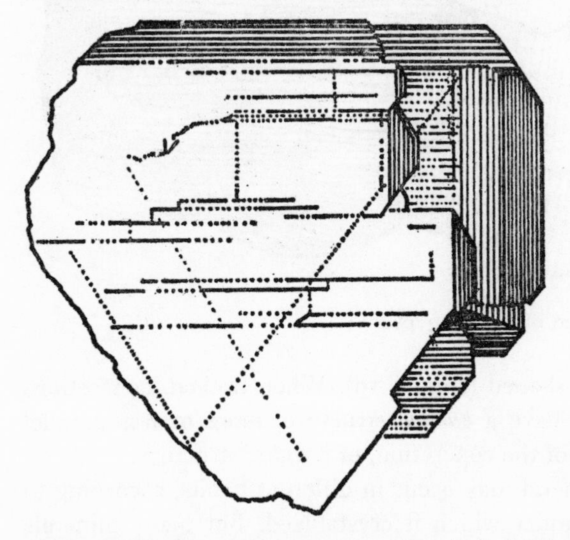

Figure 17 Specimen of barytes showing tabular habit

more or less rectangular forms, *platy* as in mica, *acicular* for needle-shaped crystals which may form radial or columnar aggregates, and rarely *fibrous* as in asbestos and some occurrences of gypsum (Figure 18).

Concretions of minerals may be massive, or earthy, but they often consist of aggregates of very small crystals. If the concretions consist of rounded masses they are often said to be

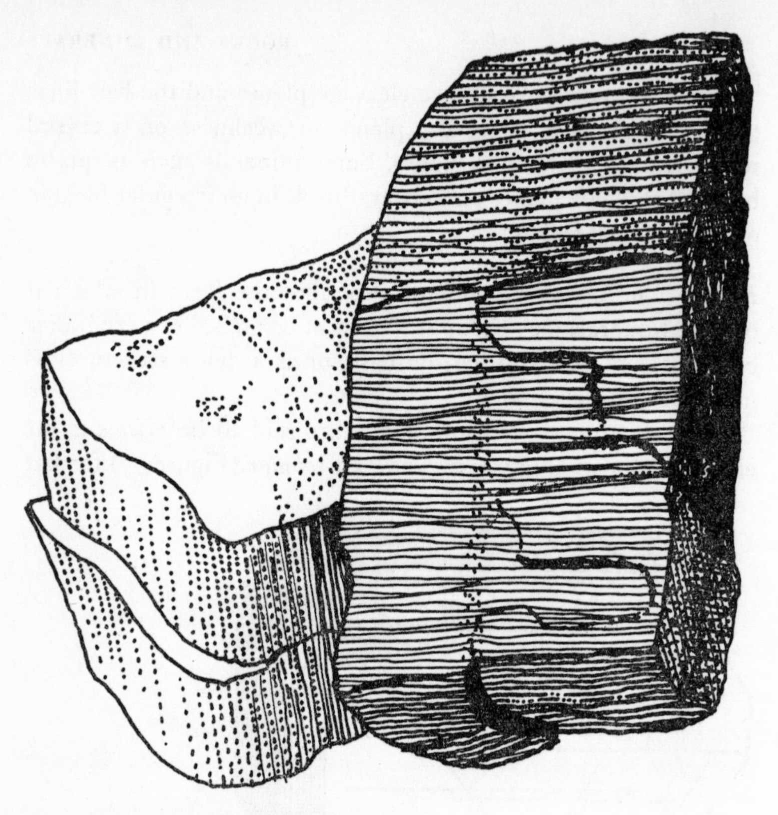

Figure 18 Specimen of fibrous gypsum

reniform kidney shaped (Figure 19). When broken, concretions may be seen to have a *banded* structure, more or less parallel with the surface of the concretion, or a *radial* structure.

The same mineral may occur in different habits, according to the conditions under which it crystallized. But many minerals have characteristic habits; for instance, quartz is crystalline, often prismatic, but more commonly it occurs in irregular grains. Hematite (iron oxide), on the other hand, may be crystalline and tabular or platy, it commonly occurs as radial reniform concretions, and is also found earthy or massive.

Colour, lustre and transparency: The different colours of minerals are one of their most obvious properties. Although some colours can be taken as characteristic of a particular mineral,

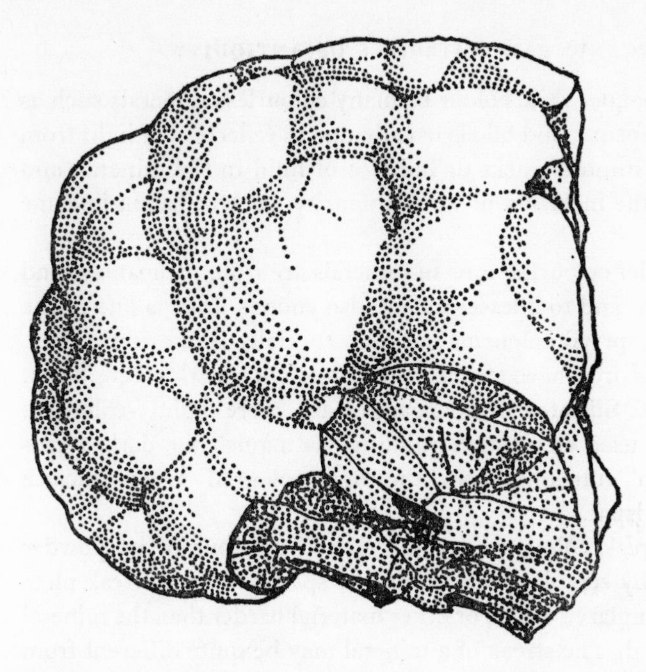

Figure 19 Specimen of hematite (kidney ore) showing reniform habit

such as green malachite, or yellow sulphur, many other minerals can occur in a number of colours. Quartz, for instance, is normally colourless, it is sometimes purple (amethyst), yellow or smoky (citrine), or pink (rose quartz). Tourmaline may form clear green crystals, it may form pink crystals, or both colours may occur at opposite ends of the same crystal. Yet another form of tourmaline is jet black. It is clear, therefore, that only in some cases can colour be considered diagnostic of a particular mineral. There are also a large number of minerals which have the same colour.

When the colour of a mineral depends on its chemical composition it is said to be *inherent*. Many minerals have no inherent colour in the pure state, they are colourless or white. Such minerals may be coloured by minute inclusions of an impurity in chemical combination, or disseminated as small particles in the mineral. This type of colouration is called *exotic*. The exotic colours of minerals vary quite widely according to the type and amount of colouring material.

The opaque white colour of many colourless minerals such as quartz, gypsum, and talc is usually due to reflection of light from countless minute cracks or bubbles of fluid in the mineral, and rarely to the inclusion of white impurity, such as kaolin in some felspars.

The chief colouring ions in minerals are iron, manganese, and chromium, and to a lesser extent also copper. Iron is one of the most widespread colouring agents, expecially in the ferric state. Silicates of iron have strong inherent colours, dark green, black, or brown. Silicates of manganese are more lightly-coloured. Colour is used as a rough guide to distinguish the dark 'ferro-magnesian' minerals from the light-coloured alkali silicates such as felspar.

The streak colour of a mineral is the colour of its powder obtained by scraping or rubbing the specimen on a streak plate made of unglazed china, or other material harder than the mineral to be tested. The streak of a mineral may be quite different from its colour. It is used in the identification of a number of oxides and sulphides of metal as well as some other minerals.

One quality of the mineral colour is its lustre. A number of different types of lustres have been described, but none can be accurately defined. The *metallic* lustre of some metal ores is characteristic, for instance copper pyrites, galena, and the native metals, gold, and copper. A *vitreous* lustre is that of broken glass, it is found on many minerals including quartz, calcite, and fluorspar. Other minerals have a *resinous* lustre, a *pearly* lustre, or a dull surface. There remains one visual property of minerals, which is their transparency or opaqueness. Many minerals, however, occur in different habits displaying varying degrees of transparency or opaqueness.

Specific Gravity: The density of a mineral is a property both of its chemical composition, and of the closeness of packing of the atoms. The specific gravity is defined as the ratio of its weight to that of an equal volume of water. There are a number of ways of determining the specific gravity of a mineral depending on the nature of the material and on the accuracy required. Rough estimates of specific gravity can be obtained by weighing a specimen and determining its volume by displacement in water. The specific gravity is obtained from the ratio of the weight (measured in grammes) to the volume (measured in cubic centimetres). More accurate methods rely on the difference in weight in air and in water. Special apparatus have been designed for specific gravity measurements, but with samples of about one to two centimetres in diameter the weight can be determined on a chemical or jeweller's balance. The sample is suspended from one arm of the balance, and weighed, first in air, and secondly immersed in water. The specific gravity is given by

$$\frac{W_a}{W_a - W_w}$$

where W_a is the weight in air and W_w is the weight in water. For accurate work much smaller fragments are usually measured to ensure that the sample is homogeneous and pure.

Heavy liquids such as Bromoform (S.G. 2·9), are used to separate minerals of different specific gravities, for instance – when dealing with unconsolidated sediments. Rock and mineral grains of lower specific gravity will float on bromoform, while the heavier fragments sink. By using a mixture of liquids it is possible to find the specific gravity of a mineral or rock. When the rock neither floats nor sinks in the mixture, it has the same specific gravity as the liquid mixture, and this can be determined in the normal way with a specific gravity bottle, or by a similar method.

Since the chemical composition of some minerals is variable, the specific gravity is valuable in determining the actual composition. For instance, in the olivine group of minerals the two end products are pure magnesium silicate (fosterite), specific gravity 3·2, and the pure iron silicate (fayalite), specific gravity 4·3. The intermediate olivine has an intermediate value of specific gravity, directly dependent on the relative amounts of iron and magnesium present. It is possible to distinguish between iron olivine and magnesium olivine grains by measuring their specific gravity, and to separate them by the use of a suitable heavy liquid.

Hardness: The hardness of minerals varies considerably, and it is an extremely useful criterion in the identification of minerals. Hardness determinations are based on the simple principle that a harder material can scratch a softer one, but not vice versa. The greater the difference in hardness between two materials the more powder will be formed in scratching. It is also useful to note the noise made in scratching, for this is louder when there is little difference in hardness.

A standard reference scale of hardness is required to compare mineral hardnesses. An arbitrary scale, in which ten minerals have been chosen as standards is commonly used (the Mohs scale of hardness). The minerals are listed in order of increasing hardness, but it is important to note that the steps in hardness are not regular or systematic.

Hardness		
	1	Talc
	2	Gypsum (or rock salt)
	3	Calcite
	4	Fluorspar
	5	Apatite
	6	Felspar (orthoclase)
	7	Quartz
	8	Topaz
	9	Corundum
	10	Diamond

Some of the minerals in this scale are common and an incomplete set of standard hardness minerals can easily be collected. It is a useful tool in the identification of specimens. Two other useful tools are a steel penknife which has a hardness between quartz and felspar (about 6·5) or a small steel file, and a finger nail which is normally harder than gypsum and softer than calcite (about 2·5).

Certain precautions must be taken when using the hardness test. It is important that the surface tested is fresh and not covered by a thin layer of weathering product (patina). When the minerals in a rock specimen are tested great care must be taken to confine the scratch to individual mineral grains.

The scratch mark should be carefully examined – with a lens

if necessary – to make certain that the test mineral has in fact been scratched. A softer mineral drawn across a harder one may leave a trace of powder which can be mistaken for a scratch mark. Similarly a steel knife drawn across a substance harder than 7 leaves a dark line.

CHAPTER TWO

The Rock-forming Minerals

THE igneous rocks are formed by the cooling and crystallization of liquid rock magma into an aggregate of mineral grains. The variety of minerals formed varies according to the composition of the magma. The minerals which make up the greatest proportion of igneous rocks may be considered as the essential rock-forming minerals. They are *quartz*, *felspar*, *mica*, *pyroxene*, *hornblende*, and *olivine*.

These essential rock-forming minerals are made up very largely of the eight common elements shown on Table 1 (p. 7). Besides these, igneous rocks and hence also the rock magma from which they solidify, contain a number of other substances in small quantities. Rock magma contains a variable amount of volatile constituents and these play an important part in the formation of some of the rarer minerals. The volatiles consist to a great extent of superheated water vapour which carries other substances and gases in solution. Some of the principal volatiles are fluorine, chlorine, phosphorus, sulphur, carbon dioxide; other substances carried in solution are metals and silica. The water of the magma is often called *magmatic water* to distinguish it from the water in the hydrosphere. It is of course the same substance. As the magma begins to solidify to rock, the volatiles become concentrated in the cavities and fissures of the main mass of the rock, or they may be injected into the surrounding country rock. The rock which crystallizes in the volatile enriched fissures is known as *pegmatite*. Pegmatite veins are normally associated with large masses of igneous rock such as batholiths, and not with the smaller intrusive dykes and sills. In rock cavities and in pegmatites, minerals grow into large, well developed crystal shapes. In some pegmatites, mica crystals of

1 metre diameter are known and much larger crystals have been found. Besides the essential rock-forming minerals other less common minerals are found which form in the presence of volatiles, such as *tourmaline* and *topaz* in granite pegmatite veins. These minerals are rare or absent in the main body of the rock mass.

The interaction between the hot volatiles of an intrusive igneous rock and the surrounding country rock gives rise to the formation of new minerals, the minerals formed depend to a great extent on the nature of the country rock and the emanations from the magma. Sedimentary rocks can be very greatly altered by such metamorphic processes, while older igneous rocks are affected to a much lesser degree. Only a few of the important minerals associated with such contact metamorphism need be considered here: those that have been used in antiquity – *garnet*, *corundum*, *zircon*, and *beryl*; and a few of the important minerals associated with metal ores – *fluorite* and *barytes*. Many metal ores are formed by contact metamorphic processes, but these will be discussed separately in the chapter on metals.

The alteration of the primary minerals by water vapour occurs frequently in the older igneous rocks. The changes may result in the formation of new minerals which entirely change the character of the original rock. Some important alteration products are *serpentine*, *chlorite*, *kaolinite*, *talc* and *turquoise*.

Quartz

Quartz is one of the commonest and most widely distributed minerals. It consists of silicon dioxide (SiO_2) in its crystalline form. There are a number of other forms of silica which are not crystalline, opal and chalcedony and related forms. These are rare as primary minerals in igneous rocks, but play an important part in the formation of sediments. The description of these forms of silica can be found in the chapter on chemical and organic sediments.

Description: Good crystals of quartz are not infrequent in rock cavities and fissures. Quartz crystallizes in the hexagonal system in six-sided prisms with pyramidal extremities. The crystal faces may be extremely regular (as in Figure 13 and 20b) and the crystal is said to have six-fold symmetry, i.e. if the crystal is turned about its vertical axis (the c-axis) there are six positions in which an identical form is seen. In another form, also in the hexagonal system, alternate faces of the pyramid are much smaller (Figure 20a), and in this form the crystal has only three-fold

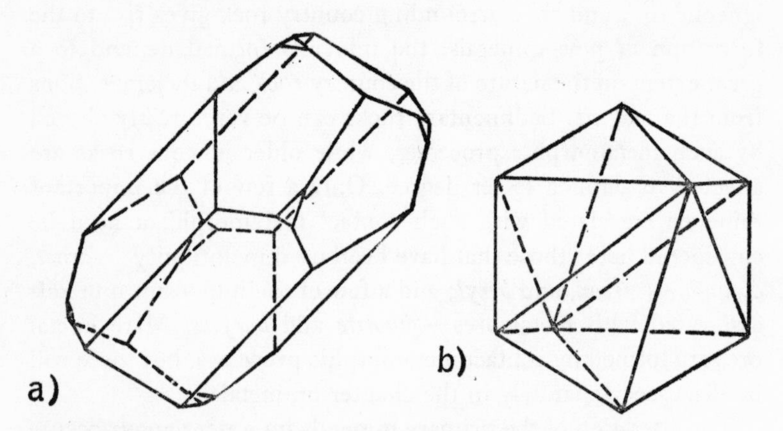

Figure 20 Crystals of quartz. (a) Six-fold symmetry of high temperature quartz (b) Three-fold symmetry of low temperature quartz

symmetry. These two forms are interesting in that they depend on the temperature at which the quartz was formed. The high temperature quartz which has crystallized above 573°C has six-fold symmetry. Low temperature quartz which has crystallized below 573°C has three-fold symmetry. There are other differences between the high and low temperature forms of quartz but these are not apparent in a macroscopic examination of specimens.

Quartz has no cleavage and it breaks with a characteristic conchoidal fracture which may serve to distinguish it from the felspars in rock specimens. Sometimes the fracture is brittle and irregular when several adjacent crystals are involved.

Pure quartz is colourless, greyish, or milky white. In igneous rocks the quartz grains are frequently greyish, or rarely black, the pure transparent variety occurring most frequently in rock cavities. Small amounts of impurities impart exotic colours to pure quartz. Hematite colours quartz red or brown, the purple variety is known as *amethyst* and probably owes its colour to manganese, a yellow variety of quartz is known as *citrine*, a yellowish brown variety as *smoky quartz* or *Cairngorm*, and a pink variety as *rose quartz*.

The hardness of quartz is 7 and it is used as a standard on Mohs' scale of hardness. The specific gravity is 2·56.

Occurrence: Quartz is found as an important constituent of igneous and metamorphic rocks, particularly in granite and gneiss, and in smaller amounts in syenites, diorite, and other rocks. Irregular masses of pure crystalline quartz are found in pegmatite veins, sometimes referred to as *veinquartz*.

Since quartz is extremely resistant to weathering, it is frequently an important constituent of sedimentary rocks. Many sands and sandstones consist predominantly or even entirely of quartz.

Silicates

The classification of the silicate minerals into the mineral groups felspar, mica, pyroxene, hornblende, and olivine is based on their atomic structure which has been outlined in Chapter 1. Each group consists of a number of closely related minerals which arise from the substitution of certain ions.

Felspars

Felspars are the most abundant of the rock-forming silicates, they are present in most igneous rocks.

There are three 'pure' felspars, and two series of intermediate groups which arise from the partial substitution of ions. The pure felspars are:

Orthoclase:	$KAlSi_3O_8$	potassium felspar
Albite:	$NaAlSi_3O_8$	sodium felspar
Anorthite:	$CaAl_2Si_2O_8$	calcium felspar

The intermediate groups are generally known as:

Alkali felspars $(K,Na)AlSi_3O_8$, which may be considered as mixtures (or more accurately – solid solutions) of orthoclase and albite, in which orthoclase generally predominates.

Plagioclase felspars which may be considered as mixtures (or more accurately – solid solutions) of albite and anorthite.

The pure felspars are relatively rare, and for the purposes of rock classification it is more important to distinguish between the alkali felspars and the plagioclase felspars. A number of distinct varieties of plagioclase felspar are defined on the basis of the relative amounts of sodium and calcium. Broadly speaking the plagioclase felspars are said to be *sodic* when albite predominates and *calcic* when anorthite predominates.

Description: In well formed crystals the characteristic crystal form is as shown in the diagram (Figure 21).

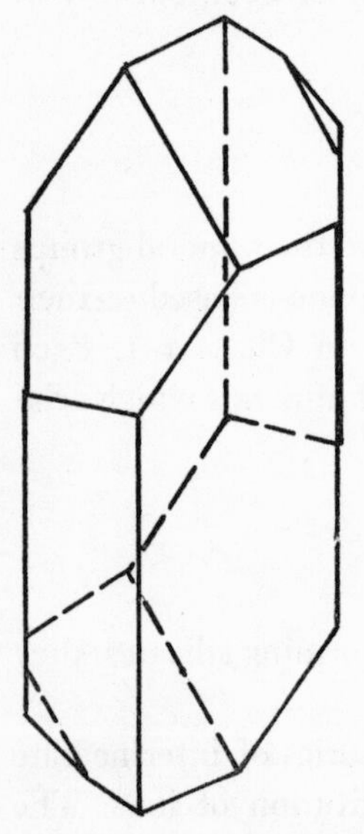

Figure 21 Crystal of orthoclase

Orthoclase felspar is monoclinic, so that the angle between the axes b and c is a right angle, axis a is inclined. In albite and anorthite, as also in mixtures of orthoclase and albite, the crystals are triclinic but the difference from a right angle between the b- and c-axes is so small, being only a few degrees, that it cannot normally be observed by eye. In hand specimens the difference in crystallography cannot be used successfully to distinguish between the alkali and the plagioclase felspars.

All felspars have two good cleavages, one well developed parallel to the base (marked c on the crystal diagrams), and a slightly less distinct cleavage parallel to the side marked b on the diagrams. In cleavage fragments the third plane of breakage shows a brittle, uneven fracture. Felspar grains in rocks often show good flat cleavage facets which reflect the light evenly. On a fresh break, the cleavages may form a step-like surface; on plagioclase felspars they are inclined but the difference in angle are so small that they cannot usually be distinguished, even with a hand lens.

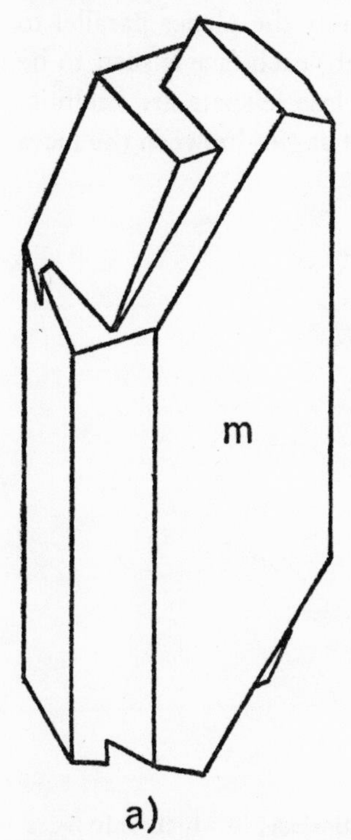

Figure 22 Twinning of felspar crystals. (a) Carlsbad twin of orthoclase

Crystals often appear to consist of two halves which have grown together in opposite directions, as if their axes had been turned through 180°; this is known as *twinning* and occurs very commonly in felspars. For instance, in the *carlsbad* twin of orthoclase shown in Figure 22a, the twinning may be visualized as though the crystal had been sliced in half parallel to the plane marked b, and one half rotated about the vertical axis through 180°, the two halves then pushed together so that they interpenetrate. The b- and c-axes of the twin are in opposite directions. This type of twinning is very common in felspars, and may be seen in rocks where the felspars have developed good crystal forms.

In the plagioclase felspars, another form of twinning is very characteristic, the *albite twin.* In this case, as before, the halves are sliced by a plane parallel to b. One half is rotated through an angle of 180° about the horizontal b-axis. Taking, for the sake of simplicity, a crystal form in which only the planes parallel to the three axes are developed (Figure 22b) each face is seen to be inclined to the other two, since plagioclase felspars are triclinic. An albite twin, therefore, has re-entrant angles between the faces

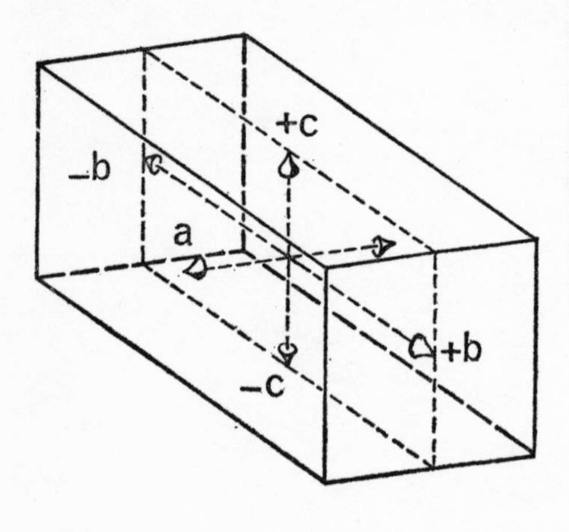

Figure 22 (b) Simple crystal of triclinic plagioclase, in which only faces parallel to the three crystal axes are developed

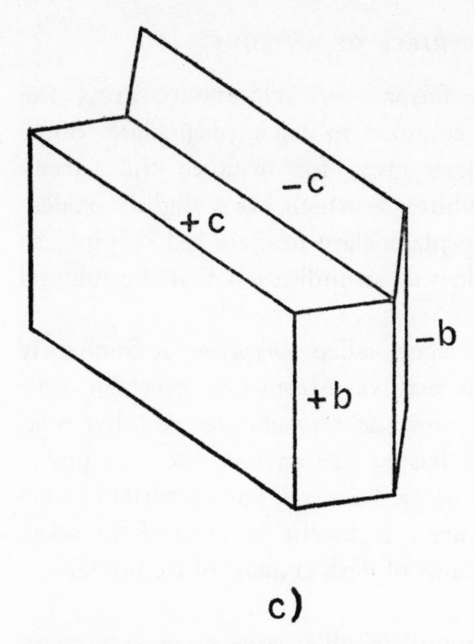

Figure 22 (c) Albite twins of plagioclase

of the twin halves, as shown in Figure 22c. In the plagioclase felspars the twin halves are often extremely thin lamellae, and a large number of these lamellae grow together in alternate directions. The lamellae may be so thin that they can only be seen under high magnification. In the more calcic plagioclases however, the twinning is frequently coarse enough to be distinguished with the naked eye or with a hand lens. If light is allowed to fall obliquely on the crystal or cleavage surface, a striped effect is obtained – caused by the reflection from alternate twin surfaces. The multiple albite twinning is diagnostic of plagioclase felspars, but it cannot always be seen.

Felspars have a hardness 6 and are used as standard on the Mohs' scale of hardness. The specific gravity varies with the chemical composition, it ranges from about 2·5 for orthoclase to 2·6 for albite and 2·67 for anorthite.

Felspars have no inherent colours. The transparent colourless felspars are relatively rare, usually they are opaque white, greyish, or yellowish white. Orthoclase felspar is commonly tinted pink (often referred to as flesh coloured) and may sometimes be dark red. The colours are exotic, due to the presence of iron oxides as impurities. Plagioclase felspars are commonly grey, the darker shades being more common in calcic plagioclase. Some plagioclase felspars are dark grey, for instance the variety *labradorite* (anorthite 50: albite 50) which has a slightly opalescent lustre. Only rarely are plagioclase felspars red or pink, so that this colour may be taken as an indication that the mineral is probably orthoclase.

A variety of potassium felspar, called *microcline*, is frequently coloured green. The colour may vary from pale greenish tinge to grass green, when it is known as *amazonstone*. Another relatively rare variety of alkali felspar has an opalescent to pearly lustre, and is known as *moonstone*. Less well known varieties such as *sunstone* and *aventurine* are translucent varieties of the alkali felspars with minute inclusions of dark crystals of iron oxides.

Occurrence: Felspars are found in all classes of igneous rock. Some igneous rocks such as syenite are composed very largely of felspar. In granite diorite, and the metamorphic gneisses, felspars predominate. The alkali felspars are found more commonly in rocks which contain free silica (quartz) and the calcic plagioclase felspar. In granite, diorite, and the metamorphic gneisses, felspars gabbro. A number of rocks contain both alkali and plagioclase felspar.

Felspathoids

These minerals, like the felspars, are also silicates of aluminium and the alkali metals, sodium, potassium, and calcium. They differ from the felspars in two ways. Additional elements such as sulphur or chlorine may be present, and the proportion of silica to alkali metals is generally lower than in the felspars. From this it follows that most of the felspathoids are not found in rocks containing free silica (quartz), since if sufficient silica had been present in the magma, true felspars would have formed. Felspathoids are found in the more basic rocks (see below) such as syenites and basalts, where they may take the place of felspars.

The felspathoids are relatively rare. *Leucite* ($KAl(Si_2O_6)$)

is found in the lavas of Vesuvius where it can be seen as white rounded crystals in a black fine-grained matrix. *Nepheline* (a rather complex felspathoid, probably a mixture of sodium and potassium aluminium silicate: $NaAlSiO_4$ and $KAlSiO_4$) is an important constituent of some syenites, known as nepheline syenite.

In the present context only one of the felspathoids need be considered in any detail. This is the relatively rare mineral *lazurite* or *lapis lazuli*.

Description: Lazurite is a silicate of sodium and aluminium which also contains sodium sulphide in chemical combination. This is expressed in its chemical formula $3(NaAlSiO_4)Na_2S$. It is a bright blue mineral vitreous, translucent or opaque. It crystallizes in the cubic system, but crystals of lazurite are extremely rare, and it is usually found as a compact mass which breaks unevenly. The specific gravity is 2·4 to 2·5, somewhat lower than the felspars. The hardness is 5·5.

Occurrence: Lazurite is somewhat exceptional among the felspathoids in that it is not a mineral which crystallizes out of the magma in igneous rocks, but it is found as a secondary mineral in crystalline limestones near granite, presumably as the result of contact metamorphism. Lazurite occurs in the Lake Baykal region, in Persia and in Afghanistan.

Mica

The micas are characterized by the excellence of their cleavage, which allows the mineral to split into extremely thin sheets. This cleavage results from the sheet-like structure of the mineral. Thin-cleavage sheets of mica are transparent, tough and flexible.

Description: For the practical purposes of identification of hand specimens, mica may be divided into two groups. The light-coloured mica, called *muscovite* and the dark-coloured mica called *biotite*.

Muscovite and biotite have complex chemical formulae. The principal difference between them is that muscovite is essentially a silicate of potassium and aluminium, while biotite is a silicate of iron and magnesium. The presence of iron accounts for the dark colour of biotite.

Muscovite $KAl_2(AlSi_3O_{10})(OH,F)_2$

Biotite $K(Mg,Fe'')_3(AlSi_3O_{10})(OH,F)_2$

In rocks, micas are seen as small flat six-sided prisms or as irregular cleavage flakes. The surface of the cleavage plates is bright and glistening, sometimes nearly metallic. The side faces of the prisms are rough and striated, and cleavage platelets can easily be detached by inserting a thin point, such as a penknife blade, into the side of the crystals. The hardness of mica varies from 2 to 3, it can be easily scratched with a penknife.

Occurrence: Micas are extremely widespread as rock constituents. *Biotite* is found as an important constituent of many igneous rocks rich in felspar, such as granite and syenite and more rarely in the dark (basic) igneous rocks which are rich in ferromagnesian minerals (i.e. silicates of iron and magnesium). It is also commonly found in metamorphic rocks. *Muscovite* also occurs in igneous rocks such as granites, but it is most abundant in many metamorphic rocks, schists and gneisses, where it may be the most important rock constituent. The decay of felspars sometimes gives rise to a variety of white mica known as sericite.

Muscovite, unlike biotite, is extremely resistant to weathering processes and it features in many sedimentary rocks, even where most other minerals save quartz have disintegrated. Biotite, on the contrary, decays easily and is therefore rare in sedimentary rocks.

Pyroxenes

The pyroxenes comprise a number of minerals which are silicates of iron and magnesium with a silicate chain structure. The differences between the pyroxene minerals are largely differences of chemical composition, in the relative proportions of iron and magnesium, and in the presence of calcium, sodium, and aluminium. These differences in composition result in variations in the optical properties of the minerals, which can be measured by microscopic examination. On macroscopic examination alone the pyroxenes are difficult to distinguish. The most typical and common pyroxene is *augite* with a rather complex chemical formula ($(Ca,Mg,Fe,Al)_2Si_2O_6$). The only pyroxene which requires special treatment here is *jadeite*, a variety of jade ($NaAlSi_2O_6$).

Description: Most pyroxenes crystallize in the monoclinic system, a small group are orthorhombic, but they all have two cleavage planes nearly at right angles. Well formed crystals sometimes occur in igneous rocks, especially in lavas. More commonly, pyroxenes occur as irregular masses of grains in rocks. The nearly right-angled cleavage can then be used to distinguish pyroxenes from the amphiboles (considered below). When they do not break along the cleavage planes, pyroxenes are brittle and have an uneven fracture. The colour of the pyroxenes is largely due to the presence of iron and hence varies according to the chemical composition. A pure calcium and magnesium pyroxene can be white or pale green. The presence of iron gives rise to green and black colours. Augite, the most commonly occurring pyroxene, is a dull dark green or black. The streak colour is always white to murky green.

The hardness and specific gravity also vary with chemical composition. Pyroxenes are among the heavier of the rock-forming minerals. The specific gravity of augite ranges from 3·2 to 3·5. The hardness ranges from 5 to 6.

Jadeite: This variety of pyroxene is not found in igneous rocks. Its mode of occurrence is not fully understood, but it is probably of metamorphic origin. Jadeite crystallizes in the monoclinic system and has two cleavage planes nearly at right angles. It is, however, rarely found in crystal form and usually occurs in massive and fibrous forms in shades of green or a brownish green. It has a hardness of 6·5 to 7 and a specific gravity of 3·3. These properties serve to distinguish it easily from serpentine, which may have a very similar appearance.

When jadeite is evenly coloured and translucent, it is very highly prized as a variety of jade. More opaque and banded varieties of jadeite are less scarce.

Occurrence: Pyroxenes occur chiefly in igneous rocks rich in calcium, magnesium and iron and are rare in rocks which contain free quartz. Igneous rocks containing pyroxenes are usually dark-coloured, green or black, such as basalt and gabbro. In some basaltic lavas, good crystals of augite may be formed.

Jadeite is a rare mineral, especially the translucent varieties. Jadeite occurrences are known in Burma, South China, Tibet, New Zealand, and Mexico. There is evidence from prehistoric axes of the occurrences of jadeite in Europe – but the localities are not accurately known.

Amphiboles

The amphiboles, like the pyroxenes, are also complex silicates of iron and magnesium with variable amounts of the metal ions aluminium, calcium, and sodium. Amphiboles differ from pyroxenes in two fundamental respects. Their atomic structure is the double chain structure in which the silicate group has the composition Si_4O_{11} (or Si_8O_{22}) whereas in the pyroxenes it is Si_2O_6. The chemical composition always includes *hydroxyl* ions, that is ions of a hydrogen and an oxygen atom held together by a homopolar bond (OH). The presence of the hydroxyl ions shows that the amphiboles have crystallized in the presence of water vapour in the magma. In the absence of water vapour, pyroxenes would have formed. Amphiboles are also formed by the hydrothermal alteration of pyroxenes, but the process is more complex than the simple addition of an hydroxyl ion to a pyroxene molecule, for there are also changes in the proportions of calcium and other metals to silica.

Description: Amphiboles comprise a large group of related minerals, the great majority of which crystallize in the monoclinic system. Among the more common amphiboles, *hornblende* is the most widespread. Rarer varieties of special interest as raw minerals are *asbestos* and *nephrite*, a variety of jade.

Good crystal forms of hornblende are found in some rocks, but the mineral frequently occurs in long blade-like forms, or as irregular grains. Hornblende has two good cleavage planes at an angle of 125°, parallel to the length of the crystal. The cleavage angles are one of the important criteria used to distinguish the amphiboles from the pyroxenes. Pyroxene cleavage planes are nearly at right angles and generally not as clearly developed. Cleavage fragments of hornblende have a rhomboid cross-section, in which one pair of angles is distinctly obtuse (125°) and the other distinctly acute (55°). On a fresh break, the hornblende crystals have shiny cleavage faces which may appear coarsely corrugated along the length of the crystal. The fracture across the crystal is uneven.

Asbestos is a variety of amphibole in which the crystals are so elongated and narrow that they are thread-like. Asbestos fibres are strong and flexible so that they can be woven or matted into fine fireproof and hardwearing sheets which are flexible.

The colour of amphiboles varies with their chemical composition and results primarily from the iron content. The non-ferrous varieties are white or grey. With changing iron content, colour varies from pale or clear green to dark brownish green and black. Hornblende is very dark green or black. The streak colours are always pale – white or greyish, greenish or brown.

The specific gravity and hardness of amphiboles also varies with chemical composition, depending chiefly on the amount of iron. Specific gravity ranges from 3 to 3·5. The hardness ranges from 5 to 6.

Nephrite is one of the varieties of jade, the other being the pyroxene jadeite. Nephrite consists of minute fibres of a calcium-magnesium silicate which contains variable amounts of iron. The non-ferrous nephrite is a white translucent jade, while the presence of iron gives rise to pale or bright 'spinach green' jades which may be translucent to nearly opaque. The hardness of nephrite is slightly lower than jadeite, ranging from 5 to 6.

The fibrous nature of nephrite makes this material less brittle than jadeite.

Occurrence: Amphiboles are very widely distributed in igneous and metamorphic rocks. Hornblendes are found in granites, syenites, and diorite and the metamorphic gneiss. Certain schists and 'greenstones' derive their colour from the amphiboles.

Olivine

Olivine is a silicate of iron and magnesium in which the basic structure is the simple SiO_4 tetrahedron. The olivines range from pure magnesium silicate (Mg_2SiO_4) to pure iron silicate (Fe_2SiO_4). The most common forms have an excess of magnesium over iron.

Description: Olivine crystallizes in the orthorhombic system, but good crystals are rarely seen; the mineral occurs most frequently in irregular grains. Olivine has no cleavage, it breaks in an irregular or nearly conchoidal fracture.

The colour of olivine ranges from a pale yellowish green or olive green to bottle green, depending on the iron content. The grains are vitreous, transparent to translucent. The hardness ranges from 6 to 6·5, and the specific gravity from 3·3 to 3·5.

A very transparent pale green variety of olivine is known as *peridot*.

Occurrence: Olivine is the main constituent of a group of dark igneous rocks known as peridotites. It is found in igneous rocks rich in ferromagnesian minerals, for instance basalt, which contain no silica or alkali minerals. It occurs more rarely in metamorphic rocks. The magnesium olivine is formed in the metamorphism of limestones which contain magnesium carbonate, i.e. dolomites.

Olivine becomes altered to serpentine by hydrothermal action and in ancient igneous rocks, it is largely replaced by serpentine.

Tourmaline

There are many varieties of tourmaline which can be distinguished by colour and which differ in chemical composition. Tourmaline is a rather complex silicate of aluminium which may contain either sodium or calcium, or both, and either iron or magnesium, or both, in combination with the volatile constituents of rock magma: fluorine, boron, and water (hydroxyl). The chemical formula varies according to the type but a generalized formula is $XY_3B_3Al_3(AlSi_2O_9)_3(OH.F)_4$, where X=Na, Ca and Y=Al,Fe″,Mg.

Description: Tourmaline crystallizes in the hexagonal system and generally forms long prismatic crystals, terminated by three flat faces. The prism faces often have a striated appearance due to the frequent alternation of prism faces and seen from above, the crystals appear to have three curved prism sides (Figure 23). Tourmaline crystals may occur singly or in masses of acicular

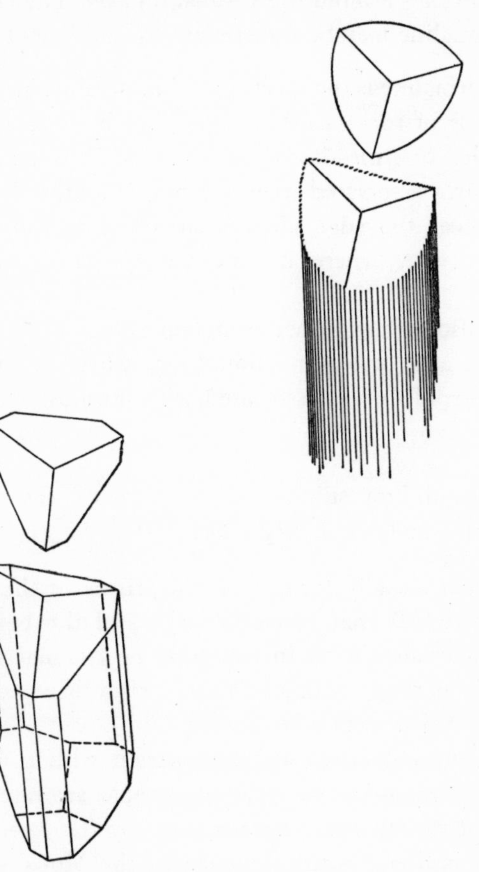

Figure 23 Tourmaline crystal

crystals. Black tourmaline commonly occurs massive or columnar, or in clumps of radiating acicular crystals.

Tourmaline has no cleavages and breaks with an irregular or conchoidal fracture. Its hardness is 7 to 7·5 and the specific gravity is 3·1 to 3·2.

Common tourmaline, or *schorl*, is jet black; it may be highly lustrous or dull, and is always opaque. Rarer varieties of tourmaline may be pink or green, and sometimes crystals are green at one end and pink at the other. Pale smoky yellow tourmaline is also known. The colour may not be evenly distributed, but may form concentric zones around the vertical (c) axis. The coloured varieties of tourmaline may be transparent to translucent.

Occurrence: Tourmaline is the most typical mineral formed in the cavities and veins of rocks where magma has become enriched with the volatiles fluorine, boron and others. It is commonly found in structures associated with granite batholiths. It occurs in the granite near the edge of batholiths and in the contact metamorphic aureole, where it may be associated with ore deposits.

Tourmaline also occurs in some metamorphic rocks such as gneisses, schists and crystalline limestone, where it indicates that the metamorphism was associated with igneous activity.

Topaz

Topaz is an aluminium silicate which contains the volatile substances fluorine and water, $Al_2SiO_4(F,OH)_2$.

Description: Topaz usually forms pointed prisms in the orthorhombic system (which may resemble prisms of the hexagonal system) but it may also occur in columnar or granular masses. The cleavage is perfect, parallel to the prism base, and the fracture in any other direction is uneven.

Topaz is usually colourless and transparent with a vitreous lustre. Yellow or brown-yellow varieties of topaz are rare, and a white translucent variety is also known.

The hardness is 8 and is the standard on the Mohs' scale of hardness; the specific gravity is 3·5.

Occurrence: Topaz is a relatively rare mineral. It is most commonly associated with granite or felsite and occurs in rock cavities or pegmatite veins where the magma was enriched with volatiles. Its occurrence is a useful indication of the permeation of rocks by magmatic vapours, as in contact metamorphism and it is then usually associated with quartz and tourmaline.

Garnet

The common garnet is a silicate of iron and aluminium ($Fe_3Al_2(SiO_4)_3$) also known as *almandine* or *almandite*. A number of other varieties of garnet exist in which the iron is replaced by other metal ions. In some garnets the aluminium is also replaced by ferric iron or chromium.

Description: All garnets crystallize in the cubic system. When crystals develop they are the rhomdodecahedron (i.e. 12 rhomboid faces, as illustrated in Chapter 1), or a slightly more complex form as shown in Figure 9, with 24 faces. Commonly, however, garnets occur as irregular rounded grains.

Common garnets are dark red or red-brown in colour. Most garnets are translucent or opaque but deep-red transparent varieties are also known. A pale olive green to greenish yellow variety of garnet is known as *grossularite* or *cinnamon stone*.

Occurrence: Garnets are widespread in metamorphic rocks. They are found in mica schists, gneisses, and also in veins in granites. The calcium garnet grossularite is commonly found in metamorphosed limestones.

Garnets are very resistant to weathering and are therefore found concentrated in alluvial deposits.

Zircon

Zircon is a silicate of the metal zirconium $ZrSiO_4$.

Description: Zircon crystallizes in the tetragonal system and normally forms a simple crystal consisting of a rectangular prism with pyramidal extremities (Figure 10).

The mineral has a poor cleavage parallel to the faces of the prism and a conchoidal fracture.

Common zircon is normally opaque, pale grey, yellowish, or reddish brown with a colourless streak. Transparent varieties of zircon also exist; they are smoky grey or brown, and a red transparent variety is known as *hyacinth.*

The hardness of zircon is 7·5 and its specific gravity is 4·7.

Occurrence: As a primary mineral of igneous rocks, zircon is fairly widespread in granites and syenites, but it normally occurs in relatively small quantities as compared to the essential rock-forming silicates. Zircon also occurs in a number of metamorphic rocks such as gneiss. Since its specific gravity is high, 4·7, it becomes concentrated in alluvial deposits derived from such rocks.

Beryl

Beryl is a silicate of aluminium and berylium, $Be_3Al_2Si_6O_{18}$.

Description: Beryl crystallizes in the hexagonal system, forming prisms usually with a truncated pyramidal extremity. It also occurs massive and crystalline. It has a very weak cleavage parallel to the prism base and breaks with a conchoidal or uneven fracture.

Crystals of beryl are transparent with a vitreous lustre and vary in colour according to the colouring impurity. Pale greens (due to chromium) are most common. Dark green beryl is known as *emerald* and blue beryl as *aquamarine*. Yellow and white beryl is also known. The massive forms of beryl may be translucent or opaque.

The hardness is 7·5 to 8 and the specific gravity is 2·7.

Occurrence: Small grains of beryl may occur as an accessory mineral in acid igneous rocks such as granite. Prismatic crystals are found in cavities or pegmatite veins and may be extremely large (one crystal 18 feet long is known). Beryl is also found in metamorphic rocks associated with granite intrusions, particularly in micaceous schists.

Hydrous Silicates

The hydrous silicates are alteration products which are formed from pre-existing silicates by the action of water. The alteration of silicates can occur in two ways. On the surface, ground water is strongly acidified by carbon dioxide and frequently also by humus from decaying vegetation. The action of acidified ground-water on rock is an important aspect of soil-forming processes. It results in the chemical decomposition of rock minerals into a number of new substances. Silicates are decomposed into simpler silicate minerals which form the *clay minerals* and into a number of salts and silica and other oxides, including iron oxides, which gives most soils their brown colours. The salts and oxides will be considered in a later chapter.

From the point of view of rock forming silicates, another form of silicate alteration is much more important. This is the action of hot magmatic water vapour, and is called hydrothermal alteration. Hydrothermal alteration is common in the more ancient igneous rocks. Only in some of the geologically young rocks are the minerals entirely free of alteration. Hydrothermal alteration is a form of metamorphism, and there is no sharp division between igneous rocks which show some alteration and the more completely metamorphosed igneous rocks. As already mentioned, pyroxenes become altered to amphiboles in the presence of water vapour; the white mica muscovite, which is a common constituent of altered rocks, is derived from felspar, topaz, and other minerals. Amphiboles and mica have already been described since they occur also as primary rock-forming silicates. Other hydrous silicates which are characteristic of metamorphic rocks are *serpentine*, *talc*, and *chlorite*.

Clay Minerals

Clay minerals are hydrated aluminium silicates which result chiefly from the alteration of igneous rocks. Clays have extremely small crystals, which can only be seen with the magnification of an electron microscope. They have a silicate sheet structure and tend to form plate-like crystals which are similar to those of mica, but on a much smaller scale. When wetted, clay absorbs water molecules between the platelets. This water acts as a lubricant which gives wet clays their plasticity. The absorption of water molecules also results in a considerable expansion on wetting, and equivalent contraction on drying. The degree and manner in which water can be absorbed varies according to the different clay minerals so that all clays are not equally plastic. The finer the clay platelets the more water can be absorbed by a mass of clay, so that the plasticity of any clay is greater when the grain size is small.

The different clay minerals vary principally in the amount of *water of crystallization* they have. The water of crystallization consists of molecules of water which form part of the crystal structure. The water of crystallization, unlike the absorbed water between the crystal platelets, is not lost by normal drying processes, but only by strong heating. When water of crystallization is lost, changes in the crystal structure also occur. Thus two clay minerals *kaolinite* and *halloysite* differ only in the degree of hydration. This is most clearly expressed in their chemical formulae: kaolinite $Al_2Si_4O_{10}(OH)_6$ and halloysite $Al_2Si_4O_{10}(OH)_6.4H_2O$. The water molecules in a halloysite crystal form part of its structure and are arranged between the silicate sheets, resulting in some distortion of the sheet structure. Halloysite crystals consist of tubes and curled platelets which split and unroll on dehydration.

There are also differences in the proportion of aluminium to silicon ions in the clays and in the extent to which substitution of ions takes place, such as magnesium or iron for aluminium. In the clay mineral *montmorillonite* $Al_4Si_8O_{10}(OH)_4.nH_2O$ (where n is a whole number) some of the aluminium is always replaced by magnesium. Since aluminium forms a *tri*valent ion (Al^{3+}) and magnesium only *di*valent ion (Mg^{2+}), the substitution of magnesium for aluminium leaves the mineral unbalanced. The remaining negative charges are balanced by the addition of cations such as sodium (Na^+), potassium (K^+) or calcium (Ca^{2+}). This is one of the ways in which these alkali metals are retained in a clayey soil. There are also unbalanced charges around the edges of the silicate sheets, where the structure is incomplete, and this is another way in which metal ions and other soil substances (e.g. humus) are retained by clay minerals. The capacity of soils to retain ions is greater when the clays are very fine-grained; sandy soils without clay are generally very poor in bases.

Clays are formed by normal soil weathering processes. When the weathering product remains in situ, the thick deposits of 'residual clays' are formed, which may consist of one type of clay mineral only. Many important clay deposits are alluvial and consist of a mixture of clay minerals and other weathering products. Hydrothermal processes also result in the formation of clay minerals, particularly *kaolinite* from felspars and *chlorite* from silicates containing iron and magnesium.

Kaolinite

Kaolinite is hydrous aluminium silicate ($Al_2Si_2O_5(OH)_4$) and is also known as *kaolin* or *china clay*.

Description: Kaolinite is a crystalline clay mineral which forms small six-sided plates similar to mica, but the platelets are generally so small that the crystal structure cannot be observed even with an optical microscope. Kaolinite forms a compact friable mass which has a smooth greasy feel when rubbed between the fingers. The colour of pure kaolinite is white, but it is often stained grey, yellowish, or brownish. The specific gravity is 2·6. The hardness of the mineral (2 to 2·5) cannot be used as a diagnostic feature since individual platelets are much too small to be tested.

Occurrence: Kaolinite is found as large deposits of china clay in deeply altered granite, for instance in Cornwall, Saxony, and other localitities in many parts of the world. The mineral is also a common constituent of many fine clay sediments. Since the flakes of kaolinite are so small they are carried in suspension for a very long time, and very pure sedimentary deposits of kaolinite are found. These are distinguished from residual kaolinite by the absence of undecayed rock grains, particularly quartz.

Kaolinite is probably formed from felspars and other aluminous silicates by normal soil weathering processes. The very large and deep deposits of china clay in the granite of Cornwall and Dartmoor are more probably of hydrothermal origin, for the kaolin is there associated with other minerals characteristic of hydrothermal activity, such as tourmaline and tinstone.

Chlorite

Chlorites are a group of minerals which are very closely related to the micas, but forming very small crystals, so that they are sometimes classed with the clay minerals.

Description: Like mica, chlorite occurs as platelets of six-sided prisms or as irregular plates. It forms finely granular masses with a slightly greasy feel. Chlorites are various shades of green, frequently with a pearly lustre, subtranslucent to opaque. The hardness 2 to 2·5 cannot often be determined, since the platelets are generally too small; the specific gravity is 2·7.

There are also hydrated forms of chlorite, such as *vermiculite*, in which the water of crystallization is arranged between the silicate sheets, and the crystals are tubular or curled as in halloysite.

Occurrence: Chlorites are derived from the hydrothermal alteration of silicate minerals which contain aluminium, iron, and magnesium, such as biotite, hornblende, and augite. The chemical composition of chlorites varies, depending on the original mineral from which they are derived. Chlorite occurs in the more basic altered igneous rocks and imparts a greenish colour to them. In metamorphic rocks such as schists and slates chlorite may be the most abundant mineral.

Serpentinite, Serpentine

Serpentine or serpentinite is a hydrous magnesium silicate which occurs in a variety of colours and forms. It is an alteration product of magnesium silicates and its composition is expressed by the formula $Mg_3Si_2O_5(OH)_4$, in which some replacement of the magnesium by ferrous iron is common.

The mineral should, strictly speaking, be referred to as serpentinite. Serpentine refers to the rock which consists solely or predominantly of the mineral serpentinite. It is common practice, however, to use the word serpentine indiscriminately – whether referring to the mineral or the rock.

Description: Serpentine occurs massive, and crystalline forms are not known. Fibrous varieties of serpentine resemble asbestos, but do not form threads as long and flexible as the extreme varieties of asbestos. The massive serpentine is smooth and may be soapy to the touch, or very finely granular.

Serpentine is commonly a shade of green, it varies from pale yellowish green, bright green, and dark brownish green to nearly black. The colour may grade from darker to paler shades in the same rock and serpentine rock is often veined and spotted with white, green, red, or brown. Fibrous varieties of serpentine are frequently shades of brown or near white. The lustre is waxy to dull, it ranges from opaque to slightly translucent.

The hardness of serpentine is 2·5 to 3 and the specific gravity ranges from 2·2 to 2·7.

Occurrence: Serpentine is found in altered rocks which contain magnesium silicate minerals such as amphiboles, pyroxenes, and especially olivine. In some igneous rocks the olivine crystals are largely or entirely replaced by serpentine. Serpentine is also found as large masses of intensely altered igneous rock, especially those subjected to hydrothermal action. The rock is often veined or patchy with other alteration products or with remains of original rock minerals.

Serpentine may have a superficial resemblance to certain forms of jades. It can easily be distinguished by the soapy feel, and the hardness and the specific gravity.

Talc

Talc is also a hydrous magnesium silicate but it differs from serpentine in many respects. Its chemical composition is $Mg_3Si_4O_{10}(OH)_2$ which shows it to be relatively richer in silica (SiO_2).

Description: Talc is an extremely soft mineral (the standard for hardness 1 on the Mohs' scale of hardness). Good tabular crystals of talc are rare, for it generally occurs massive with a foliaceous structure, or massive with a finely granular structure. It has perfect cleavage like mica and occurs in small platelets in rock.

Talc is colourless or silvery white, but green and greenish grey varieties also occur, often with a pearly lustre.

The specific gravity of talc is 2·7 to 2·8. Talc has a distinctly soapy or greasy feel to the touch. It marks cloth; the 'french chalk' used by tailors is a variety of talc.

An important massive variety of talc is known as *steatite* or *soapstone*. It is most frequently white or grey, but may also be green or reddish brown to black. The stone is so soft that it is easily carved with a knife and it is resistant to fire.

Occurrence: Talc is a hydrothermal alteration product of magnesium silicate minerals which forms under somewhat different conditions from serpentine. Talc forms most commonly from minerals which are free from aluminium, for instance pure magnesium olivine, some pyroxenes, and amphiboles. It is found in altered igneous rocks, but the most important source of talc is in metamorphic rocks where it forms an important component of some schists, or occurs as soapstone or steatite.

Non-Silicates

There are also a large number of minerals of igneous and metamorphic rocks which are not silicates. Some of these, such as gypsum and calcite, are so much more abundant in sedimentary rocks than in igneous rocks that they are better described in the chapter on sediments. The metal ores have special significance as raw materials and will be discussed separately. There remains a number of minerals which occur in more or less small quantities in igneous rocks. They are not diagnostic in the identification of rocks, and only those which have some revelance to human industry will be described.

Corundum

Corundum is the hardest of rock-forming minerals, hardness 9. Diamond is the only mineral which is harder.

Description: Corundum is pure aluminium oxide Al_2O_3. It crystallizes in the hexagonal system into six-sided prisms which may be terminated by a pyramid. The angles between the crystal faces are usually rounded and the crystals are rather barrel-shaped. Both crystals and shapeless grains are found in rocks such as syenites.

Corundum has no cleavage, but the crystals often have markings which resemble a cleavage parallel to the base of the prism.

The common form of corundum is greyish white or dark grey, the lustre is either vitreous or dull. *Emery* is a dark grey corundum, often with an admixture of magnetite and hematite (iron oxides). A blue transparent variety of corundum is known as *sapphire* and the red transparent variety as *ruby*. Both are very rare.

The specific gravity of corundum is very high, 4.

Occurrence: Corundum occurs as a primary mineral in some igneous rocks and may also result from metamorphic processes in rocks such as shales and limestones. Since it is exceptionally resistant to weathering and has a high specific gravity, corundum is found in alluvial deposits.

'Hard' sands which contain emery occur, for instance, on the island of Naxos in the Aegean, in localities in Turkey and in the Ural Mountains.

Fluorite

Fluorite is also known as *fluorspar*; a blue and banded variety is *Blue John* or *Derbyshire spar*, its chemical composition is calcium fluoride CaF_2.

Description: Cubic crystals are very common but it also occurs as a compact or granular mass. The cleavage is in a direction parallel to the diagonal of the cube faces, so that cubes with truncated corners are formed (Figure 16).

Fluorite is transparent and colourless with a vitreous lustre, but it frequently has an exotic colour which is commonly blue, purple, pale yellow, or green. The colour is often unevenly distributed in the crystals, so that it may shade off to nearly colourless, and the crystals may appear zoned.

The hardness is 4 and is used as a standard on the Mohs' scale of hardness; the specific gravity ranges from 3 to 3·5.

Occurrence: Fluorite occurs in veins in limestones as the result of hydrothermal activity, where it is frequently associated with certain metal ores such as copper pyrite, galena, and blende. It also occurs in the fissures and cavities of igneous rocks where the volatile constituents have become concentrated with minerals rich in volatiles such as topaz, tourmaline, and others.

Fluorite may resemble the blue to purple variety of quartz, *amethyst*, in its colouring and lustre. It is easily distinguished from quartz by the crystal system and the much lower hardness. Transparent varieties of fluorite can be distinguished from other spars, calcite, baryte, and others, by the simple physical tests of hardness, specific gravity, and crystal habit.

Barytes, Barite

Barytes is barium sulphate, $BaSO_4$. It is also known as *heavy spar* because of its superficial resemblance to iceland spar, a form of calcite (see pp. 106–9), and is called 'heavy' because it has a much greater specific gravity than calcite.

Description: Barytes crystallizes in the orthorhombic system and forms tabular crystals with tapering sides (Figure 17). It also occurs as a granular or compact mass and is then frequently banded, or as a columnar fibrous mass. The cleavage is very good in two directions, parallel to the base and parallel to the prism side.

Good crystals of barytes are usually colourless, transparent with a vitreous or slightly pearly lustre. They may be lightly tinged yellow, brown, or red by iron oxides. The massive varieties of barytes are white opaque, often also stained with iron oxides.

Hardness is 3 to 3·5 and the specific gravity is high, 4·5.

Occurrence: Barytes occurs in veins of hydrothermal origin, commonly in limestones, where it is usually associated with fluorite and quartz, and the ores of zinc and lead.

Turquoise

Turquoise is a complex hydrated phosphate of aluminium with some copper oxide. The chemical composition is variable and is possibly represented by $CuO.3Al_2O_3.2P_2O_5.9H_2O$.

Description: Its colour, which ranges from pale blue to bluish green, is probably due to the presence of copper. It occurs as massive reniform (kidney-shaped) masses with a rather waxy lustre. It may be slightly translucent but is more frequently opaque, and generally appears veined. The fracture is sub-conchoidal. The hardness is 6 and the specific gravity 2·6 to 2·8.

Occurrence: Turquoise is only found in intensely altered rock in veins or patchy deposits. Another substance called *odontolite*, or *bone turquoise*, can sometimes be mistaken for turquoise. Odontolite is fossil bone or teeth which have become stained greenish blue by ferrous iron phosphate, *vivianite*.

CHAPTER THREE

The Igneous and Metamorphic Rocks

THERE are many features of rocks which can be used as criteria for a classification. Their mode of origin gives the primary classification into igneous, sedimentary, and metamorphic rocks. Within these classes further distinctions can be made on the basis of their manner of formation; for instance, the igneous rocks have been classified according to the depth at which they are believed to have formed into *plutonic* (deep-seated), *hypabyssal* (intermediate depth), and *volcanic* (surface) rocks. This classification is, however, such an oversimplification that it is of limited practical value. Other criteria on which a useful classification of igneous rocks may be based are the mineral and chemical compositions of the rocks, their texture and colour.

Differences in the mineral and chemical composition and in the textures of rocks are gradational and sharp division drawn between features such as coarse-grained, medium-grained, and fine-grained rocks must be arbitrary. Similarly, although the difference in chemical composition and texture between an intrusive igneous rock and extrusive, or volcanic rock may be clearly defined in the extreme cases, a lava flow may be the superficial continuation of an intrusive dyke. Any plane which is drawn to separate the lava from the dyke will be arbitrary, and the rock on either side of such a division is identical. Even in the primary classification of rocks into igneous, sedimentary and metamorphic, only the distinction between igneous and sedimentary is absolute.[1] The metamorphic group includes many types of rocks, which differ from the 'fresh' rock (igneous or sedimentary) according to the nature and degree of metamorphism.

Such difficulties of classification are inherent in the nature of

[1] But see pyroclastic rocks, pp. 87–90.

the material, and they have given rise to several attempts at rock nomenclature. Ultimately, a full description of a rock can only be given by complete mineralogical, physical, and chemical analysis.

For the present purposes, a classification of rocks based on macroscopic features only is required. Before the use of the microscope this was the only type of classification available, and still has an acknowledged significance for geological fieldwork, engineering, and architecture. The terminology used is essentially the same as that obtained from microscopic examination, except that far fewer of the subdivisions of rock types can be recognized. The identification of a rock depends on an analysis of its texture and of its mineral composition.

Igneous Rocks

Texture: The texture of an igneous rock is chiefly a matter of grain size and grain shape. The rock may be coarse-grained so that individual minerals are easily distinguished by the naked eye, or it may be so fine-grained that only microscopic study will reveal its crystalline nature. The degree of crystallinity is an important aspect of texture, i.e. whether minerals occur as well formed 'euhedral' crystals, or whether they occur as irregular grains. Some volcanic rocks may be non-crystalline and are therefore glasses, or a combination of a glass with crystal structures. A third aspect of the texture of igneous rocks concerns the distribution of grain sizes. In equigranular rocks the crystals of the essential minerals are of roughly the same size, but in many rocks where cooling has proceeded in two stages, the first minerals which crystallize slowly develop into large crystals (*phenocrysts*) whereas the later minerals which crystallize more rapidly form a finer groundmass. Textures of this type are said to be *porphyritic* (Pl. 3).

Coarse-grained rocks, or *phanerites*, are those in which the majority of mineral grains are large enough to be seen by the naked eye or with a hand lens (magnification ×10) (Pl. 2). Most coarse-grained rocks are roughly equigranular and the crystals average about 1 to 2 mm in diameter, but porphyritic textures are also fairly common. Coarser-grained rocks, with average grain sizes of 5 mm or more, are less abundant.

Microphanerite is a term used to describe rocks intermediate in grain size between the *phanerites* and the *aphanites* (fine-textured rocks). They comprise rocks such as microgranite which is identical to granite in composition but of smaller average grain size than a true granite (usually less than 0·5 mm in diameter).

Microcrystalline rocks are predominantly so fine-grained that the individual crystals cannot be determined without the use of a microscope, and these are sometimes called aphanites. Microcrystalline rocks are very frequently porphyritic and comprise a number of rocks commonly known as quartz porphyry, a fine-grained rock with phenocrysts of quartz, and porphyrite, a dark fine-grained rock with felspar phenocrysts.

Glasses are rocks in which the magma on cooling has not crystallized into distinct minerals. They may be considered to have zero grain size. Glasses are recognized by their conchoidal fracture and vitreous to pitchy lustre. Combinations of glass and crystalline textures occur quite commonly, and glasses may lose some of their characteristic appearance through the inclusion of bubbles of gas or liquid. With time, glasses become devitrified, and change into fine-grained crystalline rocks, so that all natural glasses are of geologically recent date (Quaternary or Tertiary).

Mineral composition: Since igneous rocks result from the cooling of silicate melts, a classification of these rocks may logically be based on their chemical composition, and in particular on the amount of silica present. Although ultimately this requires a chemical analysis, the chemical composition of a rock is reflected in its component minerals and a good estimate of its chemical composition can be obtained from a mineralogical analysis of the rock. In Table 4 the essential rock-forming minerals are listed in order of decreasing silica content.

A rock which is rich in silica is said to be *acid*, and contains predominantly minerals of high silica content, especially quartz and felspar. A rock poor in silica is said to be *basic*, and is relatively richer in the metals iron, magnesium, and calcium, so that in a basic rock the mafic minerals (silicates of iron, magnesium, and calcium) predominate, and quartz is usually absent. The felspars of basic rocks are usually plagioclase felspars and frequently calcic, whereas the felspars in acid rocks are predominantly potassic and sodic. Thus, igneous rocks may be classified into acid and basic rocks which have different mineral compositions. It is useful to recognize a third class of *intermediate* rocks, which contain more silica than the basic rocks. They consist largely of felspars, and never contain more than ten per cent quartz. Some rocks are so poor in silica that they consist almost entirely of mafic minerals. They are known as *ultrabasic*.

TABLE 4

Mineral	Composition
Quartz	Pure silica
Alkali Felspar	Orthoclase or potassic felspar
Plagioclase Felspar	Sodic felspar Calcic felspar
Biotite Amphiboles Pyroxenes Olivines	Silicates of iron, magnesium and calcium: *mafic* minerals

The acid and intermediate rocks may each be further subdivided on the basis of the type of felspar present. The alkali felspar series *orthoclase-albite* (see pp. 45–6 is richer in silica than the plagioclase felspar series, *albite-anorthite*. Although the accurate identification of felspars is not possible without a microscope, it is frequently possible to distinguish between alkali (orthoclase) felspar and plagioclase felspar on the basis of twinning. *Lamellar* twins are characteristic of the plagioclase felspars and *carlsbad* twins of the alkali felspars (see pp. 48–9). When the alkali felspars are coloured, pink or green, this is also a useful means of differentiation from plagioclase, but both alkali and plagioclase felspars may be white or grey. Thus when a fresh break is available for study a rock sample may be named with a high degree of accuracy. When only a polished surface can be examined (as frequently happens in archaeology) the felspars can often not be identified, but it is usually possible to ascertain whether the rock is acid, intermediate or basic.

In Table 5 the classification of coarse-grained igneous rocks is summarized according to their chemical compositions, and the names of the principal rock types are given. The approximate proportion of mafic minerals in the rock types is indicated, as these minerals are a useful guide to rock identification, especially when the felspars cannot be identified.

TABLE 5

	ACID	INTER-MEDIATE	BASIC	ULTRABASIC
Proportion of quartz	>10%	<10%	<10%	No quartz
Mafic minerals and Orthoclase predominates	<25% GRANITE	<25% SYENITE		
Mafic minerals and Plagioclase predominates	25 – 50% GRANODIORITE (Quartz diorite)	25 – 50% DIORITE	50 – 75% GABBRO	>75% Hornblendite Pyroxenite Peridotite

As with all other characteristics of igneous rocks the series from acid to ultrabasic rocks is a gradational one, and the position of any rock within this series can be expressed in terms of its mineral composition. For example, the term granite comprises both rocks consisting solely of felspar and quartz, in which the relative amounts of orthoclase to plagioclase may vary widely, as well as quartz-felspar rocks which also contain small quantities of biotite and hornblende. Granites grade on the one hand into granodiorites with increasing plagioclase and mafic mineral content, and on the other into syenites with decreasing quartz content. In some cases therefore, it is not easy to determine whether a rock should fall in one or other of two neighbouring classes.

The fine-grained igneous rocks are classified on the same basis as the coarse-grained igneous rocks. For each class of coarse-grained igneous rock there is a fine-grained (microphanerite) equivalent which results from the rapid crystallization of magma of the same composition. Thus granites grade into microgranites, gabbros into microgabbros (commonly called *dolerite* or *diabase*). The conditions of temperature and pressure for the formation of fine-grained rocks differ from those of the large masses of plutonic rocks. This is especially marked in the formation of volcanic rocks, which crystallize at the earth's surface. This leads to differences in both chemical and mineral composition, particularly the loss of volatile components of the magma in volcanic rocks. Thus, although *rhyolite* is the fine-grained volcanic rock formed from an acid magma of similar composition to that which formed granite at depth, it is not true to say that rhyolite is a fine-grained variety of granite, and granites and micro-granites do not grade into rhyolite. The acidity of rhyolite, i.e. its silica and mafic mineral contents, are, however, the same as those of granite, and it is often said to be a fine-grained equivalent of the plutonic acid rocks. In Table 6 the nomenclature of the volcanic and corresponding plutonic igneous rocks is given.

TABLE 6

TEXTURE	ACID		INTERMEDIATE		BASIC	ULTRA BASIC
Coarse	GRANITE	GRANO-DIORITE	SYENITE	DIORITE	GABBRO	Pyroxenite Horn-blendite Peridotite
Medium	MICRO-GRANITE	MICRO-GRANO-DIORITE	MICRO-SYENITE	MICRO-DIORITE	MICRO-GABBRO Diabase Dolerite	
Fine	RHYOLITE	DACITE	TRACHYTE	ANDESITE	BASALT	

In practice, the full identification of fine-grained rocks can only be achieved with microscopic study, and only a rough approximation into acid, intermediate or basic can be attempted in hand specimens. The full nomenclature of igneous rocks is however given here, as the terms are often encountered in the literature.

Colour: The colour of igneous rocks depends entirely on their mineral components. In general, the silica-rich minerals – quartz and felspar – are light-coloured, white to grey or pink to red, and the mafic minerals are dark-coloured ranging from grey to black or green. Thus, acid rocks are usually light-coloured, and basic and ultrabasic rocks are dark-coloured. Granodiorites and diorites, in which approximately a quarter or a half of the rock constituents are dark mafic minerals, have a characteristically speckled appearance.

The difference in colour between acid and basic rocks is particularly useful in the identification of the fine-grained igneous rocks in which individual minerals cannot be identified. In hand specimens, such rocks can only be classified according to texture and colour. Many fine-grained rocks are porphyritic and the identification of the phenocrysts is very useful in identifying these rocks. Acid rocks generally have quartz or orthoclase phenocrysts; intermediate rocks have felspar phenocrysts in a darker groundmass; and the basic lavas are generally dark with augite or olivine phenocrysts.

Granite

Granites are coarse-grained igneous rocks which are composed of felspars, quartz, and generally also biotite, but granites which consist solely of felspar and quartz are also known. Sometimes hornblende is also present, occurring with or without biotite. White mica and muscovite are also found in granites. Other minerals may occur in small quantities but they are not diagnostic of the rock type; for instance, tourmaline, topaz, garnet, and others (Pls. 1 and 2).

The felspars are the most abundant mineral of granites. Sometimes only orthoclase felspar is present, but generally both orthoclase and plagioclase are found, with orthoclase always predominating. When the orthoclase is pink or red, it is easily distinguished from the white or grey plagioclase, but in many granites the two felspars are white or grey and can be distinguished by their twinning which can only be observed on a fresh break. Quartz may be of the same colour as the felspars. It can be distinguished by a number of properties: its greater hardness, its irregular or conchoidal fracture, and its lack of cleavage. In addition, the felspars normally show shiny cleavage planes, while quartz has a more vitreous lustre. Quartz is among the last minerals to crystallize out of the magma, so that it is normally found in irregularly-shaped grains, filling the interstices between the other minerals (Pl. 1).

Mica is normally present as biotite, but both dark and white mica may be found in the same rock. The micas may be distinguished by their excellent cleavage; by using a pin (or similar fine point) thin cleavage flakes can easily be detached, and this cannot be done with the other rock minerals. The cleavage planes of mica have a high, nearly metallic, lustre and a low hardness. The other dark mineral which may occur in granite, hornblende, is easily distinguished from biotite by its greater hardness and lack of flaky cleavage.

Granites are equigranular in texture, i.e. the principal mineral components are of *roughly* the same size. In some granites the range of grain size may be quite wide, but all mineral grains normally fall between 1 mm and 5 mm in diameter. Finer-textured and also coarser-textured granites are known. In some instances, the outer zone of the Dartmoor granite for example, some felspars occur as phenocrysts of orthoclase, up to several centimetres long. This gives the rock a porphyritic texture and the granite is then called *porphyritic granite* (Pl. 4).

The colour of granites varies according to the colour and relative amounts of their component minerals. They may be nearly white or pale grey depending on the abundance of the darker minerals. Pink, red, and purple granites occur when the orthoclase felspars are highly-coloured.

Jointing is often well developed in granite and the rock generally breaks up into rhomboidal blocks. The size of the blocks varies considerably; they are generally smaller in dykes than in large rock masses. In some granites the jointing may result in the rock breaking up into fragments too small even for most building purposes. Less commonly, very large blocks can be obtained, as in the Aswan region in Egypt where the granite quarries yielded blocks large enough to carve the great obelisks, but such large blocks are relatively rare.

Granite is a hard rock with a high crushing strength and it can be used for massive constructions which bear a heavy weight. It is a poor conductor of heat, so that it does not withstand fire well. When subjected to fire, strong temperature gradients are set up in the rock which cause it to crack and eventually to crumble to a friable mass.

Pegmatite is the rock formed in the volatile enriched fissures of a large rock mass, and it is most characteristically associated with granite. In fact when the name pegmatite alone is used, it normally refers to a granite pegmatite. Pegmatites are found as dykes or veins, in which very large crystals are found and in which the less-common rock minerals such as tourmaline, topaz, and others occur more abundantly than in the main mass of the rock. Pegmatites are exploited for these rarer minerals and for the large crystals of minerals, for instance, muscovite masses, which can be split into large transparent sheets up to 1 m in diameter. The potassium felspar *microcline*, including the green variety *amazonstone*, is usually found in pegmatite veins of acid igneous rocks.

Granodiorite

Granodiorite is very similar to granite, the main difference being the preponderance of plagioclase felspars over alkali felspars. Granodiorites commonly have a higher proportion of hornblende and/or biotite than granites and are therefore often darker grey in colour. Pink and red shades are much less marked than granites, since this results from the orthoclase felspars. Many of the rocks commonly referred to as hornblende granite or biotite granite, are in fact granodiorites, and this rock is more widespread than granite.

The occurrence of granodiorite is the same as for granite, forming large plutonic intrusions known as batholiths. The associated features, such as pegmatite veins and the system of jointing in granodiorite are also very similar to those described for granite.

When a rock specimen cannot be chipped to obtain a fresh break on which the felspars can be examined, it is frequently impossible to distinguish between a granite and a granodiorite. Since the appearance and the physical properties of these rocks are very similar, they were used and worked in the same manner in antiquity. When considering problems of ancient technology, therefore, the accurate identification of these rocks is not necessary. In problems of origin of archaeological specimens, the distinction is clearly highly relevant.

Syenite

Syenites differ in composition from granites principally in the absence of quartz. Felspar is the most abundant constituent of syenites, and it may be the only mineral present. The felspar is chiefly orthoclase and plagioclase generally occurs in smaller quantities. As with granites, when the two felspars are of different colours they may easily be distinguished, but when both orthoclase and plagioclase felspars are white or grey it is difficult to differentiate between the minerals in hand specimens, except on a fresh break.

Generally biotite, hornblende, and pyroxene are present, or a combination of these minerals, but they only occur in small quantitites, not exceeding a quarter of the rock constituents. Syenites may be called *biotite syenite* or *hornblende syenite* or *augite syenite* when one or other of these ferromagnesian minerals occurs alone or is markedly more abundant than the others. These variations do not to any great extent affect the physical properties of the rocks.

One other variety of syenite recognized by petrologists is

nepheline syenite. This rock contains, in addition to the normal syenite minerals, the felspathoid *nepheline.* The coloured varieties of nepheline, pink or red, are easily distinguished from quartz. But since the vitreous lustre and conchoidal fracture of nepheline resemble that of quartz, white or grey nepheline may be mistaken for quartz. When the rock is sufficiently coarse-grained the inferior hardness of nepheline, less than 6, is a useful criterion by which to distinguish it from quartz. Nepheline and quartz do not occur in the same rock (see pp. 50–1). and it is important to recognize these minerals in order to distinguish a nepheline syenite (poor in silica) from a granite (rich in silica and harder). Nepheline syenites frequently also contain small quantities of other felspathoids which are bright blue. Their presence in a rock is a useful indication that the rock is a nepheline syenite and not a granite.

Syenite, and especially nepheline syenite, are much less abundant than granite. They usually occur in smaller intrusions or as border facies of granite or granodiorite basoliths, where the magma was locally poorer in silica.

The texture of syenites resemble that of granites. It is roughly equigranular, generally coarse-textured, and grades into the finer-textured aphanites. Porphyritic textures are also found and such rocks are known as *porphyritic syenite.*

The colour of syenite varies as in granite. Greys are especially common; white, pink, and red occur according to the colour of the felspars.

In other physical properties, such as jointing and strength, syenite very closely resembles granite. The absence of quartz makes it less hard and hence easier to carve and polish; it also makes it somewhat more resistant to fire.

Some syenites which have crystallized from a magma with an excess of alumina contain appreciable quantities of corundum (Al_2O_3). Corundum is formed when the alumina present cannot be entirely used up in the formation of felspars $(K,Na)AlSi_3O_8$, in the same way that quartz (SiO_2) is formed from a magma in which all the silica cannot be used up in the formation of felspars and other silicates. It is through the weathering of such rocks that sands with a high concentration of the hard mineral corundum (emery) arise.

Diorite

Diorite is a coarse-grained igneous rock composed of felspar and ferromagnesian minerals. The felspars are predominantly plagioclase felspars; commonly the felspar of diorite is an intermediate form of the albite-anorthite series, but this cannot be determined in hand specimens.

The ferromagnesian minerals are biotite, hornblende, and pyroxene, or any combination of these. On a fresh break, hornblende and pyroxenes can be distinguished by the angles between their cleavage planes: on pyroxenes this is nearly a right angle, 89°, whereas on hornblende the angle is markedly obtuse, 124° (or 56°). It is difficult, and frequently impossible, to distinguish between hornblende and pyroxene on a polished specimen of diorite. Both usually occur as black or dark green crystals or grains with shiny cleavage planes. Sometimes hornblende can be distinguished by its bladed habit.

Quartz is generally present in extremely small quantities as an accessory mineral, or it is totally absent. Some granodiorites, similar to diorite but with at least 10 per cent quartz, are sometimes referred to as *quartz diorite*.

The texture of diorites resembles that of granites, being roughly equigranular, but very coarse-grained textures are less common than in granite, and porphyritic textures in diorite are uncommon.

The colour of diorite is largely determined by the proportion of dark minerals. It varies from light to dark grey or greenish grey, the felspars are either white or grey. Diorite is typically a black and white speckled rock (Pl. 6).

Jointing is common in diorite and blocks suitable for monumental purposes are comparatively rare, as with granite. The greater abundance of the heavier ferromagnesian minerals makes diorite a somewhat heavier rock than granite; the absence of quartz makes it less-hard than granite, whereas the relatively higher proportion of hornblendes makes it a tougher rock.

Gabbro

Gabbro is a coarse-grained igneous rock in which the ferro-magnesian minerals predominate. They are hornblende, pyroxene and olivine, or any combination of these. Biotite rarely occurs. The felspar of gabbro is *labradorite*, a dark grey plagioclase felspar, intermediate in composition between albite and anorthite. It is more 'calcic' than the felspar of diorite, but this can not be determined in hand specimens. Labradorite is sometimes nearly black, and it is then difficult to distinguish from the ferro-magnesian minerals. The striae of multiple albite twinning are often very clearly developed in labradorite and can sometimes be seen even on a polished surface. These are diagnostic of a plagioclase felspar.

It is often difficult to distinguish between hornblende and pyroxene, but hornblende is comparatively rare in gabbro. The pyroxene in gabbro is sometimes a greyish green variety known as *diallage* instead of the usual greenish black augite. Diallage is easily distinguished by its colour, its high nearly metallic lustre and by an excellent 'apparent' cleavage in one direction (this is not a true cleavage, but a parting which develops perhaps as a result of stress).

Olivine may normally be recognized as yellowish green grains. It is, however, frequently altered or partially altered to serpentine, when it loses its lustre and brittleness and is less easily identified.

Gabbros vary in grain size from fine-grained equigranular rocks of the order of 1 mm, to very coarse-grained rocks. The felspars often occur as flat tabular grains, which give the rock a characteristic appearance.

The colour of gabbro is generally dark, particularly when the felspars are dark grey or black. Grey, black, and greenish gabbros occur depending on the colour of the dominant ferromagnesian mineral. Gabbros in which diallage is abundant may be greyish green in colour.

Gabbro can be distinguished from diorite when it contains olivine or appreciable quantities of pyroxene, which are not found in diorite. Gabbros are nearly always darker rocks than diorite, and sometimes considerably darker without the characteristic speckled appearance of diorite.

Iron ores, particularly *magnetite* and *ilmenite* (see p. 145) are frequently found in intrusive masses of gabbro. The iron minerals occur as minor constituents dispersed through the rock, but bodies of concentrated iron ores are found within the rock mass. The ore bodies are intimately mixed with rock minerals, particularly pyroxene and olivine, and they grade into the non-metalliferous rock. This suggests that they are part of the original rock and are not secondary intrusions. It is doubtful whether such ore deposits were of any significance in antiquity, except in so far as erosion and weathering of the rock mass might make the ores available on the land surface. Important ore bodies of this type occur notably in regions of North America and South Africa.

Dolerite: Dolerite is the name given to rocks which have the same composition as gabbro but which are much finer-grained. They are intermediate in texture between the gabbro and the fine-grained *basalts*. The French term *microgabbro* is perhaps more self explanatory. The term *diabase* is sometimes used to designate dolerite, particularly in American literature, but some authors restrict the use of diabase to an altered microgabbro, in which the original minerals are no longer recognizable. These altered rocks are often loosely referred to as 'greenstones', particularly in archaeological literature. The texture of microgabbro and of diabase rocks often consists of closely interlocked or matted mineral grains which makes such rocks extremely tough.

Ultrabasic Rocks

Ultrabasic rocks or, more correctly, ultramafic rocks, are those which consist exclusively, or predominantly, of the ferromagnesian minerals hornblende, pyroxene, or olivine.

The minerals may occur singly or in various combinations, and several rock types are recognized according to the more prominent mineral: a rock composed entirely of hornblende, or in which hornblende predominates is *hornblendite*; a rock composed entirely of pyroxene, or in which pyroxene is predominant, is *pyroxenite*. A rock composed entirely of olivine, or in which olivine predominates, is *peridotite* (after the French for olivine, *peridot*).

The felspars in ultrabasic rocks always make up less than a quarter of the rock constituents and frequently much less. They are usually calcic plagioclase felspars.

Biotite may also be present as an accessory mineral in peridotite. It is usually a pale yellowish-brown variety of biotite which is easily distinguished by its high lustre and platy cleavage.

The ultrabasic rocks are equigranular in texture; porphyritic textures are extremely rare. Hornblendites and pyroxenites are normally fairly coarse-grained. If a fresh break is not available they are difficult to distinguish macroscopically, but hornblendite is less common than pyroxenite. Peridotites are frequently less coarse-grained and can be distinguished from other ultrabasic rocks by the absence of cleavage in olivine, whereas pyroxenite and hornblendite show flat cleavage surfaces on a fresh break. Olivine is commonly pale green to olive green in colour, and pyroxenite and hornblendite are usually dark coloured rocks. The ultrabasic rocks have a high specific gravity.

Nomenclature of the aphanites

The aphanites, or fine-grained igneous rocks are those which have formed from a rapidly cooling magma. They include many volcanic lavas, and narrow dykes and sills. Aphanites can therefore be considered as the fine-grained equivalents of the rocks already described, for instance a magma which crystallized into a gabbro at depth will, if ejected as a lava, give rise to a fine-grained rock *basalt*, consisting of much the same mineral combinations.

With a purely macroscopic study, however, it is impossible to distinguish the mineral constituents of the aphanites, and their more detailed classification cannot be undertaken here. As a first approximation, the distinction between the light-coloured acid *felsites*, and the dark-coloured basic *basalts*, is useful in the nomenclature of the fine-grained igneous rocks. Dark colours in this context are black, dark grey, and dark greens. Light colours are white, pale and medium grey, pale and medium green, brown and yellow, pink, red, and purple. The intermediate lava, *andesite*, can often be distinguished from acid and basic lavas.

Felsites

Chemically, felsites are equivalents of granite, granodiorite, and syenite. With a hand lens they are generally seen to consist of fine grains too small to identify, but they may also be so fine-textured that they have a flinty or horn-like texture and the individual grains cannot be seen. The fracture of these very fine-textured felsites is generally conchoidal and some felsites are difficult to distinguish from other hard, fine-textured, rocks. Since most felsites are intrusive and not lavas, a vesicular structure is less common than in basalts which are often extrusive. Most acid lavas cool to form glasses, and these crystallize extremely slowly into rocks which macroscopically may be considered analogous to felsites, or altered felsites.

A felsite which corresponds to granite is known as *rhyolite*, one which corresponds to granodiorite as *dacite*, and the fine-grained equivalent of a syenite is known as *trachyte*. The intermediate fine-grained rocks which correspond to diorite, *andesite*, are often darker grey in colour than rhyolite and trachyte, but colour alone is not a sure guide to their identification. When these rocks are very fine-grained and homogenous in texture they cannot normally be distinguished by the naked eye.

Porphyritic textures are extremely common in the fine-grained rocks, and the identification of the phenocrysts is often easy and useful in the closer identification of felsites. Porphyries have the same composition as the homogenous felsites, with one or more of the minerals forming large crystals. Porphyritic textures result from crystallization in two stages: during the initial, slow, stage the first minerals to crystallize out of the magma form large crystals, and this is followed by rapid crystallization of the remaining groundmass. The amount of phenocrysts, and their size may vary considerably (Pls. 3 and 13).

The acid porphyries of rhyolite and dacite have phenocrysts of quartz or orthoclase, or both, whereas the intermediate andesite porphyry has phenocrysts of plagioclase in a light groundmass.

Glasses

When the rock magma cools very rapidly a natural glass forms, in which there is no crystalline structure. Glasses of felsitic composition are much more common than glasses of ferromagnesian rocks. This is because acid magmas (those rich in silica) are considerably more viscous than basic magmas at comparable temperatures. On cooling, the movement of ions to form crystal structures is more restricted in an acid magma than in a basic one. On rapid cooling the ions are not able to form regular crystal structures. In the basic magmas a fine crystalline structure can form even under conditions of very rapid cooling such as is encountered by lavas. Glasses are recognized by their lustre and homogenous texture. They have a conchoidal fracture, and can be flaked into delicate long blades with thin, razor-sharp, edges. *Obsidian* is a highly lustrous variety of volcanic glass. It is normally translucent especially on the edges of the flakes, but it may be opaque. Obsidian may be nearly colourless, but it is usually found coloured by extremely finely disseminated magnetite, which gives it a black or smoky colour. Greenish varieties of obsidian are known, and rarely the magnetite has been oxidized to hematite, resulting in a red obsidian. The colour is often not regularly distributed. Many obsidians also contain bubbles of gas or inclusions of crystallized minerals, particularly felspars which grow into small globular clusters of needle shaped crystals (Pl. 7). Flow structures may be seen, especially when the obsidian contains inclusions, for these become drawn out into bands.

Pitchstone is a dull variety of glass which has similar properties to obsidian.

Pumice is a glass froth which is ejected when the lava contains a high proportion of steam.

Basalt

Basalt is the fine-grained equivalent of gabbro. Basalts always have a fine 'stony' appearance, not a glassy texture. They do not have the horn-like lustre of felsites, but are of a dull black, dark grey, or green colour. Basalts can be flaked, but they have a flat fracture, not a true conchoidal fracture.

Porphyritic textures are very common in basalts. Olivine is the most common porphyritic mineral found in basalts. Felspar is also very common and is often the plagioclase felspar *labradorite*. It occurs characteristically as white tabular crystals disseminated in the dark groundmass and forms a distinctive rock, commonly known as porphyrite. Augite phenocrysts in basalt are not uncommon, but other minerals are rare.

When a basalt lava which contains a high proportion of volatile components, particularly steam, is cooled rapidly, the steam and other gases are trapped in the rock and the resulting structure resembles that of a sponge. This is known as *vesicular basalt*. The size and frequency of the holes varies considerably (Pl. 8).

The cavities of a vesicular basalt often become filled with soluble salts such as calcite or other substances carried in solution. These substances may be precipitated, lining the walls of the cavities. When this process is slow and undisturbed, good crystal forms may develop which grow in towards the centre of the cavity. In other instances a fine-grained aggregate is formed. Columnar jointing is often very clearly developed in large basalt flows.

Pyroclastic Rocks

As rock magma rises to the earth's surface in a volcanic vent, the intense pressure on it is reduced to normal atmospheric pressure. Dissolved gases are released from solution and the magma may appear to 'boil'. The release of gases is sometimes violently explosive in an upward rush which carries with it liquid magma and fragments of rock torn from the sides of the vent. After most of the gases have escaped the remaining liquid can erupt quietly as a flow of *lava*.

The material carried up by the escaping gases is called *pyroclastic material*. It falls as blocks of rock ranging in size from *bombs*, greater than 32 mm, to *lapilli*, between 32 mm and 4 mm, to fine volcanic *ash* and *dust*, smaller than 4 mm. Much of this material still contains some volatiles and a spongy texture is common in the bombs, lapilli, and ash of pyroclastic rocks.

The coarser fragments fall out near the volcanic vent, and build up a steep cone of debris around it. The finer particles may be carried by the wind, and ash and dust may be carried in suspension over vast distances. Normally the greater proportion of the ash, dust, and lapilli fall in the vicinity of the volcano, building up a cone of clastic material with horizontal grading from coarse to finer material outwards. As successive outbursts of pyroclastic material are added to the deposits, a rough bedding may be produced as in sedimentary rocks. Since the explosive phase of a volcano is frequently (but not always) followed by the eruption of liquid lava, layers of pyroclastic material may be found interbedded with layers of lava.

A deposit of volcanic ash and dust may become compacted by its own weight and it is partially cemented by percolation of soluble substances which fill the voids between the particles. The resulting rock is called *tuff* if the particles are fine-grained, and *agglomerate* when it consists largely of bombs and lapilli. Tuffs are frequently light in colour and have a chalky consistency. They are rougher than chalk to touch, since the ash particles are irregular and angular and consist of hard silicate minerals. In hand specimens, some indurated tuffs are very difficult to distinguish from felsite.

Whether a volcano erupts quietly or explosively, depends largely on the chemical composition of the non-volatiles. Magmas which are rich in silica and correspond in composition to felsite, are much more viscous than those poor in silica which correspond to basalt. In a viscous magma the gases escape with difficulty and accumulate until they are released with violent explosion, whereas in basaltic magmas the gases can escape much more easily. Explosive eruptions are, therefore, much more commonly associated with volcanoes with a silicic magma. The tuffs and other pyroclastic materials are frequently found with obsidian and pumice. Basaltic lavas are highly mobile and may flow over vast areas before solidifying.

Pyroclastic rocks are not very important as raw material used by man, unless consolidated into hard homogenous rock. Both tuff and pumice can be used as mild abrasives, and some indurated tuffs are hard and tough enough to be worked into tools. The sedimentary nature of pyroclastic rocks however, makes them valuable stratigraphic horizons when interbedded with deposits of archaeological interest. Distinct beds of volcanic ash can form in a short time, in a matter of weeks or even days. Thus a bed of ash (and also lava) forms a very distinct datum in a series of deposits. Since the activity of volcanoes is normally sporadic, important eruptions which result in a large amount of ash being distributed over a considerable area give rise to stratigraphic horizons which can be used for purposes of correlation, and of relative dating. An example is the volcanic eruptions from volcanoes in the Eifel mountains in West Germany during a late stage of the Pleistocene. A thin but distinct bed of tuff is found at a number of localities, interbedded with other late Pleistocene deposits, notably loess. The presence of this band of tuff is a valuable guide to recognizing the contemporaneity of loess deposits, throughout the Mainz basin area. At the famous site of Olduvai gorge, similar widespread occurrences of beds of volcanic ash in the sequence of lake deposits has enabled Dr L. S. B. Leakey to obtain not only firm base lines within the broader sequence of lake sedimentation, but also direct dating evidence by applying radiometric methods of age determination to the stratified volcanic material (potassium-argon estimations, see Chapter 8).

Lava flows are highly destructive, and archaeological evidence overrun by lava is only rarely of much interest, but there are instances in Mexico, e.g. Cuicuilco, of prehistoric pottery found in soil overrun by lava flows. The lava flows can be dated and a maximum date for the prehistoric pottery deduced. Beds of ash and tuff are less destructive, in so far as objects buried under the ash may become fossilized. The percolation of soluble substances, and their precipitation, can sometimes form a cast of perishable buried objects, as in the case of the many well known examples from Pompeii.

Pyroclastic rocks are thus seen to exhibit many of the

characteristics of sedimentary rocks. They are stratified and may show a rough bedding and they may also contain fossils. Their origin is strictly igneous and they are composed of the primary rock-forming minerals found in similar combinations in other igneous rocks.

Metamorphic Rocks

The nature and composition of newly-formed rocks are controlled by their geological environment. The minerals and rock texture are formed according to the chemistry of the magma and according to conditions of temperature and pressure. If these conditions are changed, the rock is no longer stable and changes take place to achieve a stable form under the new conditions. Such processes lead to the formation of metamorphic rocks. The surface weathering and erosive processes are not included in the term metamorphism. They also lead to the formation of new minerals and new rocks – the sedimentary rocks. These will be dealt with in a later chapter, for the processes of weathering differ significantly from those of metamorphism.

The chief agents of metamorphism are mechanical stress, heat and the resulting chemical activity.

The pressure due to the weight of overlaying rocks rarely has any metamorphic effects. It results in compression and compaction of sediments but does not affect the igneous rocks, the majority of which have crystallized below the earth's surface as intrusives. Lateral shear stresses are, however, among the chief and most powerful causes of metamorphism. The lateral forces acting on rocks are normally associated with folding and uplift of parts of the earth's crust which result in mountain building. Intensely folded rocks are frequently metamorphosed and sometimes occur as the core of large mountain masses. Shear stresses usually generate considerable heat, so that recrystallization of the rock components takes place under pressure. This causes the minerals to crystallize in aggregates of more or less aligned bands or lenses. Foliated or banded structures are characteristic of very highly metamorphosed rocks. Minerals which have distinct directional properties such as mica, are often very markedly aligned with the cleavage planes perpendicular to the direction of the pressure.

The magmatic liquids and gases which are associated with igneous activity are often chemically highly reactive. They consist to a great extent of water vapour which at high temperature and pressure becomes a chemically active substance. Water vapour promotes recrystallization and enters into chemical combination, forming an essential component of hydrous minerals such as amphiboles, micas, serpentine, talc, and the clay minerals. Other substances which are carried in solution by magmatic water include fluorine, boric acid, sulphur, and metals. These react chemically with existing rock minerals to form new minerals, some of which are characteristic of metamorphosed rocks. This last form of rock alteration which involves the addition of new elements to the existing rock is called *metasomatism*. Metasomatism is typically associated with the metamorphic aureoles around large igneous intrusions, and besides altering the existing country rocks it also results in the filling of fissures and cavities with new minerals, including metal ores and gangue minerals such as quartz, fluorite, baryte, and others.

Metamorphism is rarely the effect of heat alone, but by increasing the chemical reactivity of substances, and by melting rock minerals, heat does play an important part in metamorphism. Its effect may be most clearly seen on zones of contact between intrusive igneous rocks and the surrounding country rocks, or on a smaller scale on rocks overrun by a lava flow.

The metamorphic agents may act on any existing rock, so that there is a great variety in the composition of metamorphosed rocks. The nature of metamorphic rocks is, however, strongly dependent on the type and intensity of metamorphism concerned. The nomenclature of metamorphic rocks cannot therefore be based primarily on the mineral composition of these rocks, as it was for igneous rocks, but the texture of the rock and the type or 'grade' of metamorphism must also be considered.

The texture of metamorphic rocks: Metamorphic rocks are

crystalline and may range from very coarse- to fine-grained textures, as do the igneous rocks. Their structure often shows a more or less distinct foliation which may superficially resemble the bedding of sedimentary rocks, but when metamorphism has not involved crystallization under pressure, compact structures may result.

Rocks which have undergone strong pressure and heat, and in which the minerals are entirely recrystallized so that the original rock structure has been obliterated, are said to be 'high grade' metamorphic rocks. They are generally coarse- or medium-grained and nearly always show a banded or foliated structure (Pl. 9). These are the *gneisses* and *schists*, in which the individual mineral grains can usually be identified by the naked eye. The terms gneiss and schist are textural terms, denoting coarsely-banded structures and clearly-foliated structures respectively. They comprise rocks of widely-differing mineral constituents. Some minerals in gneisses and schists may occur as large well-formed crystals which are not necessarily aligned in the direction of the foliation. Such rocks resemble the igneous porphyries and are sometimes called *pseudoporphyries* or *porphyroblasts*. Garnets typically occur as well formed crystals of this type in micaceous schists (Pl. 1c). Some large crystals in gneiss and schist are, however, relics from the original rocks, such as large felspars in a metamorphosed porphyritic granite. Large, rounded concentrations of silicic or felspathic minerals in some gneisses have been identified as the partly recrystallized remains of pebbles in a highly metamophosed conglomerate. When, however, such high grade metamorphism results in the complete melting of a rock, it recrystallizes much in the manner of igneous rocks. It has been suggested that the process of rock formation may be cyclical, from igneous intrusions through sedimentary rocks and high-grade metamorphism back to igneous rocks. In less intense forms of metamorphism, the nature of the original rock has a stronger influence on the resulting metamorphic rock. Fine-grained sedimentary rocks under the action of pressure may be converted to slates, sandstones may be recrystallized to quartzites, and limestones to marble. Such 'low grade' metamorphic rocks will be discussed in the context of their corresponding sedimentary parent rocks.

Metamorphic rocks which have been altered by metasomatic processes are not influenced by pressure, and their structure is generally compact and not foliated or banded. When the alteration has not proceeded very far the structure of the original rock may be preserved. Most old igneous rocks, for instance, show some degree of alteration of the felspars to sericite (a form of white mica), or of the pyroxenes to amphiboles, or olivine to serpentine. When alteration is intense, the original structure of the rock may be largely or completely obliterated and new rocks result, such as serpentine, soapstone, 'greenstone', kaolinite, and others.

Gneiss

A gneiss is a coarsely-banded or lenticular rock which may range from coarse-grained to fine-grained in texture. The banding is often rough and poorly defined (Pl. 9a), and it may be replaced by lenses or roughly circular structures. Gneisses in which the lenticular structure is clearly developed are sometimes called *augen gneiss* (Pl. 9b). The mineral constituents normally correspond to those of the acid and intermediate igneous rocks, granite, syenite, and diorite.

Since the minerals have crystallized under pressure, good crystal forms are rare and the minerals may be more difficult to identify than in the coarse igneous rocks. Cleavage is the most reliable guide to distinguish quartz from felspars. Hornblende occurs as small elongated black grains, roughly aligned parallel to the direction of foliation. Both muscovite and biotite occur commonly, and muscovite is more common in metamorphic rocks than in the igneous rocks. The micas occur as irregular platelets, often markedly aligned in the direction of foliation. Consequently, a gneiss fractures relatively easily parallel to a band of mica along the cleavage of this mineral. This may give an exaggerated impression of the abundance of mica in the rock, and transverse sections of micaceous rocks should be examined to assess their mineralogical composition.

In gneisses which are poor in mica, or in hornblende, the foliation is generally less clearly developed.

Schist

Schists are closely related to gneisses in structure and origin, but they exhibit a much more distinct banding and alignment of the minerals. The mineral grains are usually large enough to be seen by the naked eye, but their identification is not always easy, since most minerals occur as irregular or elongated grains without good crystal form. The mineral composition of schists varies very widely, depending on the origin of the rock, but mica, chlorite, or hornblende are very common constituents of most schistose rocks. Many varieties of schists can be distinguished by the predominant minerals present.

Mica schist consists of quartz and mica (Pl. 1c), often muscovite and a very dark variety of biotite. The schistose structure of these rocks results from nearly parallel alignment of the mica platelets and on fracture planes along this direction, the rock appears to consist solely of mica. Along these planes the rock usually has a silky or pearly lustre ranging in colour from silvery white to grey, or from yellowish brown to dark brown when biotite predominates. As with gneisses, rock fragments should be examined in transverse sections to establish their mineral contents.

Other minerals include garnets, which may occur as large perfectly formed crystals. Hornblende may occur, and mica schists grade into hornblende schist with an increase in hornblende content. Other metamorphic minerals may occur in smaller quantities. Sometimes graphite is found, either finely-disseminated, or in bands integrated with the schistose structure of the rock. The graphite is probably the fully carbonized form of organic matter in the parent rock, and indicates that this is likely to have been a sediment.

Chlorite schist consists largely of the green mineral chlorite. The other minerals include quartz and sometimes mica or other minerals associated with metamorphism. The chlorite platelets are markedly aligned, as are the mica platelets in mica schists. Since chlorite usually forms very small platelets, chlorite schists are generally very fine-grained, and should more accurately be called chlorite phyllite. They are very soft rocks with marked schistosity.

Chlorite schists result largely from alteration of basic igneous rocks by the conversion of the ferromagnesian minerals to chlorite. They have sometimes been referred to as greenstone, or greenstone schist. The term greenstone should – if used at all– be confined to the tough hornblende rocks which are much harder than chlorite schists, and which usually show a less distinct foliation, or are massive.

Talc schist is a schistose rock in which talc predominates. The rock is extremely soft (hardness of talc =1). Talc schist is usually white to pale green in colour but dark varieties occur due to the presence of magnetite, chromite, and other minerals. Talc schists are derived from ultrabasic igneous rocks.

Soapstone or *steatite* is closely related to chlorite and talc schists. It is a structureless rock of metamorphic (often metasomatic) origin consisting largely of talc and chlorite. It is extremely soft and is very resistant to fire.

Hornblende schists comprise many metamorphic rocks of more or less schistose structure, and consisting largely of amphiboles. The amphibole is commonly hornblende which occurs in irregular, often elongated grains. The grains form more or less aligned aggregates which may be separated by lenses of quartz, felspar, or small quantities of other minerals associated with metamorphism. The minerals may be difficult to identify with the naked eye, and hornblende schists may be distinguished from other schists by their dark green or nearly black colour and generally more moderate schistosity. They are harder than chlorite or biotite schists. Hornblende schists are not always easily distinguished from some igneous rocks such as diorite or dolerite, particularly when the rocks are fine-grained and the schistose structure is not highly developed. Any alignment of minerals does, however, point to crystallization under pressure.

Hornblende schists may result from the alteration of either basic igneous rocks or from some sedimentary rocks rich in iron and magnesium.

The alteration of pyroxenes in basic igneous rocks, such as basalt or dolerite, may occur without changes in structure which can be observed by the naked eye. This alteration gives rise to rocks similar in composition to hornblende schists.

Fine- or medium-grained hornblende rocks of this type are often collectively referred to as *greenstone*. They are fairly hard (hardness of hornblende = 5 to 6), very tough rocks, except when the schistose structure is strongly developed.

Serpentine, Serpentinite

This rock has already been described in the section on the mineral serpentine. Serpentines are formed directly by the hydration of basic and ultrabasic igneous rocks, or as a secondary alteration from metamorphic rocks such as hornblende schists.

Other minerals commonly associated with serpentine, are the remains of the primary minerals of the igneous rocks from which the serpentine was derived: pyroxenes, hornblendes, and olivine. Iron ores, especially *pyrites* are also very commonly found disseminated through the rock, in irregular grains or as good cubic crystals.

CHAPTER FOUR

The Products of Weathering

AS SOON as rock is exposed to the surface of the earth, it begins to disintegrate. The processes of breakdown and decay are known as weathering and consist of the mechanical disintegration of rock into smaller and smaller fragments, and the chemical disintegration of minerals into simpler substances.

Ground water carries carbon dioxide and the decay products of vegetation in solution, all of which are acid and have a corrosive effect on the rock minerals. The system of joints in rocks and the numerous smaller cracks and fissures, down to the cleavage cracks of the minerals, afford passages through which the acidified water can penetrate the rock mass. Chemical corrosion by ground water can therefore penetrate below the rock surface, depending on the porosity of the rock. Some minerals such as quartz and muscovite are extremely resistant to acid corrosion whereas others, especially those rich in iron, are altered comparatively rapidly. Biotite and hornblende are amongst the first minerals to be altered to clays, iron oxides, and salts.

In climates with a period of frost, water also causes the mechanical disintegration of rock, for on freezing water expands by approximately 10 per cent of its volume. This causes stresses within the rock fissures and they are gradually enlarged by repeated alternate freezing and thawing until the rock is broken into angular fragments. The rate at which rocks are broken down in this way depends on a number of factors: on the availability of water and the porosity of the rock, and on the frequency of freeze and thaw; for instance, whether diurnal or only seasonal, as in extremely arctic conditions.

Surface rock is also broken down by stresses caused by temperature changes. This form of weathering is particularly common in hot deserts, where daytime insulation may considerably heat the outer surface of the rock. Since most rocks are poor conductors of heat, a steep temperature gradient is set up in the rock's surface which causes stresses and the fracture of the rock into slabs roughly parallel to the exposed surface.

Whichever form of disintegration is prevalent, the result is a continuous destruction of rock and the production of a mantle of rock waste which is carried away chiefly by running water.

The Insoluble Products of Weathering

On steep slopes in mountainous regions, the rock waste can be carried down to the valleys by gravity alone, and large talus heaps of angular and unsorted scree accumulate at the foot of the slopes.

In the valleys the scree is removed by streams and rivers and is roughly sorted according to size and weight by the stream current. The lighter material comprising small particles is carried downstream, whereas the heavier particles, mostly large fragments, are carried and rolled over each other only in times of flood. The corners become abraded and more or less rounded pebbles are formed. The effect of river transport is thus to wear down the softer rocks and carry away the fine particles, whereas the harder rocks and those of high specific gravity become concentrated in the river bed. Near the source of rock waste in the mountains and foothills, fresh material is continually being added, so that the stream bed contains large blocks of most of the surrounding rocks. In the lower reaches of the river, where it forms wide flood plains, only the more resistant rocks and minerals are left, such as quartz (hardness 7), felspar (hardness 6), garnet (hardness 7 to 7·5), zircon (hardness 7·5), tinstone (hardness 7), and corundum (hardness 9). Zircon, tinstone, and corundum also have high specific gravities, which further aids the concentration of these materials in alluvial deposits. Native gold, which is a soft metal, is easily abraded, but its specific gravity is exceptionally high (12 to 20) so that even very small gold grains are left behind by the stream and become concentrated in river beds.

When the particles are small the shape of the grains affects the ease with which they are transported by water. The plate-like grains of mica, chlorite, and the clay minerals are carried in suspension longer than quartz grains of similar size, which are roughly spherical. Thus the very fine-grained deposits characteristically contain clays, micas and chlorites, whereas, in the somewhat coarser deposits of sand, quartz is usually the dominant material.

The grain size of a deposit is the most important criterion for its identification. Terms such as boulders, gravel, sand, silt, and clay are accurately defined terms of grain size, but the grains may consist of the same materials (see Table 7). For instance, a fine gravel grades imperceptibly into a coarse sand, and a fine sand into a coarse silt. The distinction between silt and clay is also one of grain size; the limit between clay and silt (0·002 mm), however, also corresponds to the size limit of the clay minerals, so that the clay/silt boundary usually has a mineralogical significance.

TABLE 7

SEDIMENT	DIAMETER in mm
Boulders	greater than 256
Gravel	256 to 2
Sand	2 to 0·02
Silt	0·02 to 0·002
Clay	smaller than 0·002

Conglomerate

Conglomerates are deposits of boulders or pebbles cemented into solid rock. The loose deposits before cementation are known as *gravel*, and this may be described as a boulder gravel, a coarse gravel (256 mm to 64 mm), or a fine gravel (64 mm to 2 mm). The pebbles and boulders of a conglomerate may be of any material but the harder rocks usually predominate, particularly quartz and other forms of silica, felspar, and compact rocks composed of these minerals.

The cementing material may also vary considerably; it may be consolidated sand, silt or clay, or calcite, silica, or iron oxide cements. When the pebbles stand out clearly in a fine-grained matrix the rock is known as *puddingstone*, but a conglomerate may consist of completely unsorted material, ranging in size from boulders or pebbles through sand to clay (Pl. 5).

Breccia is a consolidated scree. It is similar to a conglomerate, except that the rock fragments are angular and not rounded in outline (Pl. 10).

Sandstone

Sandstones may consist of any material of sand-grain size. Most sandstones consist predominantly of quartz, and some are pure quartz sandstones. Other minerals which are commonly found in sandstones in small quantities are felspars, generally the alkali felspars, white mica, garnet, tourmaline, and magnetite. Other minerals, such as corundum and zircon, which are hard and have a high specific gravity also occur but they are relatively rare.

The range of sand-grain sizes found in sandstones varies. Some are extremely homogenous and well sorted, particularly if they are of aeolian origin (i.e. wind-transported), such as dune sand which has become consolidated into a sandstone. Other sandstones contain a wide range of sand grain size (0·02 to 2 mm) and grade into fine conglomerates.

Sandstones also vary in their structure according to the conditions of sedimentation. Some are very thinly bedded and split easily into thin slabs, others may be homogenous throughout a considerable thickness without showing any stratification. Such rocks break equally easily in all directions and are therefore called *freestones*. Joints and fissures occur in sediments, although their origin is different from the jointing of igneous rocks. Jointing in sedimentary rocks results partly from contraction on compaction of the sediments; fissures also result from disturbances such as folding. Joints usually develop in two more or less perpendicular directions, but sometimes three or more directions of jointing exist, which may be inclined to the bedding.

The sand grains may be cemented by a variety of substances: clay, silica, calcite, iron oxides, or iron carbonate. The properties of sandstone depend on the cementing material, and also on the degree of cementation. The colours of sandstones range from nearly white or buff, through yellow, to brown, red-browns, and red. Some sandstones of marine origin are green in colour, due to the presence of ferrous salt *glauconite*; these are also known as greensand.

The porosity of sandstones varies considerably and depends on how well the cementing material has penetrated the cavities between individual sand grains. Most sandstones are porous, but some highly-siliceous sandstones have a very low porosity compared to igneous rocks. The strength of sandstones also depends on the nature of the cementing medium and on its penetration between the individual sand grains.

Fractures of sandstone usually occur through the cement so that a fracture surface has a coarse, gritty feel and the sand grains stand out from the surrounding cementing material. Poorly cemented sandstones may be quite friable and are easily eroded.

Graywacke

Graywacke is a type of sandstone which consists of sand-grain size fragments of rock as well as quartz, felspar, and other mineral grains. It results from the breakdown of fine-grained rocks, particularly rocks such as shale, slate, chert, quartzite, basalt, and felsite, but other rock fragments may also occur, such as fine-grained granite, etc. Most graywackes are grey, greenish, or black. The cementing medium is commonly clay, but it may also be silica or calcite.

Shale

Shales are sediments so fine-grained that the individual particles of the silt and clay grades cannot be seen by the naked eye. They consist largely of clay minerals, chlorite, and mica platelets. During sedimentation these platy minerals tend to be aligned with the bedding, and under pressure from the weight of overlying sediments this alignment is increased. Shales, therefore, have a very distinct fissile structure which is parallel to the bedding, and the rock splits easily into thin flat slabs.

Shales are usually soft rocks, unless they have become indurated with silica or iron oxides. They are often brittle and crumbly and give off a 'clayey' or 'earthy' odour, particularly when damp. Shales are usually grey or black in colour, depending on the amount of carbonaceous matter they contain, and fossils are quite commonly preserved.

Mudstone

As with shale, mudstone or claystone consists of extremely fine-grained particles, but these are not of a distinct platy nature as in shales. Mudstones are more homogenous than shales and do not have a distinct fissile structure, although they may show bedding or lamination. A highly indurated mudstone may be very homogenous and break with a nearly conchoidal fracture. In hand specimens indurated mudstones (or shales) are not always easy to distinguish from the fine-grained igneous or metamorphic rocks.

The Alteration of Sediments

Metamorphic processes act on sedimentary rocks in the same way as on the igneous rocks and the end products are very similar and often indistinguishable. When a rock is only partly altered, the original sedimentary structure may still be recognizable in the metamorphic rock. For instance, in a metamorphosed conglomerate which is altered to gneiss some of the larger pebbles or boulders may be only partly crystallized and remain as a lenticular structure or pseudo-phenocryst. Conglomerates and sandstones are altered to gneiss and schists. The fine-grained sediments, shales, and mudstones, are altered to very fine-grained metamorphic rocks known as *slates*, or to fine-textured schists. The very pure quartz sandstones are altered to hard siliceous rocks called *quartzite*.

Slate

Slate is a lightly-metamorphosed rock in which the crystal grains are too small to be seen, even with an ordinary microscope. X-ray analysis shows it to consist of quartz, chlorite, and a variety of white mica called sericite, with varying amounts of carbonaceous matter of organic origin.

Intense metamorphism of shales and mudstones results in the complete recrystallization of their constituents and the formation of schists, but when the alteration is primarily due to pressure only slight recrystallization takes place, particularly of the clay minerals to chlorite and sericite. Under pressure these platy minerals are aligned perpendicular to the direction of pressure, and the resulting slate has a distinct fissile structure which frequently cuts across the original bedding of the shale (Pl. 11). The 'cleavage' of slate is quite different from that of minerals. The cleavage of minerals is a result of the atomic structure and the nature of the chemical bonds within the mineral, whereas the 'cleavage' of slate simply results from the alignment of mineral grains.

Slates often have a slight lustre parallel to the cleavage, but across the cleavage the fracture is dull and irregular.

Slates are frequently grey or black, depending on the amount of carbonaceous matter present. Some slates have a green tinge from chlorite or reddish, purple or yellow shades from iron oxides.

Phyllite is a metamorphic rock which is slightly coarser-grained than slate, but finer than schist. Phyllites usually contain much mica which gives them a glossy lustre. They are often silvery white and may be tinged with red, yellow, or green from iron oxides or chlorite. Phyllites grade into mica schist and the division between mica schist and phyllite is arbitrary and ill-defined.

Quartzite

Quartzite is a hard (hardness 7) and compact rock in which quartz grains are closely cemented with silica. Quartzites fracture equally across the silica cement and quartz grains, so that fractures are nearly conchoidal and even. In hand specimens the fracture is the only means of distinguishing between quartzites and siliceous sandstone, and the two grade into each other.

Quartzites usually result from the metamorphism of sandstones which involves a certain amount of recrystallization of the quartz grains. Pure quartzites consist only of quartz, but other minerals are often present in small quantities: muscovite and biotite are commonly formed and if iron was present in the original rock, hematite and magnetite are formed. Carbonaceous matter may be altered to graphite (see pp. 126–7).

Some siliceous conglomerates acquire properties resembling those of quartzite and fracture across the cement and the pebbles.

The Soluble Products of Weathering

Many products of chemical weathering are soluble and are carried away in solution by streams and rivers to the oceans. The high salinity of sea water is largely the result of vast amounts of salts brought down by rivers over many millions of years. The soluble substances are largely salts of sodium, potassium, magnesium, and calcium. Iron oxides are also soluble under acid conditions and may move with ground water, but only small quantities are normally carried very far in solution. Silica is slightly soluble, particularly in warm water such as is found in the soils of tropical regions, and silica is also carried by running water in small quantities. These slightly soluble substances and also calcium carbonate play an important part as cementing media of sediments.

If a branch of the sea becomes cut off from the ocean either by a reef or bar in a hot and arid region, water evaporates to such an extent that its salts are precipitated. The dissolved salts are precipitated in the order of decreasing solubility, the least soluble first: calcium carbonate, calcium sulphate (gypsum, or anhydrite if the temperature is above 25°C), sodium chloride, and finally potassium and magnesium salts which are highly soluble.

In lakes of internal drainage basins similar conditions prevail, and since rivers are continually bringing down more dissolved salts to these lakes, thick deposits of salts may be formed and the lake water becomes highly saline, as exemplified by the Dead Sea. Deposits of this type are called *evaporites*, and the commonest evaporites are *gypsum*, *anhydrite*, and *rock salt*.

In arid and semi-arid regions, the evaporation of moisture from the soil may exceed the precipitation received as rain or dew. Under these conditions the movement of ground water is upwards, and not downwards as in humid and temperate regions. Salts in solution are brought up to the surface by the ground water and precipitated as a powder, a crust or excrescences on the desert surface. The salts are brought up in order of their solubility, depending on what is available in the subsoil. Many desert pans formed by the evaporation of ground water consist of gypsum; more arid conditions result in the upward movement of calcite also, and the surface soil and rock waste may be cemented by calcite forming a hard surface crust called *calcrete* (from its resemblance to concrete). Calcrete usually contains the coarse angular fragments of rock which result from insolation weathering (pp. 97–8). In sand deserts a surface of calcareous sandstone may be formed.

When the subsoil contains iron oxide or silica in solution, these substances are carried up to the surface to form hard crusts known as *ferricrete* and *silcrete* respectively.

The soluble weathering products which are precipitated from solution under various conditions form minerals, many of which are crystalline, and some which are non-crystalline or amorphous.

Calcium Salts

In the presence of carbon dioxide and water the calcium from disintegrating silicates forms *calcium carbonate*. Since carbon dioxide is always present in the atmosphere, all soil water contains carbon dioxide in solution and wherever calcic silicate minerals are weathered, calcium carbonate is one of the weathering products. It is therefore extremely widespread and abundant. In slightly acidified water, calcium carbonate is readily soluble; it is leached out by ground water and may be reprecipitated near the water table, or carried by streams to the seas.

A common but less abundant calcium salt is *calcium sulphate*. Sulphur occurs as a trace element in many rocks particularly in the more basic rocks, where it is commonly found as a constituent of the metal ores iron pyrite, copper pyrite, and marcasite. Many of the sulphate salts, including calcium sulphate, are derived from the weathering of metal sulphides.

A less common calcium salt is a *calcium phosphate*. A crystalline form of calcium phosphate, *apatite*, occurs in very small quantities as a primary mineral of igneous rocks. Most calcium phosphate is probably of organic origin and forms in the presence of calcium and decaying animal matter, particularly bone. It is an abundant mineral of some very localized sediments.

Calcium fluoride is a mineral of igneous or hydrothermal origin and has already been described in the appropriate section (p. 67) on rock-forming minerals.

Calcium Carbonate

There are two crystalline forms of calcium carbonate, the very common hexagonal form, known as *calcite*, and a rather less common orthorhombic form known as *aragonite*. Calcite and aragonite have the same chemical composition $CaCO_3$ but differ in their crystallography. In aragonite the atoms are more closely packed together, so that this mineral is slightly harder than calcite and has a somewhat higher specific gravity.

Calcite

Description: Calcite crystals commonly form six-sided prisms with a pyramidal extremity, known as *dog-tooth spar* (Figure 24) and crystals also occur as six-sided prisms with a flattened extremity formed by three-crystal facets, known as *nail-head spar* (Figure 25). The dog-tooth crystals differ from quartz crystals in that the pyramid facets each cut across two prism faces, whereas in quartz each pyramid facet cuts across one prism face only.

Good calcium crystals are found where calcium carbonate has been precipitated slowly in protected surroundings in rock pools or fissures. More commonly, calcite occurs as either a crystalline

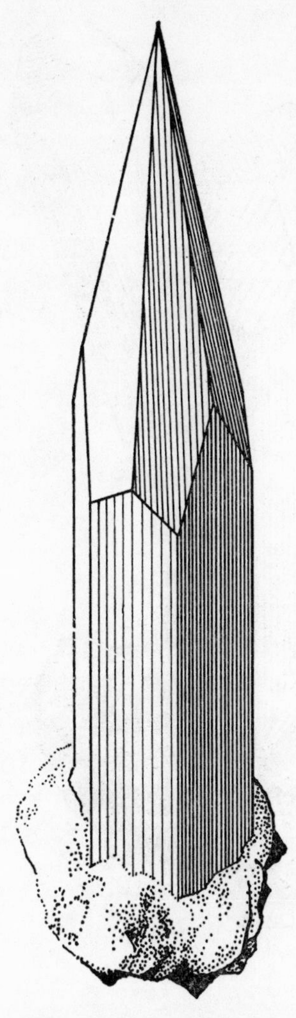

Figure 24 Calcite crystal: dog-tooth spar

mass or a finely-granular mass of minute crystals or disseminated as a cementing medium of sediments.

Calcite has an excellent cleavage in three directions, breaking into rhomboid cleavage fragments. On a broken surface of a crystalline mass of calcite, shiny cleavage facets are always seen and fracture along other directions is rare.

Pure calcite is colourless and transparent, but it is commonly

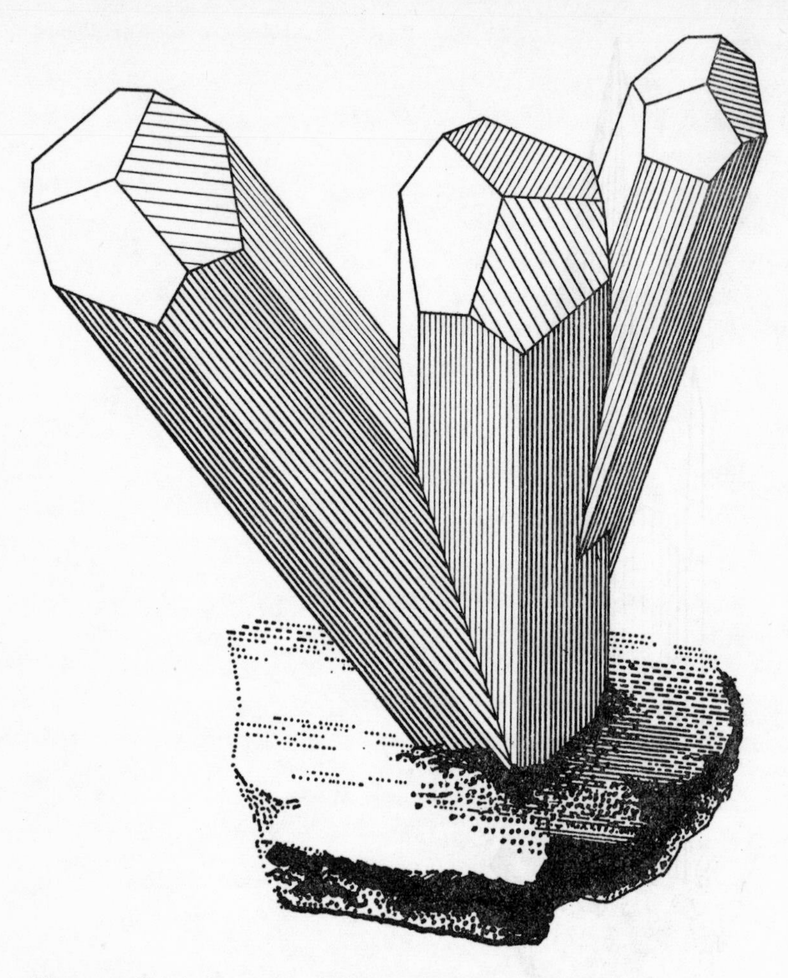

Figure 25 Calcite crystal: nail-head spar

translucent or opaque white due to the reflection of light from cleavage planes and to the inclusion of air or water bubbles. Calcite is easily stained by other substances in the solution from which it has been precipitated and yellow, brown, or red staining by iron is common; manganese staining occurs giving black or purple varieties of calcite.

The hardness of calcite is 3 and its specific gravity 2·7. Calcite effervesces in acid. All carbonates are corroded by acid with the formation of carbon dioxide, but amongst the commonly occurring carbonates only calcium carbonate reacts with cold dilute acid. It briskly effervesces in hydrochloric acid and weakly in acetic acid (e.g. vinegar), or citric acid (e.g. lemon juice).

Iceland spar is a very pure transparent variety of calcite which breaks easily into regular rhomboid slabs.

A compact fibrous variety of calcite which can be highly polished is sometimes called *satin spar*, but the name is more commonly applied to a fibrous variety of calcium sulphate which is very similar in appearance. Since calcium sulphate does not react with cold acid these two minerals can be distinguished by the acid test.

Stalagmite is a crystalline form of calcite deposited by slowly running water in caves and it may be concretionary or banded; another common name for it is *dripstone.*

Tufa or Travertine is a calcium carbonate deposit precipitated around springs of lime-charged water. Tufa often contains fossil material and detailed imprints of organic perishable objects may be very clearly preserved. Tufa and travertine are usually granular deposits of calcite which may be loose or very compact depending on the conditions of precipitation. In some lake beds granular calcite deposits, closely resembling tufa, are precipitated by algae.

Banded varieties of calcite are often mistakenly referred to as alabaster (Pl. 12), a variety of calcium sulphate, or less commonly as onyx, a variety of silica.

Occurrence: Calcite is extremely widespread as a product of weathering and hence as a component of soils and sedimentary rocks. Calcite may occur as a cementing medium of sediments such as sandstones (e.g. calcareous sandstones), as nodules or concretions, or as finely-disseminated granules throughout a sediment. Pure deposits of calcite occur in caves or rock fissures as secondary infiltrations.

The more abundant occurrence of calcite is as the principal constituent of limestones and chalk.

Aragonite

Description: Aragonite is the orthorhombic form of calcium carbonate, and also forms prismatic crystals with pointed pyramidal extremities. The crystals frequently occur as acicular crystals, or as bunches of long thin crystals packed parallel to each other forming a radiating or columnar mass. Aragonite also occurs as crystalline concretions. The cleavage of aragonite is in one direction only and is much less clearly developed than in calcite; it is brittle and has a subconchoidal structure.

Aragonite is generally white or greyish, but it may be stained in the same way as calcite; it is transparent to translucent or opaque. It is somewhat harder than calcite, 3·5 to 4, and has a specific gravity of 2·9.

Like calcite, aragonite effervesces with cold dilute acid.

Occurrence: Aragonite is much less abundant than calcite, but it can occur almost everywhere where calcite is found. The conditions under which aragonite is formed are not fully understood. It seems certain that crystallization from hot solutions, above about 40°C, results in the formation of orthorhombic crystals, so that aragonite is found in the travertines from hot springs. A number of reef-building corals, some algae, and molluscan shells contain aragonite, so that deposits formed from the debris of such organisms contain appreciable quantities of aragonite. Aragonite is also found in stalagmitic formations often in bands interbedded between bands of calcite, or as secondary crystal growths on calcite stalactites. How these changes from calcite to aragonite formation occur is still unknown, in many cases it is clearly not the result of temperature changes.

Aragonite is less stable than calcite and when subjected to heat and pressure, the aragonite of rocks is transformed to calcite.

Differentiation between calcite and aragonite: When good crystal forms are available it is generally possible to distinguish the mineral visually. The hardness test, carried out with care, may distinguish between calcite, hardness 3, and aragonite, hardness 3·5; but this is unreliable when the calcium carbonate occurs as a finely crystalline or granular mass. In the latter case it is difficult to distinguish the two minerals by visual means or by the simple hardness or specific gravity tests, particularly if the two minerals are interbedded. A simple chemical stain test can be applied, known as *Meigen's test*. Aragonite is stained pink with a solution of cobalt nitrate, whereas calcite is not. The mineral to be tested is boiled for a quarter of an hour in a cobalt nitrate solution and then washed. (There are also more sensitive tests which are particularly useful for fine intergrowths and which may be found in any of the more specialized works on mineral identification.)

Dolomite

Dolomite is a carbonate of calcium and magnesium. It contains approximately equal weights of calcium and magnesium carbonate; it is not a mixture of the salts but a complex chemical substance containing calcium, magnesium, and carbonate ions.

Description: Dolomite crystallizes in the hexagonal system into rhomb-shaped crystals and the crystal faces are often curved. The cleavage is perfectly parallel to the rhomb faces of the crystals. Dolomite also occurs massive or granular.

Dolomite is white, translucent, or opaque, but it may be stained by impurities to yellowish or brown, and sometimes red, green, or black. The hardness is 3·5 to 4 and the specific gravity 2·8.

In cold acid the mineral dissolves very slowly, but in warm acid it dissolves readily with effervescence of carbon dioxide.

Occurrence: The mineral dolomite occurs as rhomboid crystals in veins, often associated with the metal ores galena and blende. It forms thick beds of granular or finely-crystalline rock which is also called dolomite.

Calcareous Rocks – Limestones

Limestone is a general term referring to all sedimentary rocks which consist wholly or largely of calcite. They are therefore soluble in acid, and limestone rock may be identified by its effervescence in acid.

Most limestone rocks are of marine origin, some are lacustrine while the rarer clastic limestones, which are limestone breccias, may be subaerial or marine.

Calcite may be precipitated directly from sea water, either chemically or by the action of living organisms which abstract calcium carbonate from the sea water. Much of the organically produced calcium carbonate occurs in shells or other hard parts of primitive marine organisms, such as coral. These fall on the sea floor when the creatures die and very extensive deposits of limestone rock, thousands of feet thick, may be formed in this way.

A pure limestone contains at least 90 per cent calcium carbonate. Sand or clay may be deposited on the sea floor at the same time as calcite, and this results in the formation of sandy (*arenaceous*) limestones, or clayey (*argillaceous*) limestones. There are an infinite number of possible gradations between a pure limestone, an arenaceous limestone and a calcareous sandstone, and similarly between argillaceous limestones and calcareous mudstones.

As the calcite bed thickens, compression results in the expulsion of sea water and the formation of consolidated rock. This may be accompanied by some recrystallization of the calcite, but fossils are often extremely well preserved in limestones.

Bedding may be distinct in limestones if the conditions of sedimentation change from time to time, and limestones may be interbedded with shales or mudstones. But in many limestones the bedding is so thick that its composition remains homogenous over hundreds of feet. Joints are normally developed and on exposure to the surface, these joints are rapidly enlarged by weathering processes since drainage of a limestone region may become engulfed in a system of subterranean streams.

Limestones vary considerably in their physical properties. Limestones with a firm and compact texture are strong, but the *hardness* of limestones is the same as for calcite, 3. The porosity of limestones also varies depending on their texture; loosely cemented limestones are more porous and they are therefore also less resistant to weathering than the massive varieties.

Mountain limestone is a term often used to refer to the very pure massive limestones, particularly of the Carboniferous period. They range in colour from pale grey to dark greys, and may be stained red shades by iron oxides or greenish, usually as a result of dolomitization. Black limestones often contain carbonaceous matter originally of organic origin; some black limestones have a pungent tarry smell, particularly on fresh breaks; they contain considerable quantities of organic matter and are called *bituminous limestones.*

Chalk is a soft friable limestone. Pure chalk is white and consists almost entirely of calcium carbonate. It largely consists of the minute disc-shaped skeletons of marine algae, foraminifera, and plankton, but larger fossils also occur and may be very abundant. The non-calcareous parts of chalk consist largely of the siliceous skeletons of diatoms and other organisms. Most chalks are very pure and were formed in seas which received no land sediments, but impure grey or red chalks are known, which contain clay, silt, and iron oxides.

Oolite, or oolitic limestone, consists of minute spheres of precipitated calcium carbonate cemented together. These spheres may range from minute specks, which are not easily seen by the naked eye, to the size of a pea. They generally contain a small quartz or other sand grain at the centre, around which the calcium carbonate has been precipitated in concentric layers.

The properties of oolite depend largely on the size of the calcite spheres and the degree to which they are cemented. Some compact oolites are quite strong, but oolites are usually more porous than massive limestones, and therefore more easily weathered, particularly by frost.

Marl is a loose, impure limestone which contains appreciable quantitites of clay and/or sand.

Dolomite is a limestone in which all or most of the calcite has been replaced by the mineral dolomite. Dolomite may be formed directly by precipitation from sea water or by the action of sea water on calcite before it is covered by a later deposit; but in many dolomite rocks the calcite has been altered to dolomite at a later stage, by the infiltration of magnesium-bearing solutions.

This process, which is known as dolomitization, is usually most marked along fissures in the rocks, and limestones in which the replacement of calcite by dolomite is not complete are often referred to as *magnesian limestone*.

Since dolomite is a denser mineral than calcite, the secondary alteration of limestone to dolomite is usually accompanied by a decrease in volume, so that many dolomites are porous rocks and may be traversed by veins of various kinds.

Marble is a metamorphosed limestone in which the calcite has been entirely recrystallized, so that the original sedimentary structure is lost. A dolomite is recrystallized to a marble consisting entirely of crystalline dolomite. Marbles may vary in texture from coarse-grained rocks with calcite crystals 1 cm long, to very fine-grained rocks in which individual calcite grains cannot be distinguished by the naked eye. If the texture is not too fine, the rhomb cleavage facets of calcite are clearly seen on a fresh break. Fine-textured marbles have a shimmering lustre on a fresh break.

A pure calcite marble is snow white, but during metamorphism the non-calcareous impurities of the limestone, i.e. sand, clay, and iron oxides are also recrystallized to form new minerals. These may be disseminated throughout the rock, giving it an exotic colour, or they are irregularly distributed in patches and streaks giving the characteristic 'marbled' appearance. Iron oxides give yellowish or reddish colours, and black or grey colours are frequently due to substances of organic origin.

Marble is a soft rock, hardness 3, and may be easily distinguished from sandstones or felsites which may superficially resemble it; marble also dissolves in cold acid with effervescence.

Unlike most metamorphic rocks marbles are rarely foliated, but they occur massive and have a homogenous texture.

In architecture and statuary any limestone which takes a high polish is called marble. This also includes a large number of partly altered or unaltered compact crystalline limestones. Limestones which have been lightly altered by shear stresses or pressure alone may be so compacted and partly crystalline as to have physical properties similar to a true marble. In such rocks, the

a

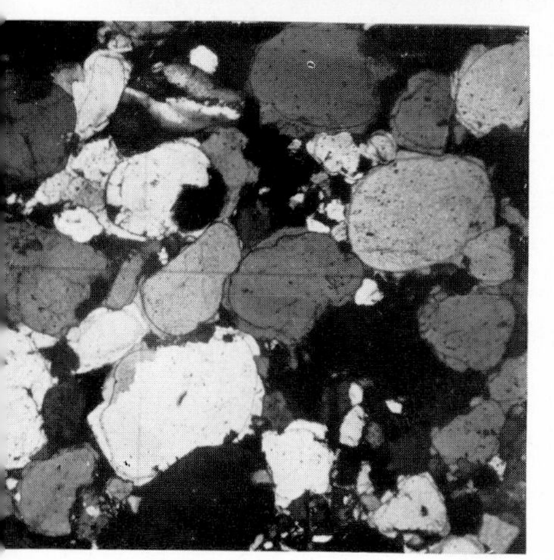

b

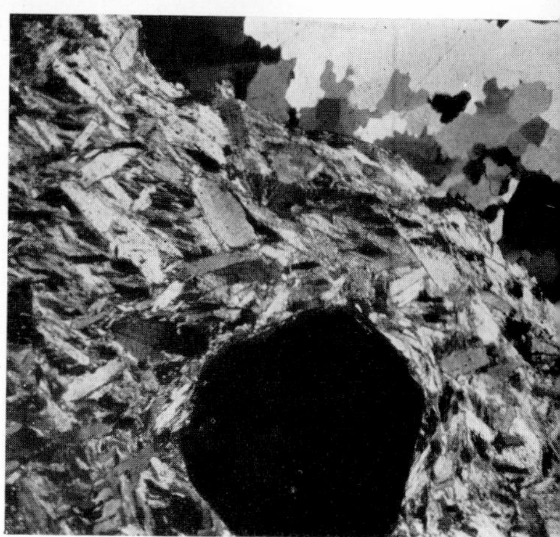

c

1 Microphotographs of thin sections of igneous, sedimentary and metamorphic rocks. All three are taken in polarised light with crossed nicols. This results in light being transmitted only when the minerals are aligned in certain directions. Since the minerals are randomly aligned (except in the schist), grains of the same mineral may appear white if aligned parallel to the direction in which polarised light is transmitted, black if perpendicular to this direction, or grey in intermediate positions. (Magnification × 37)
(*a*) Granite (Granodiorite) showing interlocking crystals: quartz with small 'bubble' inclusions and irregular outlines; felspars showing parallel and some perpendicular cleavage cracks; hornblende showing rhombic crystal outlines and two sets of cleavage cracks inclined at 120°. (*b*) Sandstone showing the rounded outlines of the original quartz sand grains through the silica cement which fills the interstices between the grains. (*c*) Schist with bands of mica and quartz. The platy mica crystals are aligned parallel to the shistosity of the rock, and around a large garnet crystal; the inregularly shaped quartz crystals are less clearly aligned, but the large structureless white patch shows some degree of alignment in the quartz band of the schist.

2 Granite showing equigranular texture of a coarse grained rock: grey quartz, white felspar, black hornblende and biotite.

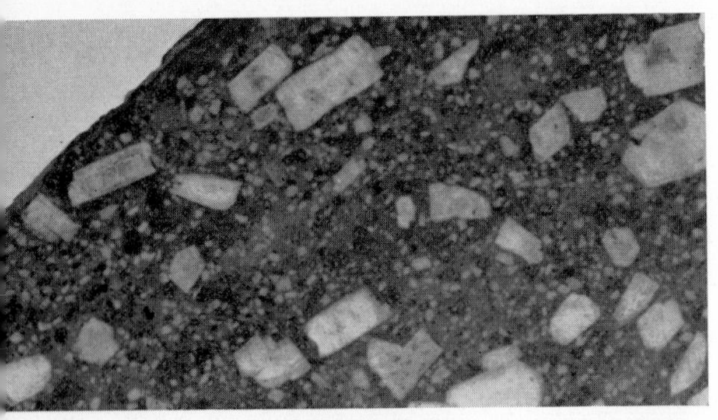

3 Quartz Porphyry with large and small phenocrysts of quartz and felspar in a fine-grained dark groundmass.

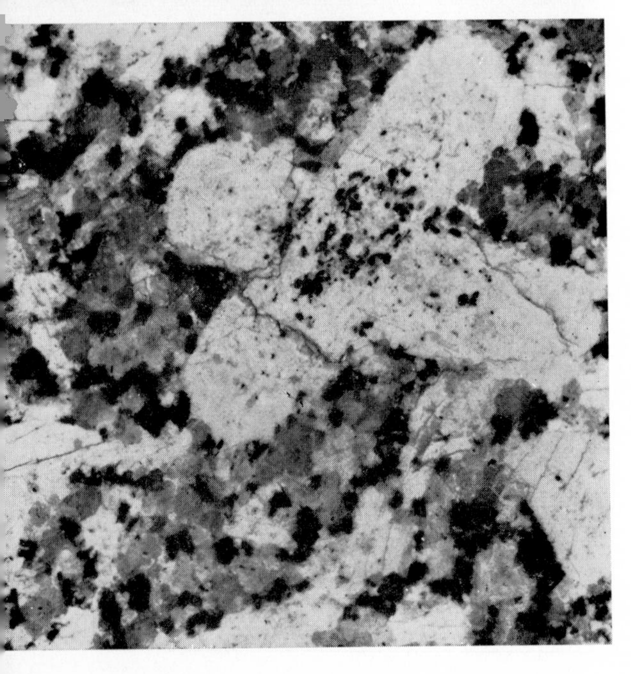

4 Porpyhyritic Granite with phenocrysts of felspar in a coarse-grained groundmass. In the centre is a cruciform twin of orthoclase felspar.

5 Pebble conglomerate with large subangular pebbles and smaller, more highly rounded, pebbles grading into sand grains.

6 Predynastic Egyptian (Amratian) disc mace-head of *diorite*. (5 cm high)

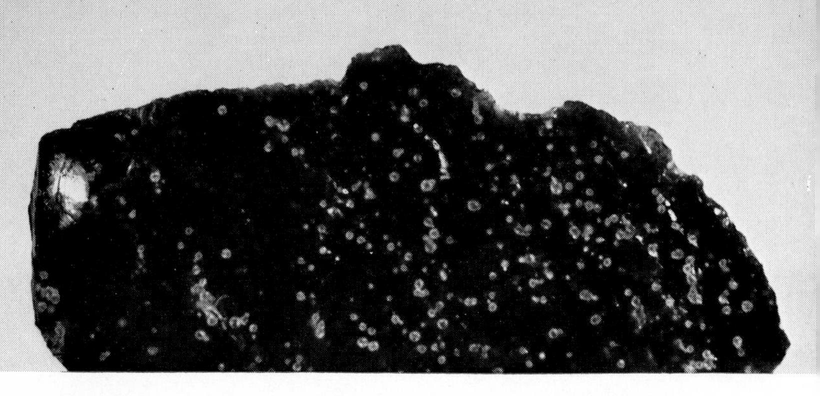

7 Blade of spherulitic *obsidian* showing small spherical clusters of white crystals (felspar) in a translucent glass matrix.

8 Vesicular basalt with roughly spherical cavities and a few white phenocrysts of felspar in a dark fine-grained matrix.

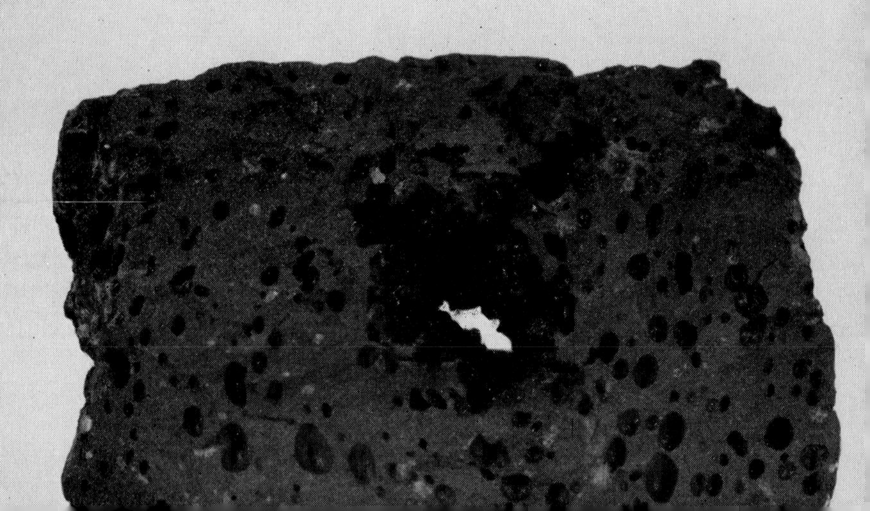

9 (*above*) Gneisses. Banded gneiss in which the minerals show a clear parallel alignment, but are not separated into broad distinct bands. (*below*) 'Augen' gneiss in which the minerals are clearly separated into distinct bands and lenticular masses.

11 Predynastic Egyptian palette of *slate* in the form of an hippopotamus. The regular and distinct fissility of slate has been exploited in making this palette which has a uniform thickness of a few mm. (18 cm long)

10 Predynastic Egyptian (Gerzean) vase of *breccia*. (11 cm high)

12 Archaic Egyptian (Dynasty I–II) dish of *banded calcite* known as 'Egyptian alabaster'. The colours grade from a creamy white to ochreous yellow and brown. (32 cm diameter)

13 Archaic Egyptian (Dynasty I–II) cup of *felspar porphyry*. (7 cm high)

14 Prehistoric Sickles. (*above*) Clay sickle of very highly fired and vitrified pottery, from the Ubaid period of Ur. (33 cm long) (*below*) Flint sickle made by mounting short flint blades in a wooden handle, (25 cm) from the Fayum Neolithic of Egypt.

15 Axes. Left: Polished axe of diorite with wide angle cutting edge, from the Neolithic of Yorkshire (East Riding). (14 cm long).
Centre: Axe (pallstave) of bronze from Bronze Age Dorset. The casting technique made it possible to shape elaborate devices, such as the phlanges and ridge, to prevent the axe head being driven into the haft with use, and a small loop to facilitate lashing the head into its haft. The splayed shape of the cutting edge results from hardening by hammering.
Right: Axe of iron from Saxon London (?). Forging techniques resulted in a return to more simple shapes than could be made in bronze. This axe shape with shaft hole could be forged by folding a long strip in two and welding and hammering one end to a tapering edge.

18–19 (*above*) Miniature bottle of variegated black and white glass with applique handles, probably of Saitic date (Dynasty XXVI–XXX). (7 cm high) Blue faience Ushabti figure of Queen Henut-tawy of Dynasty XXI with wig, flail and inscription in deep blue. (11 cm)

16 Bronze dagger and sword and imitations in flint from the Early Bronze Age in Denmark; imported bronze dagger from Jutland and Danish flint copy; bronze slashing sword from West Zealand and flint copy from Funa.

17 Oval pedestal dish of clear glass from the Roman period in Egypt (4th–5th century A D). (16 cm diameter)

20 Pink granite statue of Rameses II, the high state official, from Memphis in Egypt (XIXth Dynasty). This statue shows the compact form of Egyptian formal statuary even when interest is shown in the realistic representation of detail, as in the face and hair. The style may, in part, result from the use of hard brittle rocks such as granite.

21 (*right*) Marble statue of 'crouching Aphrodite' from Rhodes (2nd–1st century BC?). It shows the delicate work achieved in marble, for instance in the treatment of the hair and arms.

23 Flint handaxes from gravels of the Somme river in Northern France. (*left*) 'Fresh' unrolled Acheulean handaxe in which the edges are still quite sharp. (14 cm high) (*right*) Rolled and abraded handaxe in which the projecting ridges have been heavily rounded.

22 The unfinished obelisk at Aswan, showing the quarrying technique employed to detach blocks of hard rock.

24 Fragment of coarse sandstone (millstone grit) weathered under acid, humid soil conditions. C is the pale creamy unaltered rock. The dark line B is a narrow deep brown zone in which iron salts are highly concentrated. A_2 is the white leached zone consisting solely of quartz, from which all traces of iron have been leached down to B. A_1 is the leached surface of the weathered rock, also devoid of iron, but stained dark grey with humus.

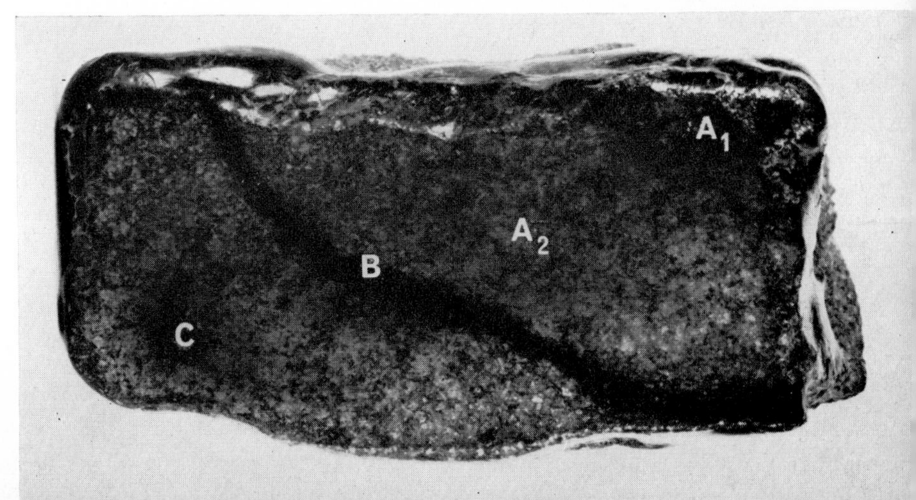

25 The effects of salt infestation on a Palestinian pot.

26 Thin sections of Windmill Hill pottery (magnification $\times$ 10). Naturally occurring clay with rounded, corroded, flint weathered from chalk (plane polarised light). (*right*) Clay with added filler of uncorroded sand grains of quartz, felspar and hornblende (crossed nicols).

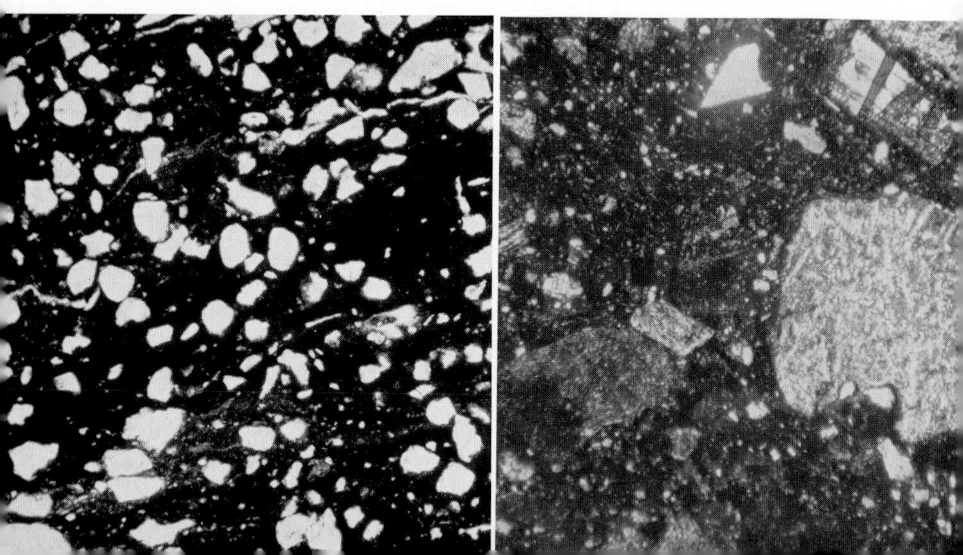

original structure including fossils may be preserved intact, but fossils are often distorted, elongated or flattened and give rise to a patterned surface when polished.

Marbles are found in many parts of the world in regions of metamorphosed rocks associated with gneiss, schists, or phyllites. They are also formed by contact metamorphism around intrusive igneous rocks, but such occurrences are usually of smaller extent and grade into the bedded sedimentary rock.

Calcium Sulphate

There are two forms of calcium sulphate, the pure crystalline form, *anhydrite* – $CaSO_4$ and a hydrated form of calcium sulphate which is much more abundant, *gypsum* – $CaSO_4.2H_2O$.

Gypsum

Description: Gypsum crystallizes in the monoclinic form and crystals of gypsum are generally flat with lozenge shaped facets bounded by tapering sides, as shown in Figure 26. Twinning is

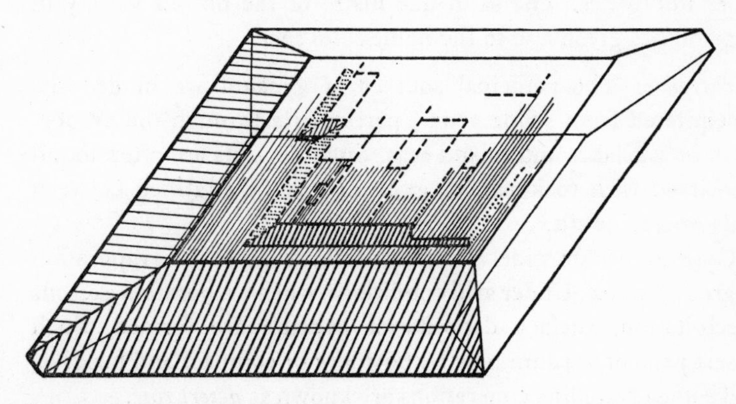

Figure 26 Specimen of gypsum

fairly frequent, and twin crystals are either very pointed, or have a wide re-entrant angle. This characteristic has given rise to the names 'arrowhead' and 'swallow tail' types.

As a rock constituent, gypsum is commonly granular, massive, or fibrous (Figure 18), or less commonly – foliated. It has a perfect cleavage parallel to the side facet so that very thin flat plates can be obtained.

Gypsum is colourless and transparent, but crystals are often white to translucent or may be stained with iron oxides to pink or brown. Massive varieties of gypsum are translucent to opaque and may be snow white or stained pink, brown, or black. The lustre is glassy or pearly but the massive varieties may be dull.

The hardness of gypsum is 2 so that it can be scratched with the fingernail, and it has a slightly soapy feel to the touch; the specific gravity is 2·3.

If heated moderately, not above 200°C, gypsum loses some of its water of crystallization (if powdered it is then known as plaster of Paris); it readily reabsorbs moisture to return to gypsum, $CaSO_4.2H_2O$. If heated more strongly it may lose all its water of crystallization and be converted to anhydrite, $CaSO_4$.

Selenite is a very pure transparent variety of gypsum.

Alabaster is a fine-grained compact variety; it may be pure white but it is often banded or veined and stained with iron oxides or other impurities. The satin-like lustre of the fibrous variety of gypsum has given rise to the name *satin spar*.

Occurrence: The principal sources of gypsum are in deposits precipitated from saline water, particularly through the evaporation of salt lakes and inland seas. Such deposits are often found associated with rock salt, or gypsum may be stratified between beds of clay or silt.

Gypsum occurs widely in desert soils owing to the evaporation of ground water. Under arid conditions, when evaporation exceeds precipitation, surface deposits of gypsum are formed. Such desert pans of gypsum may be powdery or compact and massive, and some crystalline concretions are known as *desert rose*.

Gypsum crystals (*selenite*) are commonly found in marine clays where they are most probably formed by the interaction of the sulphur from iron pyrites on the calcium carbonate of shells.

Anhydrite

Description: Anhydrite crystallizes in the orthorhombic system into prismatic or tabular crystals, but in rocks it is usually granular or nearly massive; fibrous anhydrite is less common than fibrous gypsum. Anhydrite has three good cleavages at right angles, so that cubic or rectangular forms are seen on a fracture.

Anhydrite is white, translucent, or opaque, sometimes with a bluish tinge, but it may be stained like gypsum. It has a pearly to glassy lustre, but in massive varieties the lustre is usually dull.

The hardness of anhydrite is somewhat greater than that of gypsum, ranging from 3 to 3·5, and the specific gravity is 2·9, somewhat greater than that of gypsum.

Occurrence: Anhydrite is less abundant than gypsum, but it is commonly found associated with gypsum deposits and with rock salt. There is some evidence that gypsum is formed from salt water at temperatures above 25°C, so that alternations of gypsum and anhydrite beds may reflect temperature changes.

Differentiation between anhydrite and gypsum: The hardness and specific gravity may be used to distinguish these two minerals, but when they occur as patchy intergrowths they are not easily distinguished. A simple test may be carried out to observe whether water of crystallization is evolved on heating. A small amount of the powdered mineral is placed in a small heat-resisting glass tube and is strongly heated over a bunsen flame (this test is known as the 'closed tube test', since one end of the tube is sealed). Gypsum gives off water which condenses on the upper walls of the tube; anhydrite does not give off water.

Calcium Phosphate

The crystalline form of calcium phosphate, *apatite*, is extremely widespread and occurs in very small quantities in most rocks. Calcium phosphate is also an essential component of most animal life, particularly of bones and teeth, and many sedimentary occurrences of calcium phosphate are of organic origin. They are therefore of very variable chemical composition, and may not be crystalline. One non-crystalline variety of calcium phosphate is *collophane*, and there are a number of other terms used to refer to particular types of phosphatic deposits, such as *phosphorite*, *guano* and others.

Apatite

Apatite is a calcium phosphate with fluorine, $Ca_5F(PO_4)_3$, in which the fluorine may be wholly or partly replaced by chlorine or more rarely by hydroxyl (OH) or carbonate (CO_3) ions.

Description: Apatite crystallizes in the hexagonal system, forming six-sided prisms with truncated pyramidal extremities. It also occurs massive, or as very small shapeless grains.

Apatite varies in colour from a yellow or yellowish green to a bluish green. It may be transparent, but frequently occurs as opaque resinous crystals or grains. The fracture is uneven and the cleavage is very poor, and may not be apparent.

The hardness of apatite is 5, the specific gravity is 3·2.

Occurrence: Large well-formed crystals of apatite occur in rock veins, particularly in pegmatite veins. Small grains of apatite are widely distributed in most igneous and metamorphic rocks and become available to living organisms when such rocks weather into soil. Phosphates of organic origin may be in the form of apatite as in bone and teeth and in deposits derived from these materials. Other organic phosphate deposits are usually mixtures of apatite and other substances.

Phosphorite results from the accumulation of organic remains (particularly bird or bat droppings) on limestone. The calcite of the limestone becomes partly altered to apatite and the resulting rock which is a mixture of calcite and apatite is known as phosphorite.

Guano are deposits of a high phosphatic content derived from bird or bat droppings. They are usually found in caves, at the foot of cliffs, or in other localized deposits where birds or bats habitually congregate in large numbers.

Bone beds are accumulations of the bones and teeth of animals which have become concentrated, usually by the activity of running water or by the accumulation of bones near water holes or rock fissures. Bone beds are therefore commonly found in caves or rock fissures, or in certain fluviatile deposits. In calcareous surroundings, such bone deposits may be partly converted to a non-crystalline form of calcium phosphate known as *collophane*. Collophane is a yellowish-brown substance, with a very resinous lustre, which may occur as concretions or in stalagmitic form.

Sodium Salts

Sodium salts are very soluble and therefore only occur in appreciable quantities in solution in sea water or salt lakes and in regions of high aridity. Sodium minerals are found principally as evaporites or in small quantities as efflorescences on desert soils. Sodium chloride (NaCl), *halite* or common salt, is by far the most abundant of sodium salts. Other sodium salts are often associated as impurities with sodium chloride. Several sodium carbonate minerals are known which differ in their degree of hydration; the most common are *natron* and *trona.*

Halite, Rock Salt

Halite, rock salt, or common salt, are all terms commonly used to refer to sodium chloride. Halite is the mineralogical term, whereas rock salt usually refers to the deposits of halite which may contain small quantities of impurities.

Description: Halite forms simple cubic crystals and occasionally cubes with concave facets; its cleavage is also cubic. Pure halite is colourless and transparent, but it often appears white owing to reflection from cleavage and other cracks. Halite may be coloured bright red due to the inclusion of hematite, or black from organic impurities. Its hardness is 2 to 2·5 and the specific gravity is 2·2. It is easily soluble in water and has a distinctive salt taste.

Occurrence: Deposits of rock salt occur as extensive beds, and are commonly associated with gypsum. They may also be interbedded with thin strata of clay or other sediments. The beds vary greatly in thickness and may range from 1 centimetre to over 40 metres thick. The thick deposits are very probably formed by continued evaporation associated with subsidence of the lake or sea floor.

Rock salt also occurs as large intrusive domes or plugs in sedimentary rocks. These are formed when salt deposits become buried beneath a great thickness of rock. Since salt is comparatively plastic it is 'squeezed' up towards regions of weakness by the downward pressure of overlaying rocks.

Natron

Natron is a very hydrated form of sodium carbonate:

$$Na_2CO_3.10H_2O.$$

Description: Natron crystallizes in the monoclinic system, but it is usually found massive, granular, or as efflorescences on the desert floor. Natron is white, grey, or yellowish, with an earthy and dull lustre, but the crystalline form may be vitreous. The hardness is 1 to 1·5 and the specific gravity is 1·5, but since natron usually occurs with other sodium salts, this may be difficult to determine.

Natron is highly soluble in water, and it effervesces with cold dilute acid.

Occurrence: Natron occurs in evaporites or on desert soils in arid regions, usually with other sodium carbonates. It is the last of the sodium salts to be precipitated out of solution, after trona and halite.

Trona, Urao

Trona is a less hydrated form of sodium carbonate and bicarbonate (i.e. basic sodium carbonate), $Na_2CO_3.NaHCO_3.2H_2O$.

Description: Trona crystallizes in the monoclinic system and generally forms fibrous or columnar masses or bands. Trona is of the same colour as natron but it has a vitreous, nearly translucent lustre. The hardness is 2·5 to 3, and the specific gravity is 2. Trona is highly soluble in water, and effervesces in cold dilute acid.

Occurrence: Trona occurs with other sodium salts in evaporites or as desert crusts. It is precipitated out of solution before natron, and before halite if this is present.

Potassium Salts

Potassium salts are very soluble and occur in saline residues in arid or semi-arid regions, and in solution in sea water and salt lakes. Most potassium minerals of saline residues are hydrated salts of potassium, magnesium, and sometimes calcium. *Nitre*, potassium nitrate (KNO_3), also forms thick deposits of organic origin, and is found in the soils of certain arid regions.

Nitre, Saltpetre

Description: Nitre forms acicular crystals or columnar masses of crystals with a silky lustre. It also occurs as thin crusts particularly in soils. Nitre is white when pure, vitreous and translucent to transparent. It is soluble in water and has a salt taste. The hardness is 2 and the specific gravity is 2.

Occurrence: Nitre deposits of organic origin occur in the arid regions of Northern India, Persia, Egypt, and other countries; and, in smaller quantities, associated with other potassium salts and sodium salts in saline residues.

Silica

Silica is only slightly soluble in water, but its solubility increases with temperature, so that in tropical regions quartz is corroded by ground water, whereas in temperate and arid zones quartz is one of the most stable minerals.

When silica is precipitated out of solution, it normally does not form crystalline quartz but remains in a colloidal state. Colloidal silica consists of an intimate random mixture of silica (SiO_2) and water, with no definite structure. When little water is present the colloidal silica forms a structureless solid mass known as *gel*. The properties of colloidal silica depend on the amount of water present and on any impurities. On dehydration of a silica gel, some of the silica begins to crystallize. The crystals formed are so small that they are sub-microscopic, or *cryptocrystalline*.

Three principal types of silica minerals are distinguished according to the proportions of colloidal and crystalline silica.

Opal is a purely colloidal form of silica. *Chalcedony* silica is the cryptocrystalline form, which frequently also contains variable amounts of opal. The crystalline form of silica is quartz which has been described under rock-forming minerals (pp. 43–5).

Opal

Opal is an amorphous form of silica, in which the amount of water is usually less than 10 per cent.

Description: Pure opal is translucent or opaque milky white. It often has a bluish or grey tinge, and may display different shades of colour according to the direction in which the stone is viewed, reflecting bright primary colours (rainbow colours) from minute cracks or irregularities of composition in the stone. Traces of impurities may colour opal yellow, red, brown, or black.

The fracture is conchoidal and opal occurs as structureless masses or concretions. The hardness is less than that of quartz, 5·5 to 6·5, and the specific gravity is 2·2.

A number of varieties of opal are recognized according to colour or mode of occurrence. *Wood opal*, or *fossil wood*, is wood in which all the cell tissues and cavities have become replaced by opal. The original structure of the wood may be reproduced in great detail, but it is often partly obliterated.

Diatomite consists of the small tests and skeletons of aquatic organisms, such as algae and diatoms. When the organism dies its hard parts, which consist of opal, accumulate, often on the bottom of a lake floor. The grain size of diatomite depends on the type of organism. In lakes where free silica is easily available, diatom growth is vigorous and thick deposits of pure white diatomite are found.

Occurrence: Opal occurs as concretions or linings of cracks and cavities of rocks. It is found characteristically filling the vesicles of basalts or as nodules in sandstones and shales. In old rock, opal may be partly or entirely converted to the cryptocrystalline form, *chalcedony*.

Porous opal crusts occur as deposits around siliceous springs, particularly hot springs, and form deposits resembling travertines.

Chalcedonic Silica

Chalcedonic silica usually occurs as a mixture of crystalline and colloidal silica. The crystals are fibrous and form a matted structure in which the colloidal silica remains trapped. The properties of chalcedonic silica depend on the amount of colloidal silica and water present and three main types may be recognized, although they grade into each other. *Chalcedony* – the most hydrated form, *flint* – an intermediate form, and *jasper* – with very little or no hydrous silica.

Chalcedony is white or colourless, translucent to opaque, and is often milky white with a wax-like lustre. It has a conchoidal fracture, and appears entirely structureless in hand specimens. The hardness is slightly lower than quartz, 6·5–7. A great variety of chalcedony forms are distinguished, primarily according to colour.

Carnelian is a translucent reddish or brownish variety of chalcedony, and an opaque brown variety is known as *sard*.

Agate is a variegated variety of chalcedony, in which bands or patches of different colours may range from colourless to brown red, grey, or blue. The colours may grade imperceptibly into one another, or be sharply demarcated. When the colours are in flat bands the stone is also known as *onyx* or *sardonyx*. Moss agate is a variety in which the impurities, iron oxides or chlorite, form dendritic (tree-like) patterns.

Prase, *chrysoprase*, and *bloodstone* are various green varieties, the latter speckled with red.

Flint is a compact cryptocrystalline silica with some hydrous silica. It may be black, or various shades of grey, or coloured brown with iron oxide. The colours may be patchy or banded. It has a conchoidal fracture and is nearly as hard as quartz, 6·5 to 7.

Chert is a somewhat coarser form of flint which has a subconchoidal to flat fracture. Both flint and chert appear structureless in hand specimens. Flint may be translucent on thin edges, but chert is usually opaque. It is often difficult to distinguish between flint and chert, and the former is often used to refer to the siliceous nodules which occur in chalk, whereas similar nodules in limestones are called chert.

Jasper is an opaque cryptocrystalline variety of silica, usually intensely coloured with impurities. Jasper may be yellow, red, green, or brown, and some varieties are banded. It has a flat or subconchoidal fracture, and grades into chert.

Cortex: Many siliceous concretions have a natural outer shell which is opaque or lustreless, and may be white or grey. This crust or cortex consists of a porous layer of cryptocrystalline silica from which the colloidal silica has been lost. Colloidal silica, which contains some water, is more readily soluble than pure crystalline silica. It is therefore leached out of the composite siliceous minerals such as flint, chert, and jasper – leaving a porous, minutely crystalline structure. The white colour of the cortex is due to the irregular reflection of light from the numerous crystals. Since the cortex is porous, it is easily stained by soil solutions.

Occurrence of chalcedonic silica: Cryptocrystalline silica, like opal, results from the dehydration of silica gels which have been deposited as films or concretions in fissures or cavities in the rock. In many instances rock cavities may be lined with opal which grades to the more crystalline forms towards the centre, and may end in quartz crystals in the centre of the cavity. In sedimentary rocks – such as limestones, chalk, some shales and sandstones – nodules or bands of siliceous concretions are found, which are usually flint, chert, or jasper. They are probably secondary formations in these rocks, resulting from the accumulation of silica in localized spots, but in chalk and limestones they may have been formed at the time of sedimentation, due to local conditions favouring the precipitation of silica on the sea bed.

Deposits of Organic Origin

There are a number of substances which are usually classed as minerals or rock but which are organic in origin. Some – such as limestone, phosphorite, or diatomite – are partly or entirely produced by living organisms which, after death, become incorporated in rocks by normal sedimentary processes. The calcite, apatite, and opal of these rocks is, however, indistinguishable from that produced by inorganic processes.

Other rocks or 'minerals' of organic origin are those derived from the alteration of the perishable parts of organisms; all of these contain *carbon* and *hydrogen* in combination with other elements (particularly oxygen and nitrogen).

Coals

Under certain conditions, plant remains are not entirely decomposed by bacteria but accumulate to form deposits which consist of the more or less altered plant tissues. *Peat* is a characteristic deposit of this type, in which some of the plant remains may still be identified, whereas others are decomposed to simpler organic substances (i.e. containing carbon and hydrogen).

As deposits of plant debris increase in thickness and become buried beneath later deposits, they are subjected to pressure and heat. Chemical changes take place which result in the loss of water and the more volatile components, with a consequent increase in the proportion of carbon in the deposit. *Brown coal*, or *lignite*, contains roughly 50 per cent carbon, *black coal* may consist of up to 90 per cent carbon.

Jet

Jet is a fossil wood altered by heat and pressure, but to a lesser degree than black coal, and it may be considered as a variety of lignite.

Description: Jet is black, opaque with a slightly resinous lustre, and it can be highly polished. It breaks with a conchoidal fracture. Jet frequently preserves the grain of the wood, and since it contains a high proportion of carbon, it can be burnt. The specific gravity varies according to the processes of fossilization, but it generally is 'lighter' than coal.

Occurrence: Jet occurs as nodules in shales, mudstones, and other fine-grained sediments. Most jet and lignite is found in geological formations of relatively recent date (Tertiary), whereas black coal deposits usually occur in older formations, particularly in carboniferous sediments.

Bitumens

The bitumens are probably also of organic origin. They consist of hydrocarbons, i.e. compounds consisting primarily of carbon and hydrogen. The proportion of carbon to other elements varies and – generally speaking – the richer in carbon, the thicker and blacker is the bitumen. Bitumens are roughly divided into *mineral oils* and *pitch*. Pitch is a black or brown sticky substance which can be melted by gentle heating, and which sets on cooling. The temperature at which it sets depends on the exact composition of the pitch. If it sets at atmospheric temperature, it can be roughly moulded or pressed into shape and made to adhere firmly on to other materials.

Hard pitch is brittle and breaks with a conchoidal fracture.

Graphite

Graphite is a crystalline form of pure carbon.

Description: Graphite has a sheet structure of carbon atoms bound by homopolar bonds, but there are no strong bonds between carbon atoms of adjacent sheets. It crystallizes in the hexagonal system, but crystals are extremely rare and it is usually massive or scaly. The cleavage is perfectly parallel to the carbon sheets, and the mineral has a greasy feel and stains the fingers. Graphite is iron grey or very dark grey, with a metallic lustre; the streak colour is black and, since the mineral is very soft, the streak can be obtained on paper. The hardness ranges from 1 to 2 and the specific gravity from 2 to 2·4 depending on the purity of the material.

Occurrence: Graphite is characteristically found in metamorphic rocks. It probably originates from the metamorphism of carbonaceous matter of organic origin, in which heat alteration has reduced all hydrocarbons to pure carbon. Graphite occurs as veins in crystalline limestones and marble, or as lenticular patches in gneiss or schists, or disseminated throughout the altered rock.

Amber

Amber is a fossil tree resin from an extinct conifer, *Pinus succinifer*.

Description: Amber is a resinous substance which occurs as irregular lumps. It ranges in colour from a deep orange brown to yellow, and may be almost white, rarely with a blue or green tinge. It is sometimes translucent, but it is frequently clouded or opaque. Amber may contain inclusions of insects, earth, or other impurities which were embedded in the resin at the time it was exuded from the tree.

The chemical composition of amber is complex and variable, and the formula $C_{10}H_{16}O$ represents an average composition. One of the principal constituents of amber is *succinic acid*, $C_4H_6O_{10}$, and the amount of succinic acid varies in ambers from deposits of different geological age and from different regions. Succinic acid is the only component of amber which is soluble in boiling water, so that an estimate of the amount of succinic acid in a specimen of amber can be obtained by extracting the acid in water.

Amber has a hardness of 2 to 2·5 and a specific gravity only slightly higher than water, 1·1, so that it is easily carried by water but it does not float. It breaks with a conchoidal fracture.

Succinite is a yellow to brown, translucent to opaque, variety of amber which is especially common in the Baltic Sea region. It may contain as much as thirty per cent succinic acid.

Ambrite is reddish yellow amber which is found in New Zealand.

Copaline is a dark yellowish amber which occurs as nodules in London Clay.

Copal is the resin from a living African species of tree.

Occurrence: Amber is found as nodules in deposits of Tertiary age, particularly in sediments of estuarine origin. Succinite occurs widely in the Baltic Sea region, but amber of similar composition is also found in Germany and in the North Mediterranean region. Amber occurs commonly as pebbles in beach deposits on the shore of the Baltic Sea, and to a lesser extent on the coasts of the North Sea.

CHAPTER FIVE

The Metals of Antiquity

THE terms 'Stone Age' and 'Copper', 'Bronze', and 'Iron' Ages are often used in archaeological literature to distinguish periods before and after the discovery of metals. For, whereas in the Stone Ages people relied solely on naturally occurring rocks (and organic substances) for the manufacture of tools, during the Copper, Bronze, and Iron Ages a new group of materials, the metals, became available, which for many purposes proved superior to stone. The discovery of metals is, therefore, generally considered to mark an important advance in technology, yet the distinction between the natures of stones and metals is often not fully understood.

Metals are a group of elements which, in nature, usually occur in combination with other elements, forming many of the inorganic substances which constitute the earth's rocks and minerals. Most of the rock-forming minerals, for instance, contain metals such as iron, magnesium, calcium, sodium, or potassium in combination with silicon and oxygen. There are also less abundant minerals which contain metals in combination with oxygen, sulphur, or other elements. The minerals from which the metal can be extracted in more or less pure form are known as *ores* to distinguish them from other metalliferous minerals which are not exploited in this way. The distinction between ores and other minerals is a purely practical one and whether a mineral is classed as an ore or not, depends entirely on the technological use made of it. For instance, before the Chalcolithic period, the green mineral malachite was used as a pigment and as a decorative stone; from the Chalcolithic onwards it was also used for the extraction of copper, and in this later context the same mineral is referred to as a copper 'ore'.

Metals differ from other substances in a number of ways. To the chemist, metals are a group of elements which can be distinguished from other elements by their chemical properties. Metals form positive ions (anions) in chemical combinations; one of the most important chemical properties of metals is their ability to replace the hydrogen in acids to form salts, (e.g. zinc and hydrochloric acid form the salt zinc chloride

$$Zn + 2HCl = H_2 + ZnCl_2).$$

The elements sodium, potassium, and calcium form positive ions and combine with acids to form salts. They are, therefore, metals in the chemical sense, although their physical properties differ from the popular concept of a metal: sodium for instance, is soft and has the consistency of cheese, it is extremely unstable in air and in the presence of water it ignites spontaneously and reacts chemically with the water to form the alkali sodium hydroxide (caustic soda).

From the point of view of a technologist, the physical properties of metals are more important than the chemical definitions; and to a metallurgist the concept of metal is more restricted than it is in the chemical sense. Metals are *malleable* (i.e. they can be hammered into shape); they are *ductile* (i.e. they can be drawn out into threads), and they are good conductors of heat and electricity. Metals have a characteristic lustre, they are opaque, often greyish white or yellowish in colour. Some metals are used pure, but many are used as mixtures (more accurately as solid solutions) of different metals; for instance, bronze which is a 'mixture' of the pure metals copper and tin. Metals can be molten and poured into moulds, but the temperature at which they melt varies considerably for the different metals. On solidifying, metals crystallize usually in either the cubic or hexagonal systems. The structure of metals is very much affected by impurities even in very small quantities and by the conditions of cooling and working. The study of the structure and properties of metals is a highly specialized field, which lies beyond the scope of this book. The metals known in antiquity, and the ores from which they were obtained, are described below. A few metals – gold, silver, and copper – are sometimes found in a more or less pure state and are then said to occur *native*.

Ore Deposits

There are three main types of ore deposit:

1. Those that have formed at the same time as the rock by crystallization from the magma. These deposits are usually irregular in shape and distribution throughout the rock, and were probably not a very important source of metal ores in antiquity.
2. Secondary mineral deposits which arise from metamorphic processes such as contact metamorphism and occur as veins or *lodes* in rock fissures. The latter are often of considerable depth but limited in width.
3. Alluvial or *placer* deposits, in which minerals of high specific gravity become concentrated in fluviatile gravels and sands.

Secondary enrichment of ore deposits: The outcrop of a metal-bearing lode is weathered into a deposit known as *gossan*. The gossan contains oxy-salts (i.e. oxidized minerals of the metal) whereas the original metal ores at depth are usually sulphides.

In the gossan many of the soluble substances are leached down and a concentrated residual deposit of metal oxides, carbonates, and sometimes native metal, is left. The downward leaching of metal salts produced in the gossan can sometimes result in considerable concentration of rich metal ores in an intermediate *zone of secondary enrichment* between the gossan cap and the original mineral vein (Figure 27).

Gold

Description: Pure gold is yellow with a metallic lustre and it does not tarnish. The specific gravity is extremely high, 20, and the hardness ranges from 2·5 to 3. The metal is both ductile and malleable, and can be shaped by cold hammering. The melting point is 1,060°C.

Native gold has been known to contain as much as 99 per cent pure gold, but it is usually amalgamated with silver and traces of other metals. Its colour varies in different sources, depending on the nature and amount of impurities. Traces of copper impart a reddish tinge to gold and silver gives it a pale colour; when the concentration of silver is high, around 25 per cent, the metal is nearly white and is known as *electrum*. *Black gold*, or *gold telluride*, is an ore of gold with tellurium and often also other metals such as silver, lead or antimony. There is no evidence that these gold tellurides were exploited in antiquity.

Occurrence: Gold is found in veins, particularly in quartz veins associated with granite intrusions. The gold occurs either as grains, as thread-like formations, or as fine gold dust. Gold is often associated with pyrite or other minerals of hydrothermal activity and in weathered veins the gold is found as small metallic nuggets in rusty coloured quartz.

Gold becomes concentrated in alluvial deposits by virtue of its high specific gravity. Gold placer deposits are very widespread and gold has been obtained from rivers in most parts of the world, but it is usually found in very small quantities.

Silver

Silver occurs native or as a simple ore from which the metal can be extracted. The most common silver ores are *horn silver* (silver chloride), *silver glance* (silver sulphide), and a number of sulphides of silver with other metals, such as antimony or arsenic. There is, however, little evidence that these ores were exploited in antiquity. Much of the silver obtained occurs as an impurity in other ores which are known as *argentiferous* ores. Electrum and galena are the most important argentiferous ores from which silver has been smelted.

Native Silver

Description: Native silver sometimes forms distorted cubic crystals but it usually occurs as grains, or thread-like formations.

It is a white metal which has a high lustre when freshly polished, but it tarnishes readily. The specific gravity ranges from 10 to 11 and the hardness from 2·5 to 3. It is malleable and ductile and can be shaped by cold hammering. Its melting point is 1,000°C.

Occurrence: Native silver occurs in the upper part of silver sulphide lodes in the zone of secondary enrichment. The gossan capping usually contains chlorides of silver. Primary native silver also occurs in veins associated with hydrothermal activity which are usually deep-seated veins and could not be exploited in prehistory.

The metal also occurs in alluvial deposits, but glacier deposits of silver are less widespread than those of gold.

Copper

Copper is found native, but most of the copper obtained in antiquity was smelted from ores. The ores may be grouped into the oxy-ores; the oxides and the carbonates; and the sulphide ores, of which there are three important variants.

Copper veins are found in regions of hydrothermal activity, such as contact metamorphic zones and in veins in igneous rocks. The primary ores of copper lodes are the sulphides of copper and iron *bornite* and *chalcopyrite*, usually associated with considerable quantities of the iron sulphide *pyrite*.

Copper sulphides are very unstable and are easily oxidized. The oxides and carbonates of copper are leached down to a lower zone of secondary enrichment in which native copper is also found. The upper cap, or gossan, usually consists of oxidized iron ores, *limonite*, and is frequently separated from the enriched zone by a sterile leached zone. If the enriched zone lies below the water table, the oxides are replaced by enriched sulphides of copper, *covellite*, and *chalcocite* (Figure 27).

Native Copper

Description: Native copper forms cubic crystals, but it is usually found massive in thin irregular sheets or plates, or in a maze

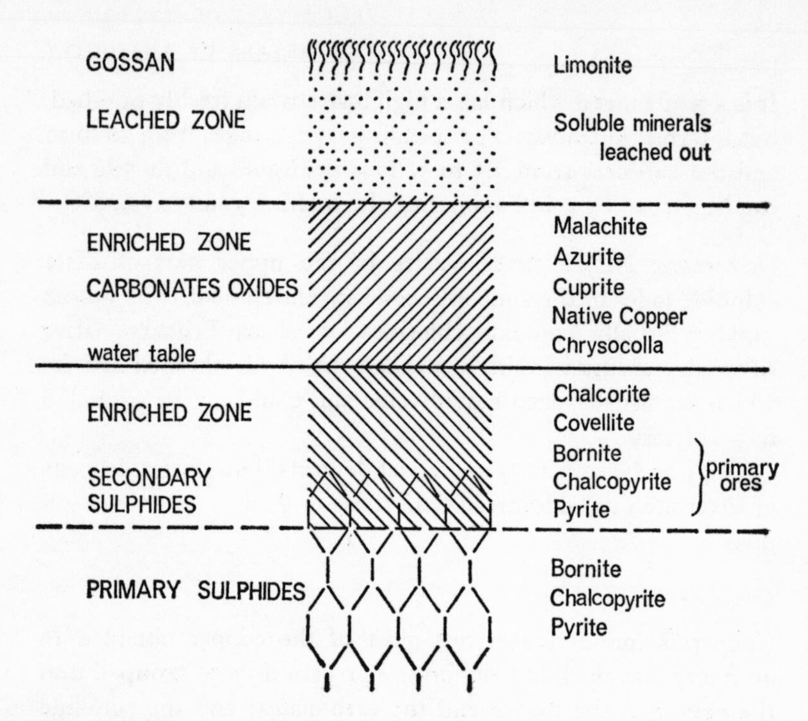

Figure 27 Diagrammatic section across a copper lode

of thin threads forming a spongy mass, also known as *moss copper*. Native copper is copper-red with a metallic lustre, but the surface may be tarnished and dull, sometimes with a black or a greenish colour. The specific gravity is 8·8, and the hardness ranges from 2·5 to 3. It is malleable and ductile and can be hammered into shape. Repeated hammering hardens the metal and it becomes brittle, breaking with an irregular fracture. On heating it to red heat, the metal becomes malleable again. The melting point is 1,100°C.

Occurrence: Native copper occurs in cracks and cavities of rocks as a result of hydrothermal activity, particularly as a secondary filling in the cavities of basic lavas. It also occurs in the enriched zone of sulphide lodes. Native copper is also concentrated in alluvial deposits.

Cuprite

Cuprite is a rich copper ore, Cu_2O, which contains 88 per cent by weight of copper.[1]

Description: Cuprite forms cubic crystals and sometimes octahedra; it is commonly found massive or in earthy friable masses. It is bright red or dark red with a submetallic lustre in the massive varieties, but dull in the earthy variety. The fracture is conchoidal, but crystals may show a weak cleavage parallel to the octahedra facets. The specific gravity is 5·8 to 6 and the hardness 3·5 to 4.

Occurrence: Cuprite is found in the zone of enrichment of copper lodes.

Tenorite, Melaconite

Black copper oxide, CuO, contains slightly less copper than cuprite, with 79·9 per cent copper by weight.

Description: Tenorite or melaconite usually occurs as dull black masses or concretions, or as a fine black powder. It is occasionally found as shining black scales. The specific gravity is 6·3 and the hardness 3 to 4, but these properties can only be tested on the massive variety.

Occurrence: Black copper oxide is found in the enriched zones of copper lodes with the more common cuprite.

Malachite

Malachite is a hydrated carbonate of copper, with a copper content of 57 per cent, $CuCO_3.Cu(OH)_2$.

Description: Malachite forms monoclinic crystals, but individual crystals are rare. The fine crystalline varieties usually form reniform concretions with a fibrous radial structure. It also occurs massive, earthy, or granular. On the outer surface of concretions the lustre may be waxy and bright; broken surfaces are dull and opaque. The colour is brilliant green and various shades of green

[1] The percentage of copper given is the theoretical value for pure ore; it is unlikely that the yield from smelting was ever complete.

may form concentric bands, particularly in the fibrous variety. The specific gravity is 4 and the hardness 3·5 to 4.

Occurrence: Malachite is found in cavities and fissures in the enriched zone of copper lodes, where it has accumulated by gradual precipitation from solution. The banded nature of the concretions is the result of minor changes in precipitation.

Azurite

Azurite is a less hydrated form of copper carbonate

$$2CuCO_3.Cu(OH)_2$$

which contains 55 per cent by weight of copper.

Description: Azurite differs from malachite primarily in its brilliant blue colour. Its form and habit are the same as for malachite, but the specific gravity is slightly lower, 3·7. The colour of azurite may range from light blue to a very greenish blue and concretions of azurite frequently grade into green malachite.

Occurrence: Azurite occurs with malachite and the two minerals may be found intergrown in the same concretions. Azurite is somewhat less common than malachite.

Chalcopyrite, Copper Pyrite

Chalcopyrite is a sulphide of copper and iron $CuFeS_2$ which contains 34·5 per cent copper.

Description: Chalcopyrite forms tetragonal crystals and is usually found in masses of ill-formed crystals which are nearly massive. It is brass yellow in colour and has a strong metallic lustre, but the streak colour is black or greenish black. The specific gravity is 4 to 4·3 and the hardness 4.

Occurrence: It occurs in copper lodes as a primary ore of copper, and is not normally found near the surface where the primary ores are replaced by the oxidized ones.

Bornite

Bornite or *Erubescite* is also a sulphide of copper and iron, but its composition is variable so that no accurate chemical formula can be given. It is richer in copper and poorer in iron than chalcopyrite.

Description: Bornite forms cubic and octahedral crystals, but it is most commonly found massive. It has a reddish golden colour with a high metallic lustre, but on exposed surfaces it tarnishes to green and blue with iridescent lustre. It is also known as *peacock ore* from the bright iridescent colours. The streak colour is grey to black. The specific gravity varies from 5 to 5·5 and the hardness is 3.

Occurrence: Bornite is found with chalcopyrite as a primary ore and is commonly associated with the zone of secondary sulphide enrichment.

Chalcocite, Copper Glance

Chalcocite is a rich copper sulphide Cu_2S with 80 per cent copper, but iron is usually present as an impurity.

Description: Chalcocite usually occurs massive with a granular or compact structure, but orthorhombic crystals are also known. The colour is black or lead grey, with sub-metallic, almost waxy, lustre. On exposure it tarnishes easily and has a slight bluish or greenish tinge. The fracture is conchoidal. The specific gravity is 5·5 and the hardness 2·5 to 3.

Occurrence: Chalcocite is found in the zone of sulphide enrichment of copper ores.

Covelline, Covellite

Covelline is a sulphide with 66 per cent copper, CuS.

Description: Covelline usually occurs massive or as hexagonal plates forming a scaly mass. It is dark blue-black in colour with a high metallic lustre and slight iridescence, sometimes with reddish tints. Covelline crystals have a perfect basal cleavage. Across the cleavage the fracture is brittle. The hardness is 1·5 to 2 and the specific gravity 4·5.

Occurrence: Covelline is found with other copper sulphides in the zone of secondary enrichment.

Chrysocolla

Chrysocolla is a copper mineral of very variable composition which contains primarily a hydrated silicate of copper, $CuSiO_3.2H_2O$.

Description: Chrysocolla is non-crystalline and occurs amorphous and massive as concretions or encrustations. It varies in colour from bluish green or turquoise to sky blue. The lustre may be nearly vitreous or dull and on fracture surfaces it may show a bright enamel-like lustre. The fracture is conchoidal.

The specific gravity is 2 to 2·2, the hardness varies considerably, from 2 to 4, but some varieties will scratch glass and probably contain pure silica which has a hardness of 7.

The copper content of chrysocolla is variable, but it may yield up to 10 per cent, on smelting, using limestone as a flux to melt the silica.

Occurrence: Chrysocolla is formed by precipitation in the zone of enrichment of copper lodes.

Tin

The only source of tin is its oxide, *tinstone* or *cassiterite*, which has a theoretical tin content of 78 per cent. There are also sulphides of tin with other metals. These occur as minor deposits associated with cassiterite or with other metal ores, but there is no evidence that the sulphides were worked to extract the tin. Tin has a specific gravity of 7·3 and a melting point of 232°C.

Cassiterite

Description: Crystals of cassiterite form tetragonal prisms with pyramidal ends, and the mineral also commonly occurs massive or fibrous as shapeless grains. Pale yellow crystals may be nearly translucent but cassiterite is commonly opaque dark brown or black. Crystals have a brilliant lustre, but the massive varieties have a much softer lustre, often called adamantine.

Cassiterite is brittle and breaks with an irregular fracture. The specific gravity is 6·8 to 7, and the hardness 6 to 7.

Occurrence: Cassiterite occurs in veins associated with acid rock intrusions. It is found in quartz veins in granite and in the contact metamorphic zones of granite structures. Cassiterite is commonly associated with other minerals of acid rock veins such as fluorite, tourmaline and apatite. In some instances, such as the deposits of Cornwall and Brittany, it is also associated with copper ores, but the two ores do not commonly occur together in workable quantities. Tin ores are much less widespread than copper ores.

Alluvial deposits derived from tin-bearing rocks are often very rich in tinstone, since it has both a high specific gravity and a great hardness; it is also very resistant to chemical weathering.

Lead

Lead is a soft grey metal which tarnishes readily. Its specific gravity is 11·3 and the melting point is 327°C. Lead can be obtained from its three principal ores: *cerussite*, *anglesite*, and *galena*. *Cerussite* – lead carbonate ($PbCO_3$), and *anglesite* – lead sulphate ($PbSO_4$), can be smelted directly. The sulphide, *galena* (PbS), must first be roasted. The presence of zinc blende with galena makes this ore much more difficult to smelt and the two ores, when they do occur together, must be separated before smelting. It is therefore improbable that pewter was manufactured directly by smelting lead and zinc ores together, but rather by adding the zinc ore calamine to metallic lead. The red oxide, *minium* (Pb_3O_4), occurs in the weathered zone of lead veins, associated with the other lead ores.

Galena

Galena nearly always contains some silver sulphide as an impurity, and most occurrences of galena are said to be argentiferous. The presence of silver does not affect the physical properties of galena, and the presence of silver can only be determined by analysis.

Description: Galena forms cubic crystals with a perfect cubic cleavage (Figure 15), so that a crystal aggregate easily crumbles into small cubic fragments. The colour is lead grey with a light metallic lustre which is easily tarnished. The streak is also lead grey. The specific gravity is 7·5 and the hardness 2·5.

Occurrence: Galena occurs in lodes or is finely disseminated in rocks. It is predominantly of hydrothermal origin. Veins of galena are commonly found in limestones and other sedimentary rocks, where it is associated with other minerals of hydrothermal origin and commonly with *blende*.

Cerussite

Description: Cerussite crystallizes in the orthorhombic system, and forms flat prismatic crystals. It also occurs compact, granular, and massive. The crystals are white or greyish, transparent to translucent, with a vitreous lustre which sometimes borders on resinous. The fracture is conchoidal and it is very brittle. The hardness is 3·3 and the specific gravity 6·5.

Occurrence: Cerussite is found in the oxidation zone of lead veins. It is probably formed by the action of water, containing carbon dioxide, on *anglesite* (lead sulphate).

Anglesite

Description: Anglesite forms flat prismatic crystals in the orthorhombic system, occasionally showing pyramidal extremities, and the crystal faces are often striated. The cleavage directions are parallel to the long axis (c-axis) of the crystals.

Anglesite is white or greyish, transparent to translucent, with a vitreous or nearly resinous lustre. The hardness is 2·5 to 3 and the specific gravity is 6·3. It is often quite difficult to distinguish between anglesite and cerussite without chemical analysis (see below).

Occurrence: Anglesite is formed in the oxidation zone of lead veins from the sulphide galena.

Distinction between anglesite and cerussite: The two minerals anglesite and cerussite are very similar in appearance and in other properties such as hardness and specific gravity. They are commonly found associated, and both occur in the weathered zone of lead veins. They can be distinguished by simple tests: the carbonate – cerussite – dissolves in hydrochloric acid with effervescence of carbon dioxide; the sulphate – anglesite – is also soluble in hydrochloric acid but without effervescence. The solution of anglesite in acid yields a white precipitation of barium sulphate on the addition of barium chloride solution (gentle heating may be necessary to dissolve the minerals in acid).

Minium, Red Lead

Description: Minium occurs as a powdery or granular mass or as concretions. The colour may vary from scarlet to orange red, and the streak is a brilliant orange red to yellow. It is opaque with a greasy or dull lustre. The hardness is 2 to 3, and the specific gravity is 4·5.

Occurrence: Minium is found associated with galena or cerussite, and results from the weathering of these minerals in the oxidized zone of lead-bearing veins.

Zinc

Metallic zinc was not known in antiquity, but its ores were used for the manufacture of brass and pewter. The zinc ore used was chiefly *calamine*, the carbonate of zinc ($ZnCO_3$) which occurs in the weathered zone of zinc-bearing veins. The sulphide, *blende* (ZnS), may also have been smelted, as it is commonly associated with lead ores.

Blende, Sphalerite

Description: Blende crystallizes in the cubic system and commonly forms rhombdodecahedra (12-sided forms as illustrated for garnet, p. 27) but good crystals are not often found. The cleavage is good parallel to the crystal faces. Blende also commonly occurs massive and compact. It is usually a dark brown to black colour but crystals may be yellow, whitish, and rarely colourless. The lustre is resinous, translucent to opaque. The specific gravity is 4 and the hardness ranges from 3·5 to 4.

Occurrence: Blende is commonly found associated with galena in lead veins. It is particularly common in limestones but also occurs in contact metamorphic zones in other rocks. Blende is the most common zinc ore and occurs as the primary ore in the unaltered lode.

Smithsonite, Calamine

Description: Crystals of smithsonite are rare. The mineral crystallizes in the hexagonal system, with good cleavages forming rhombohedral cleavage fragments. It commonly occurs massive as encrustations or as concretions. The colour is white with a greyish or greenish tinge and the lustre is vitreous and slightly pearly, translucent or opaque. The hardness is 5·5 and the specific gravity 4 to 4·5.

Since it is a carbonate it can be dissolved in hydrochloric acid with effervescence, but much less readily than calcium carbonate.

Occurrence: Smithsonite is found in the upper parts of zinc lodes as an alteration of the primary zinc blende.

Mercury

Mercury is a silver white metal which solidfies at −39°C. Its specific gravity is 13·6. Native mercury is rare but it is known to occur associated with its sulphide ore, *cinnabar*, either disseminated through the rock, or filling small rock cavities. The metal forms amalgams with most other metals, but it does so most readily with gold and silver.

Cinnabar

Description: Cinnabar crystallizes in the hexagonal system and forms small tabular crystals. It usually occurs as granular encrustations. Cinnabar is often brilliant red and has a clear red streak, but it is sometimes dark or brownish red. Crystals may be translucent and nearly vitreous, but the granular variety is dull and opaque. The hardness is 2 to 2·5 and the specific gravity is 8.

Occurrence: Cinnabar is a rare mineral and is probably deposited from hot springs. It occurs associated with rocks of recent volcanic activity (i.e. of Tertiary or later date).

Iron

There are a large number of iron ores, many of which were already smelted in prehistory. They are conveniently grouped into oxides, carbonates, and sulphides.

The sulphide, *pyrite* or *iron pyrite*, occurs as an accessory constituent of igneous rocks but it is more commonly the result of hydrothermal activity, and it is associated with altered rocks and in veins.

The carbonate ore, *siderite* (or *chalybite*), contains between 30 per cent and 44 per cent extractable iron. Small iron carbonate deposits occur in lake beds, but most siderite occurs in altered limestones which have been infiltrated with iron-bearing solutions.

The oxides comprise a large number of minerals with varying iron contents. The pure iron oxides, *magnetite* and *hematite*, contain theoretical values of 72 per cent and 69 per cent iron respectively. The hydrated oxide *limonite* varies in iron content with 25 per cent to 60 per cent extractable iron. Magnetite is a primary rock mineral and hence is usually found in deep-seated masses which were not easily available to prehistoric smelters. Hematite and the hydrated oxides are either weathering products or secondary rock constituents and they are very widespread in surface rocks.

Native iron is known to occur as lenticular masses in deep-seated ultrabasic rocks and was therefore of very limited interest in prehistoric iron smelting. Meteoric iron, however, was probably used fairly extensively where available. The composition of meteoric iron is variable but some iron meteorites are pure enough to be worked without smelting.

Pyrite

Description: Pyrite commonly forms cubic or octahedral crystals and sometimes more complex forms of the cubic system (Figure 9). Pyrite also occurs in concretions with a radial structure. Pyrite is pale yellow or brass yellow, with a strong metallic lustre, and it is always paler than chalcopyrite. It has a dark brownish or greenish black streak. Pyrite has a specific gravity of 4·8 to 5 and a hardness of 6 to 6·5, which is considerably harder than chalcopyrite.

Occurrence: Pyrite is widely disseminated in basic rocks and in veins where it is commonly associated with chalcopyrite. Pyrite also occurs as a secondary mineral in rocks of sedimentary origin, such as chalk, where it occurs as rounded nodules.

Siderite, Chalybite, Spathic Iron

Description: Siderite crystallizes in the hexagonal system and forms rhombohedral crystals, often with curved faces. The cleavage is perfect – parallel to the rhomb faces. It also occurs massive and granular. The colour ranges from pale yellow or buff to a dark brownish black. The lustre is vitreous or pearly and opaque. The specific gravity is 3·8 and the hardness ranges from 3·5 to 4·5.

Occurrence: Siderite is precipitated in some lake or bog deposits, where it is frequently altered to hematite or limonite. It is formed by the action of ferruginous solutions on limestones and may result in rich deposits of calcareous siderite, which has retained the original rock structure. The lime in these ores acts as a flux in smelting.

Clay ironstone is an impure iron carbonate deposit which occurs as bands or nodules in sedimentary rocks, particularly in coal measures.

Oolitic ironstone is an iron carbonate which has replaced the calcite in an oolite and has retained the original rock structure. The iron content of ironstones varies considerably, and may range from 24 per cent to 46 per cent extractable iron.

Magnetite

Magnetite is the richest iron oxide with a theoretical iron content of 72 per cent, and the chemical formula Fe_3O_4.

Description: Cubic crystals are common and it also occurs massive and granular. It is black or grey-black in colour, opaque, with a black streak, and a slightly metallic lustre. The fracture is conchoidal or flat. The specific gravity is 5·2 and the hardness ranges from 5·5 to 6·5.

Magnetite is the only magnetic ore of iron and loose deposits such as sands can be tested for magnetite with a small magnet. Lumps of magnetite can 'pick up' small iron objects and are also known as *lodestone*.

Occurrence: Magnetite occurs finely disseminated in many igneous rocks and also as large lenticular masses in some deep-seated igneous rocks and schists. The hardness and specific gravity of magnetite cause it to be concentrated in alluvial deposits derived from such rocks, but under conditions of strong chemical weathering, it is weathered to hematite or limonite.

Hematite

Hematite is a more oxidized form of iron than magnetite, with the chemical formula Fe_2O_3 and 70 per cent iron content.

Description: Hematite crystallizes in the hexagonal system forming rhombohedral crystals, which are frequently flat and tabular. It also occurs massive, reniform in rounded concretions with radial structure, or earthy and amorphous.

Hematite is black or steel grey with a metallic lustre, but in very thin transparent particles it is a clear red and the earthy variety is red. The streak colour is always red.

The hardness ranges from 5·5 to 6·5 and the specific gravity from 5 to 5·3, but it may be considerably less for earthy hematite which is often impure.

Specular iron is the crystalline variety of hematite, which occurs as flat, nearly scaly crystals. It is black with a shiny metallic lustre.

Kidney ore is the reniform variety of hematite, often with radial structure. It is steel grey with a light metallic lustre, and frequently with a very highly lustrous outer surface on the concretions.

Red ochre is a red earthy variety of hematite, amorphous and easily powdered.

Occurrence: Most hematite is of secondary origin, either as a weathering product or as a product of metamorphism. It is found as concretions or bands in altered rocks, particularly limestones and as a cementing medium of ferruginous sandstones. Hematite is formed as a weathering product in the upper zones of iron-bearing lodes and as pans or crusts in soils. The red colour of many tropical soils is due to hematite.

Limonite

Limonite is a hydrated oxide of iron. Its chemical structure is not certain, but the chemical composition may be represented by the formula $2Fe_2O_3.3H_2O$. Pure limonite has a 60 per cent iron content.

Description: Limonite is amorphous and has no crystalline structure. It occurs as concretions of various forms, sometimes with a radial structure, and frequently dull and earthy. It ranges in colour from clear yellow to various shades of brown. The lustre is often dull, but it may be silky or nearly metallic in the dark concretions. The hardness is 5, but this cannot be tested on the earthy varieties, and the specific gravity is 3·5 to 4.

Bog iron ore is a very loose earthy variety of limonite which is found in swampy or marshy soils.

Ochre is the earthy variety of limonite which may be easily powdered and ranges in colour from yellow to various shades of brown.

Occurrence: Limonite is a weathering product of ferruginous rocks and minerals. Limonite caps are common on the surface of iron lodes. Limonite is precipitated as crusts and pans of soils and as concretions, and as such is extremely widespread and abundant.

The Extraction of Metals from their Ores

Amongst the metals which were known in antiquity, gold, silver, copper, lead, and iron were commonly worked as pure metals. Tin was used extensively in the manufacture of bronze, but only rare examples of its use as a pure metal are known. By Roman times, and possibly earlier in classical Greece, mercury was known and used in the purification of gold, but since it is liquid at normal temperatures (it solidifies at $-39°C$), it was not considered to be a true metal. The Romans also used zinc ores in the manufacture of brass and pewter, but they did not succeed in extracting the pure zinc metal for reasons which will be discussed below.

The first metals which were used in prehistory were those which occur native, that is gold, copper, and – more rarely – silver. Once smelting processes were discovered a variety of ores were exploited. The first ores which were smelted are the oxides and carbonates of copper (cuprite, malachite, and related ores); the sulphide ores of copper (chalcopyrite and related ores) require a rather more complicated process to extract the metal, and were probably not used before the first millennium B.C. Lead and tin ores are also comparatively easy to smelt, and recent discoveries suggest that lead may have been obtained at a very early period, perhaps from the carbonate or sulphate ores (cerussite and anglesite) which are more easily smelted than the sulphide (galena). Lead metal corrodes very rapidly, so that any evidence for its use in antiquity is less likely to survive than for other metals. The only tin ore which was worked is cassiterite.

Before the third millennium BC some silver was obtained from the rare native occurrences, but many of the early silver objects, for instance those at Ur, are in fact electrum, which appears to have been treated as silver. Silver was considered to be an extremely rare metal, and was valued more highly even than gold. Gold was obtained from alluvial and vein deposits. During the third millennium, probably in the Black Sea region, a process was devised to obtain the silver which exists as an impurity in some occurrence of the lead ore, galena. With this discovery, argentiferous galena became the principal source of silver, and many deposits of galena were worked primarily for their silver content. In Roman times, silver was also obtained as a by-product of the purification of gold which frequently contains small quantities of silver.

Iron was discovered comparatively late, probably around 1200 B.C. Iron ores are very widespread and abundant and many different ores were exploited depending on their availability in different regions. It is unlikely that the sulphide ore, pyrite, was much exploited, for the presence of sulphur, even in minute quantities, has a detrimental effect on the properties of iron. Since iron has a high melting point, 1,500°C, it is much more difficult to purify than the other metals known in prehistory, for it is improbable that temperatures as high as 1,500°C could ever be attained in primitive smelting furnaces. Meteoric iron was also used, but meorites form a very small proportion of the sources of metallic iron. Some of the earliest iron objects known however, are of meteoric iron.[2] Meteoric iron can often be distinguished from smelted iron by its high nickel content.

Little is known of the first uses of mercury and since the metal remains liquid at normal atmospheric temperatures, direct archaeological evidence of its use is not likely to survive. Mercury was known in classical Greece, but it was probably first used by

[2] e.g. Iron beads from Gerzeh, Egypt, dated to the Predynastic (SD 60–63) by Wainwright (1936), p. 7. See Coghlan (1956).

the Romans to purify native gold. It was obtained by distillation of cinnabar.

It seems highly probable that a great variety of 'stones' must have been tested as potential metal ores by the ancient smelters. Only some of these could be made to yield their metal content by the smelting processes then known. Thus, although the ores of metals such as zinc, aluminium, magnesium, and others are fairly widespread, these metals were not discovered until much later times.

The early metal-smelters worked their ores by heating them in a reducing atmosphere, either in a crucible in a simple furnace, or in some form of shaft furnace. In the smelting process the metal ore (oxide, chloride, or carbonate) is reduced to metal in an atmosphere of carbon monoxide. The carbon monoxide results from the burning of fuel (the essential component of the fuel being carbon, C) with the production of carbon dioxide, CO_2; above a temperature of about 700°C, however, carbon dioxide is converted into carbon monoxide, CO ($C+CO_2=2CO$). The reduction of ores involves two simultaneous processes; the first reaction is the actual reduction of the metal ore by the carbon monoxide, in which the metal ore loses oxygen and the carbon monoxide is converted to carbon dioxide ($MO+CO=M+CO_2$, where M is a metal, and MO its oxide ore); the second reaction is the conversion of the carbon dioxide back to carbon monoxide (if the smelting process is carried out above 700°C).

The temperature at which ore reduction can be achieved varies for different metal ores. One important reason for this is that the relative affinities of various metals and carbon for oxygen varies with temperature. Ore reduction will take place when conditions are such that carbon has a greater affinity for oxygen than the metal to be smelted. For any substance it is possible to calculate a measure of its readiness to oxidize at different temperatures and hence to plot curves of the readiness to oxidize ($-\triangle G$)[3] with temperature (T in degrees centigrade).

[3] The calculations are based on the second law of thermodynamics which is expressed mathematically as $G=H-TS$, where G is the Gibb's free energy of a system, T is the absolute temperature and S is entropy. Since equilibrium

The oxidation curves for carbon and the metals of antiquity are shown in Figure 28. They are seen to be virtually straight

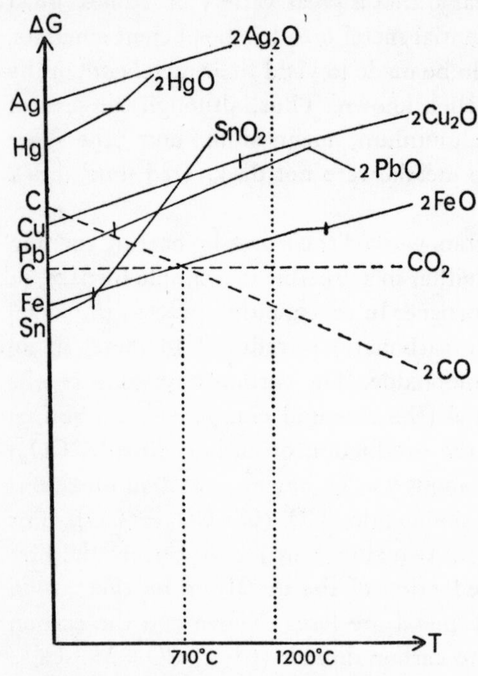

Figure 28 Oxidation curves for carbon and the metals smelted in antiquity (after D. J. G. Ives, 1962). Short vertical stroke = melting point of metal; short horizontal stroke = boiling point of metal

lines, but with a distinct change in slope at temperatures where there is a change of phase, i.e. at the melting point and boiling points of the metals. The lower the value for $-\Delta G$, the greater is the affinity for oxygen, so that when the curve for any metal lies below those for carbon, the metal has a higher affinity for oxygen than carbon and it cannot be reduced; when the curve for a metal lies above those for carbon, carbon has the greater affinity for oxygen, and the metal oxide can be reduced.

reactions will tend towards an increase in entropy, there will be a strong tendency for a reaction if it results in a large positive value (ΔS) in the equation $\Delta G = \Delta H - T\Delta S$. Hence, $-\Delta G$ may be considered as a measure of the tendency of a reaction to take place in a closed system.

There are two curves for carbon; one for the formation of carbon dioxide and one for the formation of carbon monoxide. These curves intersect at a temperature of 710°C. Thus, as already stated, below 710°C carbon is oxidized to carbon dioxide, but above this temperature the carbon is oxidized to carbon monoxide. Since most prehistoric smelting processes took place at temperatures ranging from around 900°C to a maximum around 1,200 or 1,250°C, reduction was achieved in an atmosphere of carbon monoxide.

The metals smelted in antiquity (copper, silver, lead, tin, and iron) are all seen to lie above the carbon curve in the given temperature range for smelting. When the metal oxide is heated in the presence of carbon, there will be a greater tendency for the carbon to oxidize than for the metal and oxygen is transferred from the ore to the carbon, leaving pure metal. If the smelting temperature lies above the melting point of the metal, as in the case of copper, tin, silver, and lead, pure liquid metal is separated from the slag. The comparatively late discovery of iron can probably be explained by its very high melting point, well above temperatures reached in prehistoric furnaces. The iron ore is therefore reduced in the solid state and the resulting pure iron remains as small grains embedded in a spongy mass of slag known as *bloom*. The iron can only be extracted from the bloom by repeated hammering and reheating which welds the small iron grains together while the slag and impurities are broken off.

Figure 29 shows the oxidation curve for carbon and for some of the metals which were not discovered in prehistory, although their ores were easily available. They may well have been tried and discarded for lack of success. Aluminium clearly requires very high temperatures to extract it from its oxide ore and this metal is now extracted by a rather complex method. Magnesium and manganese also lie below the carbon oxidation curve. Zinc poses an interesting problem. Metallic zinc was unknown even to the Romans who, however, used it extensively in the manufacture of the alloys brass and pewter. An examination of the oxidation curve for zinc shows that both its melting point and its boiling point lie below the carbon oxidation curves, so that at

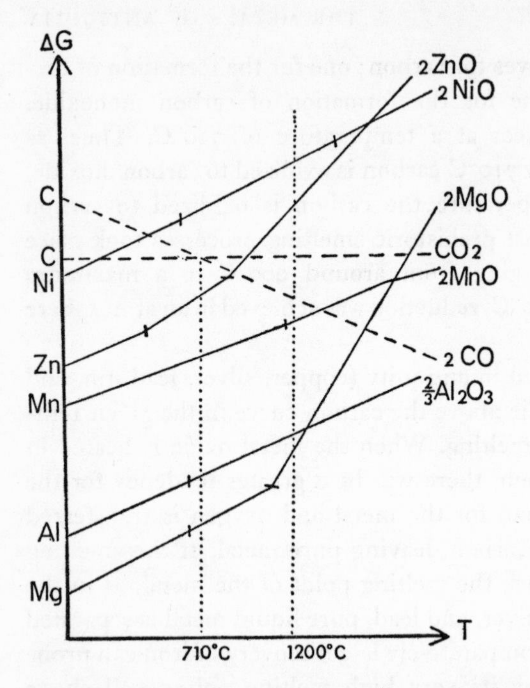

Figure 29 Oxidation curves for carbon and some metals not known in antiquity (after D. J. G. Ives, 1962). Short vertical stroke = melting point of metal; short horizontal stroke = boiling point of metal

temperatures at which zinc ores can be reduced, zinc vapour is produced and the metal can only be obtained by distillation. Thus, zinc alloys could be produced by adding zinc ores to copper or lead ores, or more probably by adding the zinc ore to metallic copper or lead, and melting the mixture, but metallic zinc could not be obtained.

Although nickel might theoretically have been reduced, nickel ores do not normally occur as pure ores but only mixed with iron or copper ores. The separation of these metals was beyond the capabilities of the prehistoric smelters.

When sulphide ores are used, the smelting process is a little more involved. The sulphide must first be converted to the oxide by roasting, i.e. by heating it strongly in a blast of air with access to oxygen. The roasted ore can then be reduced in the normal way.

Some Metalliferous Minerals not used as Ores

There are several highly-coloured metalliferous minerals which were used as pigments. Some of these, such as malachite and the ochres, were also used as metal ores; but others were minerals of metals which were not smelted – manganese, arsenic, and antimony. As already stated above, manganese could not have been smelted by the methods used in antiquity. Arsenic was probably added to copper and bronze alloys, but there is no evidence that it was known in the metallic state. The metals arsenic and antimony differ from the other metals known in antiquity in that they are very brittle and not malleable. Neither of these metals could have been worked or used as copper, lead, or iron were used, and it is possible that their metallic nature may not have been recognized. Several occurrences of the use of antimony in ancient Egypt have been claimed, but many are probably mistaken identifications (see Lucas 1962). There are small antimony beads from the Twenty-second Dynasty, but these are probably of native antimony, which, though rare, is known to occur.

The minerals used as pigments are antimony sulphide, *stibnite*, or *antimonite*, two sulphides of arsenic which are commonly found together, *realgar* and *orpiment*, and various forms of manganese oxide, the most common of which are *pyrolusite*, *psilomelane*, and *wad*.

Stibnite, Antimonite

Stibnite is a trisulphide of antimony, Sb_2S_3.

Description: Stibnite forms orthorhombic crystals, usually long and prismatic with striated faces. It commonly occurs in masses of radiating or columnar crystals, but it is also found granular. The colour and streak colour are dark grey. Stibnite has a metallic lustre, but this tarnishes to a dull surface on exposure, or sometimes to an iridescent lustre. The fracture is subconchoidal or irregular and the mineral is brittle. The hardness is 2, and and the specific gravity is 4·5.

Occurrence: Stibnite occurs in veins commonly associated with quartz. It is also found in veins of lead or zinc ores with quartz, calcite, or barytes.

Realgar

Realgar is the primary arsenic sulphide, AsS, which is altered to orpiment, As_2S_3 on exposure.

Description: Realgar crystallizes in the monoclinic system and forms prismatic crystals, but it is usually found in massive or granular concretions. The colour varies from red to orange and the streak colour is the same as the mineral colour. It is usually translucent with a resinous lustre, but transparent and nearly opaque varieties are known. The fracture is conchoidal. The hardness is 1·5 to 2 and the specific gravity is 3·5.

Occurrence: Realgar is deposited from hot springs or from volcanic fumes. It occurs as nodules in veins, and is frequently associated with orpiment and with cinnabar.

Orpiment

Orpiment is arsenic trisulphide, As_2S_3.

Description: Orpiment crystallizes in the monoclinic system, but crystals are rare, and it usually occurs massive or as aggregates of thin flakes. It is clear yellow in colour and has a yellow streak. The lustre is pearly on the crystalline form, and resinous or dull on the massive varieties. It is translucent or opaque. The hardness is 1·5 to 2, and the specific gravity is 3·5.

Occurrence: Orpiment is formed from the alteration of realgar, especially in the weathered zones of realgar veins, and on exposure to the atmosphere realgar is altered to orpiment. The two minerals are usually found together, but orpiment is more abundant.

Pyrolusite

Pyrolusite is a pure form of manganese dioxide, MnO_2.

Description: Pyrolusite may form orthorhombic crystals, but it is commonly found massive or in reniform concretions, sometimes with radial structure. It is dark grey, opaque with a metallic lustre, and has a black or bluish-black streak. The fracture is irregular. The hardness ranges from 2 to 2·5 and the specific gravity is 4·8.

Occurrence: Pyrolusite is formed from the alteration of other minerals which contain manganese. It is found in clay deposits which result from the weathering of such rocks. Pyrolusite is also precipitated from solution and occurs as nodules or concretions in sedimentary rocks which formed under humid conditions. Pyrolusite and the other forms of manganese oxide are ultimately derived from the weathering of manganese minerals in igneous or metamorphic rocks. They are usually associated with iron salts.

Psilomelane

Psilomelane is a hydrated form of manganese oxide, of variable composition.

Description: Psilomelane is non-crystalline, amorphous, and occurs as reniform or stalactitic concretions. The colour varies from black to dark grey, but the outer surface of concretions may be brownish black and the streak colour is brownish black. The lustre is greasy or dull, but on the surface of concretions it may be nearly metallic. The hardness is 6 and the specific gravity varies from 3·5 to 4·5.

Occurrence: The occurrence of psilomelane is the same as for pyrolusite.

Wad

Wad is an impure hydrated form of manganese oxide.

Description: Wad is non-crystalline, amorphous, and earthy. It occurs as irregular concretions, encrustations or as dendritic stains or crusts. Wad may be black, grey or brownish black, dull and opaque, and the streak colour is the same as the mineral colour. The hardness cannot normally be measured since it is usually very friable. The specific gravity varies with composition from 3 to 3·5.

Occurrence: Wad results from the decomposition of other manganese minerals, and usually occurs in sediments formed under damp conditions.

CHAPTER SIX

The Manufacture of Tools, Weapons and Ornaments

One of the principal purposes of identifying the materials from which ancient artefacts were made is to assess the technological problems involved in their manufacture. An understanding of the materials used for making various tools and weapons in antiquity can also give some insight into how such tools might have been used, and especially into their effectiveness. For an appreciation of the technological aspects of stone tools, it is generally sufficient to arrive at a macroscopic identification of the rock used. Thus it may be important to distinguish between, say, a diorite and a granite if these rocks are used to make celts (that is – axes, adzes, and other polished implements), for their physical properties differ. The *exact* composition of these rocks, which can only be obtained from micro-analyses, does not materially affect their physical properties and is therefore of little importance in purely technological problems.

From the descriptions of minerals and rocks given in the previous chapters, it should be possible (with a little practice!) to arrive at such macroscopic identifications. This chapter, which illustrates the uses of rocks in antiquity, is therefore a partial justification of the technical detail given in previous sections.

In this chapter, some of the most common and interesting uses of rocks and minerals in antiquity are considered. The use of different materials is discussed from the point of view of the physical properties of the rocks and their suitability for the manufacture of different artefacts. The most common tools, weapons, and other artefacts encountered by archaeologists are considered separately to illustrate how far the properties of rocks and other materials were appreciated and exploited in antiquity.

Tools

Stone Knives

The functional feature of a knife is a thin sharp edge, which is either straight or smoothly curved.

When making a thin sharp edge out of stone, the rock must be flaked, for it would be impossible to work a very thin edge, using pounding and grinding techniques of working stone, without snapping it. Rocks which have a homogenous structure break with a conchoidal or flat fracture, and can therefore be flaked. By various techniques, the approximate shape and size of the flakes can be controlled. On the other hand, if the grain-size of the rock is not very small, the fracture which is uneven across the various rock constituents results in an irregular surface and it is more difficult to obtain a smooth edge. During use, the edge on a coarse-grained rock tends to fracture more irregularly than on a homogenous rock.

The hardness of the blade is important, for it must be harder than the material to be cut. The greater the difference in hardness, the easier it is to cut. With a hard blade less pressure need be applied to cut, and therefore the risk of snapping the knife blade through uneven pressure is less than with a softer blade.

The natural materials with the best flaking properties are the volcanic glasses, notably obsidian which – since they are non-crystalline – have a zero grain-size. If the obsidian is also homogenous in structure, i.e. does not contain spherulites, gas or liquid bubbles etc., the fracture is completely conchoidal. The hardness of obsidian is approximately 7. This is harder than most organic substances used by man and also harder than some common rocks such as steatite or alabaster which were, therefore, carved with obsidian or flint knives. The brittleness of obsidian may be partially overcome by mounting an obsidian knife blade in resilient material, such as gum, wood, bone, etc. Since short blades are less liable to snap than long ones, the resilience of a long cutting tool can also be achieved by making a compound blade of several short blades mounted close together. This was frequently done, for instance in making sickles, where a long cutting blade is required. In a compound blade of this type the advantage of a smooth unbroken cutting edge is lost (Pl. 14a).

More widely occurring materials with properties similar to those of obsidian are the chalcedonic forms of silica, flint, chert, and jasper. Opaline forms of silica can also easily be flaked, but they are less widespread than flint and chert. Since chalcedonic silica has a fibrous cryptocrystalline structure, it is less brittle than obsidian. The crystal size is however so small that it barely affects the fracture, which is conchoidal. In jasper, which is the most crystalline of the three chalcedonic varieties of silica, and which contains the least colloidal silica, the fracture may be subconchoidal or even flat. The edge of flakes is very thin and smooth, and even in jasper the cryptocrystalline structure does not affect the smoothness of the cutting edges. All forms of colloidal and cryptocrystalline silica were widely used for making cutting tools throughout prehistory and later antiquity. During the Neolithic, however, there seems to have been a greater emphasis on the use of obsidian and in many regions this material replaced flint and chert. The change in materials may be seen in many regions of the Near East and Mediterranean, where Palaeolithic tools are made in flint or chert, whereas Neolithic tools are often in obsidian. Although obsidian has better flaking qualities than chert and poor quality flint, these latter materials are usually adequate for most cutting purposes and the change from flint to obsidian may not always have been a matter of choosing the better raw material. With the increase in trade or travel in the Neolithic, the use of obsidian spread over considerable distances to regions where it does not occur naturally. This is already so at the very early Neolithic site of Nea Nikomedeia in Macedonia where, in the earliest levels, flaked tools are made of locally occurring flint, chert, and quartz, while in the later levels these tools are made out of obsidian.

Where neither obsidian nor flint, chert, etc., were available other rocks were flaked into knives and various forms of cutting tools. Many rocks have been used which have a homogenous structure and a sufficiently fine-grained texture so that they can be flaked with a conchoidal or flat fracture. These rocks are largely siliceous rocks such as quartzite and the fine-grained, silica-indurated rocks such as silcrete, indurated shales, and tuffs. Vein quartz has also been flaked, particularly in some early Palaeolithic industries, e.g. at Olduvai in Tanganyika, and at Choukoutien in China. Vein quartz normally consists of a mass of quartz crystals of variable size which are randomly orientated and intergrown, thus forming a rock which has the texture of an igneous rock (such as, for example, granite). When vein quartz is flaked each individual quartz crystal breaks with a conchoidal fracture, but the rock as a whole has an irregular fracture. It is, therefore, difficult to obtain a smooth and thin cutting edge. Thus single crystals of quartz may be flaked successfully, as was done in some Indian Mesolithic cultures, but vein quartz is a poor raw material for cutting tools and tools made out of vein quartz are usually large and appear clumsily made. Some fine-grained igneous rocks, such as basalt, with a flat fracture have been flaked when better material was not available. The uneven composition of such a rock makes controlled flaking more difficult than on siliceous rocks.

When very small cutting tools were made, as in the late Palaeolithic and Mesolithic industries, there was a greater emphasis on the choice of good homogenous raw materials than in earlier periods. When necessary materials such as flint or chert were obtained through trade or travel. For the coarser tools of earlier industries, inferior raw materials were used where better ones were not readily available. Thus while in England most lower Palaeolithic tools were made out of flint, the lower Palaeolithic industries of Burma were made out of fossil wood and those of southern India out of quartzite, for in neither of these latter regions were flint or chert available in large nodules. However, in the microlithic industries of South India a variety of jasper, carnelian, and opal tools were made out of small pebbles.

Stone Axes and Adzes

When chopping with an axe or an adze, the cutting edge is subjected to repeated blows and most rocks are too brittle to withstand the impact on the edge of a thin flake. In making stone axes and adzes, the thinness of the cutting edge must be partially sacrificed for resilience and toughness of the tool. This was achieved by making a tool with a roughly cylindrical or ellipsoidal cross-section, and grinding the cutting edge to a wide angle (Pl. 15a). The strength of the tool could also be ensured by choosing a more resilient raw material than used for knives and by adapting various methods of hafting.

Flint has been used for making adzes and axes. In the woodland Mesolithic cultures of Europe a cutting-edge was obtained by careful flaking, but in later periods a smoother and less brittle edge was obtained by grinding and polishing the edge. The polishing was often carried out over the entire surface of the tool and since flint is of the same hardness as the quartz abrasives available, this required a great expenditure of labour. It seems, therefore, that much of this work must have been done for non-functional purposes, although when a blade was lashed to its haft a polished butt would lessen wear on the binding. From the many blocks of sandstone found with long, roughly parallel grooves, it seems clear that for grinding axes and adzes (and perhaps other objects) consolidated sands were preferred to loose sand. The smoothness of the surface obtained depends largely on the coarseness of the abrasive used, and partly on the texture of the material polished. Coarse abrasives leave scour marks equal in depth to the coarseness of the sand grains used; and on a rock with both soft and hard components, as most igneous rocks, the softer minerals may be ground down more rapidly than the harder minerals, thus leaving an uneven surface. With a fine-grained abrasive, a smoother surface can be obtained. Many grinding stones and whetstones for polishing adzes were in fact made from fine-grained sandstones or siltstones.

Many other rocks which are less hard and more resilient than flint were more widely used for the manufacture of celts. Fine-grained amphibole rocks with a homogeneous structure were particularly suitable. These include various rocks commonly known as *greenstone*. The amphiboles, of which hornblende is the most common mineral, have a fibrous habit and often form a matted structure which results in a particularly tough rock. The hardness of such rocks ranges from 5 to 6 and they were therefore easier to grind and polish than flint. Some fine-grained basic and intermediate igneous rocks such as basalt, dolerite, and diorite are also suitable raw materials for the manufacture of axes and adzes. Such rocks frequently show some degree of hydrothermal alteration, i.e. the pyroxenes are altered to amphiboles, and the properties of these rocks are similar to those of hornblende schists and greenstones.

In a petrological survey of the stone celts of Southern Britain and Brittany, the implements were separated into groups of tools made from the same rock. Twenty groups have been identified to date, and in several cases the exact locality of the rock source has also been found. There are also many implements which, although made of very similar rocks, show slight petrological differences and can, therefore, not be assigned to any known group. These are referred to as 'ungrouped' tools.

Taking the figures for axes, adzes, and battle axes, but excluding hammers, maceheads, etc., the results of this survey show that over 60 per cent of the tools examined are made out of one of the rock types discussed above. Axe groups I–IV, XVI, XVIII and their subdivisions are greenstones from Cornwall, and Groups X, XIII and XVIII are dolerites from Brittany, Wales, and Northern England respectively. Even among the ungrouped tools, greenstones and basic igneous rocks predominate. Six of the axe groups and many ungrouped axes, comprising nearly 30 per cent of all the tools examined, fall within a class of rocks which are very fine-grained indurated tuffs, hornfels, or altered sediments. These rocks are basic or intermediate in composition and since they are very fine-textured they are resilient, although some are less hard than the amphibole rocks. They include the Group VI axes of welded tuff from the Langdale axe factories in the Lake District of Northern England.

In a few instances, approximately 10 per cent of all the tools examined, other less suitable rocks have been employed, but these rocks generally form smaller axe groups and are less-widely distributed. Groups XV and XIX are consolidated greywackes, Group XV is partly altered to chlorite. Group XV axes occur in the Midlands, where the greywacke is the only reasonably hard and tough rock available in a region of limestone and gritty sandstones. In the region of Dartmoor, several implements of granite have been found, but a high proportion of these remained unfinished, or were found broken. The brittleness of the quartz and felspar, and the coarseness of the granite, were clearly found to be unsatisfactory substitutes for the greenstones and tuffs.

Among the ungrouped axes from England and Brittany are a few of jadeite and nephrite. These rocks are tough and hard and can make excellent axes. Jades are comparatively rare rocks and have often been considered to be precious or semi-precious. Both in modern times, and in certain cultures of antiquity such as Bronze Age China, axes made from this material were ceremonial and non-functional. However, there is no contextual evidence to suggest that jade axes in prehistoric Europe were treated differently from those made out of the more common rocks.

Elsewhere – where hard, resilient materials were not easily available – a great variety of other rocks have been employed for the manufacture of celts, including some very soft materials which could be easily polished and ground. Even serpentine and marble (hardness 2·5 and 3 respectively) have been used for small celts, as in the early Neolithic levels of Nea Nikomedeia in Macedonia, where these rocks occur locally. These tools are too small to have been used for any heavy chopping and must, therefore, have served as adzes, gouges, or hoes for working soft materials. It is possible that they were ceremonial objects.

Stone Saws

Sawing may be carried out with a saw blade or with an abrasive powder or paste. In both cases a narrow groove is abraded, so that the blade or abrasive used must be as hard as, or harder than, the material to be cut. In addition, a serrated saw-blade also cuts and tears and must, therefore, be able to withstand considerable stress on the projecting teeth. Small stone saws of Mesolithic and later date were made out of flint and chert and – although their exact use can only be guessed at – they must have been used on small objects made from comparatively soft materials such as wood, bone or antler. Saw blades must be very thin. A saw is usually subjected to considerable lateral stresses, due either to the uneven nature of the material or to irregular sawing, or both. A thin saw-blade would have to be made out of a very resilient material to withstand such stresses. No rock is both hard and elastic enough for this purpose. Before the use of metals, large wooden objects were chopped with an axe, whereas large stone objects were sawn by rubbing abrasive powder or paste along a narrow groove.

The most commonly used abrasive was sand. Most sands consist largely, or entirely, of quartz which is the hardest of the common rock-forming minerals. Thus most rocks can be cut or ground with quartz sand. Sands which also contain the hard minerals corundum, zircon, or spinel, etc. were especially valued for working hard stones. The emery (impure corundum) sand of Naxos, for instance, was imported in Roman times, and probably also in classical Greece when minerals harder than 7 were worked into gems. In earlier times, however, very few minerals of a hardness greater than 7 were cut, and there is no good evidence for the exploitation of hard sands on anything but a local scale. Although it has been suggested, for instance, that the Egyptians used emery both as an abrasive and to point copper saws, Lucas (1962) considers that the use of emery in Egypt is very improbable. He points to the fact that the only hard mineral worked by Egyptian lapidaries was beryl, hardness 7·5 to 8, and that in no case is beryl known before the Greek period.

Stone Drills

There are two types of drills: those with hard bits, and those with soft bits used in conjunction with a hard abrasive. Some small flint points found together with chipped carnelian and amethyst pebbles and unfinished beads at Hierakonpolis in Egypt are believed to have been drill bits used to make the fine perforations in the beads (diameter as small as 2 mm). Flint, carnelian, and amethyst are all of the same hardness and this must, therefore, have been a laborious work. To make long perforations drilling may have been started from opposite ends of the bead for it is impossible to make a very long and narrow bit from materials such as flint. Many beads of materials as hard as carnelian (hardness 7) have extremely fine perforations, as little as 1 mm in diameter or less, and up to 15 mm long. To make such long and very narrow perforations it is probable that a soft drill of copper was used together with a fine abrasive. The abrasive may have been fine sand or powder of the mineral to be cut. The use of crushed flint and chert is attested by an unfinished steatite bead from Armant in Egypt which still had crushed flint in the perforation.

For making a wide hollow or aperture a row of closely spaced drillings was made, but in the manufacture of stone vessels much effort was spared by using a tubular drill which cuts out a cylindrical core. Various theories have been put forward as to the exact mechanisms for hollowing out the body of narrow-necked stone vessels, but whatever the details of the operation, it seems certain that they were drilled with wide bits of a hard, gritty rock – such as sandstone or quartzite.

Metal Cutting-tools

The metals used for toolmaking in antiquity were copper, bronze, and iron. These metals are more resilient and elastic than rocks. The hardness of the different metals of antiquity varies considerably, but all are softer than quartz. The hardness of a metal can be greatly affected by very small amounts of impurity; for instance, the presence of traces of carbon in iron, or of arsenic or antimony in copper and bronze, increase the hardness of these metals considerably. Many prehistoric iron objects were in fact hardened by the addition of carbon to the iron, thus making steel; some copper and bronze objects were also hardened by small amounts of arsenic or antimony; but whether these were added deliberately or result from the smelting of impure ores is still a matter of debate. The hardness and resilience of metals also depends to a large extent on how they have been worked. The metallurgy of copper, bronze, and especially of iron, is a complex subject and beyond the scope of this book. However, some of the properties of the metals of antiquity must be understood to appreciate the technical advantages of metal tools over stone tools.

Although metal ores are less abundant than the rocks used for toolmaking, and the extraction and working of metals is at least as laborious as the manufacture of stone tools, the use of metals is not always less economical than the use of stone. A broken metal tool can be recast or reforged into new artefacts, and many hoards of broken and disused copper or bronze objects have been found which were the raw materials of ancient metal workers. A broken or heavily-blunted stone tool can often not be re-used and once a stone tool has been discarded it must be replaced by entirely new raw material.

Copper is a rather soft metal, ranging in hardness from 2 to 3. It is very malleable and ductile, so that it can be shaped by hammering and drawing. Since its melting point is about 1,100°C it could also be shaped by casting in a mould.

Bronze, which is an alloy of approximately 90 per cent copper and 10 per cent tin, is harder than copper. Its properties depend on the relative amounts of tin and copper, and the composition of prehistoric bronzes varies considerably. In regions where tin was not easily available, bronze may contain considerably less than 10 per cent tin. Besides hardening the metal, the addition of tin to copper lowers its melting point to approximately 1,000°C and makes it slightly less malleable and ductile. Bronze could be worked in the same manner as copper.

Both copper and bronze become harder when they are hammered, and if hammering proceeds too long, the metals become brittle and may crack. Copper and bronze which have been hardened in this way can be rendered soft and malleable again by heating to a dull red heat for a short period – a process known as *annealing*.

Pure iron is soft – though always harder than copper – and malleable. Its melting point is high – 1,500°C – and in antiquity the metal was only worked by hammering and drawing. Unlike copper and bronze, which can be hammered cold, iron must be hammered while red hot, a process known as *forging*. Steel was made by heating the iron to at least 900°C in a charcoal fire, which results in a slow penetration of carbon into the iron. The properties of steel can also be altered by hammering and annealing. However, to anneal steel it must be allowed to cool very slowly. If the hot metal is cooled rapidly it becomes hard and brittle. Very hard but brittle steel could, therefore, be prepared by cooling the metal quickly by immersion in water. This process is known as *quenching*. Quenched steel could again be softened by gentle heating, or by *tempering*. By controlling the temperature at which quenched steel is tempered, the hardness and brittleness of the metal can be controlled to a high degree, for the higher the temperature the softer the steel becomes.

Since copper, bronze, and iron are all softer than the various forms of silica, a metal knife-blade is no sharper than a blade of freshly-flaked flint, obsidian, or similar material. With use, the edge of a flint blade becomes blunted by chipping and it cannot be resharpened to its original sharpness; but since metals can be sharpened by grinding, a blunted metal blade is easily resharpened whenever it becomes blunted through use. Thus, when only very soft materials need be cut, even copper or bronze knives have certain advantages over stone. For many purposes, however, even hardened bronze or copper knives are too soft or would need such frequent resharpening as to be impracticable, and before the use of iron and tempered steel, many small cutting tools continued to be made in flint, obsidian, or other stone. With the discovery of tempered steel – which is not much softer than quartz – stone cutting-tools were very largely replaced by iron.

In the manufacture of axes, the resilience of metals gives them a real advantage over stone. Furthermore, since copper and bronze could be shaped in moulds, and sharpened by hammering and grinding, it was possible to make axes with thin, sharp cutting-edges, whereas stone cutting-axes always had wide cutting-edges. Thus, although the softness of copper and bronze might make them less advantageous in the manufacture of axes and adzes, their other properties gave them such great advantages over their stone counterparts that, from the Chalcolithic period on, axes began to be made in metal, and from the Middle Bronze Age, bronze axes became quite common. It is interesting to note that the prehistoric copper and bronze axes were always finished by hammering, thus increasing the hardness of the cutting-edge after casting; this process also accounts for the splayed shape of these axes. The casting process of manufacturing copper and bronze tools also had certain other advantages over stone. Various devices to improve hafting methods could be designed, which it was difficult or impossible to obtain in stone. Thus, although the earliest metal axes are flat, and were presumably hafted in much the same way as stone axes, the addition of flanges and a ridge across the width of the tool, as in palstaves, ensured that the axe-head would not be driven back into its haft with use (Pl. 14b). Later still the development of the socketed axes allowed entirely new hafting methods to be employed.

Iron is so much harder than copper and bronze that it replaced these metals for most types of tool, in spite of the very laborious forging and tempering processes. With the use of iron however, shapes such as the palstave and socketed axe were replaced by flat or shaft-hole axes (Pl. 15c).

Only very small-blade saws could be made out of stone. With the use of metals, however, it became possible to make them long, very flat and thin, and to shape and sharpen the projecting teeth. Copper saws are known as early as First-Dynasty Egypt at Saqqara when they appear to have been used for wood-working. By Middle Kingdom times in Egypt, copper saws were largely replaced by bronze. Later, with the widespread use of iron, saw blades were also made out of hardened steel. It is unlikely that metal saws were ever used for cutting hard rocks or the hard minerals used for gems, etc. Sawing of these materials continued to be done with abrasives of sand or crushed stone.

Clay Cutting-tools

Surprisingly enough, even baked clay has been used to make sickles. In the Southern Ubaid culture of Mesopotamia, where in the wide alluvial plains of the Tigris and Euphrates consolidated rocks are extremely rare, people had recourse to very highly-baked clay for hard materials. The clay sickles are of nearly vitrified pottery (see p. 174) and therefore harder and less friable than most earthenware (Pl. 13b). Many of the crescent-shaped sickles characteristic of the Southern Ubaid culture, but also occasionally found on some Northern Ubaid sites, were found broken. This has been taken as evidence that these tools were functional objects and not toys or ritual objects. Vitrified pottery has also been used in this culture to make nails, knives, axes, and adzes, but it is not clear whether these were really functional tools or not.

Hammerstones

Any stone which will withstand the shock of sudden impact without splitting may be used as a hammerstone. Thus, for hammering or pounding soft materials, such as organic substances, virtually any piece of rock of manageable size may be used. A pounder used in this way may not show any use-marks, in which case it is unlikely to be recognized as a tool by the archaeologist. Other soft materials, such as ochres and other natural pigments, could also be pounded with any suitably shaped piece of rock, often natural pebbles. The only use-marks left are the finely powdered pigments which sometimes adhere very firmly if the hammerstone is slightly porous.

When using stone on stone, however, it is the more brittle of the rocks which is most liable to split. Hammerstones used for flint knapping have commonly been found in Stone Age contexts. Quite commonly a stout roughly spherical pebble of flint was used, but in some regions, such as the Thames valley of England, the equally hard but tougher quartzite pebbles were commonly selected. Repeated use of these hammerstones has left a maze of batter marks on their surface, usually concentrated at one end of the pebble.

The use of the hammerstones to crush the ore in prehistoric metal mines and in quarrying hard rock will be described on p. 198. It is significant that pebbles of basic igneous rocks were frequently preferred to other materials. In the granite quarries at Aswan in Egypt, dolerite pebbles seem to have been deliberately imported from the desert region between the Nile and Red Sea to pound and crush the granite which is a harder, but less resilient rock.

Querns and Millstones

Querns or millstones, used to grind cereals or other foodstuffs, need not be made out of very hard or very tough rock. Grinding will be most efficient if the grinding surfaces of both querns and rubber are rough and remain rough with use. Thus many querns and millstones were made out of sandstone or other non-homogeneous rock which cannot easily be polished. A fine-structured vesicular basalt, from a locality near Niedermendig in the Eifel mountains in Germany, was widely used for the manufacture of querns in Europe in the Iron Age and the rock was even exported as far as Britain. If the quern or rubber wears down too rapidly, flour may be heavily contaminated with grit. Thus, although sandstones make very efficient querns and millstones, those in a fine-grained, highly cemented, sandstone yield a purer flour.

Weapons

In discussing the materials from which weapons were made it is convenient to group them into three broad categories: those which depend on delivering a heavy blow; those which pierce; and those which cut.

Throwing-stones, Maceheads, and Battle-axes

Some of the most primitive weapons were probably simply heavy objects, such as large pebbles or lumps of rock, thrown at a quarry; but the most sophisticated maceheads and battle-axes may be grouped within the same category, for they also depend on delivering a hard blow to kill a victim. Clearly no very specific properties are required for a weapon of this type and any consolidated rock may be used. However, maceheads, such as the

Predynastic Egyptian types and battle-axes of the Northern European Neolithic and Bronze Ages were carefully shaped and highly polished. It seems probable that the choice of rock in these instances was governed, in part at least, by aesthetic considerations (Pl. 6). Thus these weapons are generally made out of crystalline igneous or metamorphic rocks.

Arrows, Spears and Lances

Arrows, spears, lances, and similar weapons depend on their ability to pierce the soft tissues of animals or humans (except blunt arrows used on small game such as birds which are intended to stun, rather than pierce, the animal), and the tips of such weapons should therefore be sharp. The materials used for making various forms of arrow-heads, lance-heads, etc., were the same as those used for making knives, presumably for the same reasons. In making projectile points, the cheapness of these materials was also an important consideration, since the point might frequently be lost, and stone arrow-heads continued to be made long after the discovery of copper and bronze.

Daggers and Swords

Weapons which are intended to cut the victim are almost exclusively weapons of warfare, and they only become clearly differentiated from other types of weapons with the use of metals. Long pointed blades of stones such as obsidian, flint, or chert are known already in Predynastic Egypt, and these may well have been daggers used in warfare. In the late Neolithic and early Bronze Age of Northern Europe where bronze was scarce, long flint daggers were made in imitation of metal weapons made by technologically more advanced peoples farther south (Pl. 16). To make a long cutting-blade, however, the resilience of metals is a very great advantage over the brittleness of stone and the long cutting-blades of swords could not be fashioned before metal technology had become highly developed. Only in the Iron Age did sword blades become very long and thin, for by a highly complex process of tempering steel, and welding strips of different hardness and resilience, the sword-smiths of the Iron Age could make a weapon which was both resilient enough to withstand blows on a long narrow blade, and yet had hard and thin cutting-edges.

The standardization of artefacts, which could be achieved more easily with metals than with stone, also had advantages when equipping an army for warfare.

Vessels

Without any doubt, organic substances such as wood, bone, gourds, basketry, etc. must have been used as vessels from Palaeolithic times onwards. However, these are rarely preserved in the archaeological record. The earliest vessels known are shallow limestone bowls from the Palaeolithic which were used as lamps. Stone vessels only become more common in the pre-pottery Neolithic cultures; as, for instance, in the early levels of Jericho where limestone bowls were used. With the use of baked clay for making vessels, pottery became the most widely used material in many regions. Stone vessels, at this time, were usually rare and made either for decorative and ritual purposes, or as luxury goods. It must be presumed that the replacement of stone vessels by pottery vessels in every day use was due to the cheapness and ease of manufacture of baked clay. Egypt is a notable exception for in the late predynastic and early dynastic periods stone vessels were not rare, although pottery vessels were in common use. Apart from stone and pottery, other materials used in later periods are metals and, less abundantly, glass and faience.

Stone Vessels

Throughout antiquity a great variety of rocks, ranging in hardness from soapstone to granite, have been used to carve bowls, vases, etc. Among the early Egyptian stone wares, very finely-carved vessels often with lugs and some fluting, are found in virtually any available rock. Granites, including a grey granite (granodiorite?) and a pink porphyritic granite, diorite, and porphyrite (Pl. 13) were used, but basalt is the most commonly used igneous rock. Among the softer rocks, limestones and alabaster feature very abundantly; both calcite, alabaster, and gypsum alabaster seem to have been used for the same types of vessels and the two rocks are often difficult to distinguish by macroscopic inspection. Calcite occurs most commonly and was therefore also most commonly used (Pl. 12). The frequent use of hard rocks as well as softer rocks suggests that in many cases the Egyptians were influenced by aesthetic considerations rather than by ease of manufacture. However, many of the small perfume and ointment jars or bottles were made out of softer rocks, as well as many tall jars, possibly storage vessels.

The very soft rocks steatite and serpentine have also been used for vessels in Egypt, but not as frequently as their ease of working might suggest. Elsewhere, advantage was taken of the extreme softness of these rocks and in Minoan Crete and in North America steatite pots are sometimes very elaborately carved in high relief. The North American Indians both quarried and carved this rock with flint or obsidian knives and used it to make cooking-pots because of its excellent resistance to fire.

It will be noticed that in the examples of stone vessels given above, there are few sedimentary rocks. Those sediments which were commonly used, such as the two forms of alabaster, are crystalline; the common limestones used are either the fully crystalline marbles or dense compact rocks. Clearly rocks with distinct sedimentary structures such as bedding, would give rise to planes of weakness and increased porosity in a vessel. The overall porosity of sediments is generally greater than in igneous or other crystalline rocks. Several well-cemented or indurated sediments were, however, occasionally used and vessels of indurated breccia (Pl. 10), mudstone, and greywacke are known from Egypt. Poorly-consolidated sedimentary rocks have rarely been used for they are generally too friable and porous. However, the soft bituminous shale from Kimmeridge on the southern English coast was very easily carved and is naturally rendered relatively impervious by its bitumen content. It was used in Bronze Age in England for the manufacture of cups and other small objects.

Metal Vessels

All metals were considered among the more expensive materials throughout most of antiquity until iron became abundant. Gold and silver were always used for either ritual or luxury goods (except in pre-Columbian Peru where some common tools such as fish-hooks were made of gold); and gold or silver goblets, vases, and bowls feature among the riches and works of art of antiquity. From the Middle Bronze Age onwards, bronze, and later iron, became sufficiently abundant to replace weapons and certain tools previously made out of stone. As discussed in the various sections on tools and weapons, for certain objects metals have a real advantage over stone. Common pots and bowls, however, continued to be made from clay although metal vessels have certain advantages. Metal vessels can be placed directly on the fire, are impervious and less breakable. It must be presumed that bronze and iron vessels of various types were generally confined to either the ritual or luxury classes of articles because clay was an adequate and much cheaper material for household vessels.

Clay Vessels

Pottery is a clay which has been 'hardened' by firing. The plastic and cohesive qualities of 'moderately' wet clay make it possible to mould or press it into almost any desired shape, which it retains on drying. Drying at temperatures up to about 100°C causes all the absorbed moisture to be expelled and the clay becomes hard and aplastic. It can, however, reabsorb moisture and regain its original properties. When the water of crystallization is driven off, the clay changes its character entirely and no amount of wetting will cause it to become plastic again. The firing process causes first dehydration of the clay minerals by evaporation of absorbed moisture at 100°C, and the expulsion of the water of crystallization at about 400°C, depending on the type of clay mineral. This loss of water usually involves considerable shrinkage, up to 10 per cent. At higher temperatures, the clay particles begin to melt and when the clay fuses entirely it is said to 'vitrify'. The melting point varies considerably for different clays and – in practice – to obtain a dense, non-porous body, clays are fired to their 'maturing point' below the melting point, when only the edges of the clay minerals fuse without the pottery losing its shape. Much prehistoric pottery, however, was fired well below its maturing point, so that much of the early pottery remains porous. Pots could be made impervious, or at least less porous, by coating with fats or resins or finishing techniques such as burnishing and, at a later date, by glazing.

Most clays used in prehistory are naturally occurring sediments which consist of a mixture of clay minerals. Most natural clays are gritty (Pl. 26a), and when only very pure clays were available, grit was often deliberately added (Pl. 26b). The grit reduces the risk of cracking during firing, partly by reducing the shrinkage, and partly by making the pottery more porous and allowing moisture and trapped air bubbles to escape during the firing process. For certain finishes, such as very fine slips, pure clays were used, either occurring naturally or especially extracted from natural gritty clay sediments.

The colour of prehistoric pottery depends largely on the iron content of the clay and on the firing conditions. If clay is fired under oxidizing conditions, any contained organic matter is burnt out, and the iron salts are dehydrated and oxidized to hematite. Thus oxidized pottery is generally red or brown in colour. If the clay contains no iron, or only very small amounts, it may fire to buff colour. Under reducing conditions the organic matter in the clay may not be burnt out, but reduced to carbon. This may mask the original colour of the pottery and in some poorly fired pottery the core remains black, whereas the outer surface is oxidized and red. This usually results from hasty firing. A black surface was often obtained intentionally by coating the surface of the pot with fat, soot, or carbon before firing it under reducing conditions so that these organic materials remained in the pores of the pot; but black wares were also obtained, intentionally or unintentionally simply by firing a pot in a very smoky fire when the carbon adheres to the surface of the clay and partially fills the pores. Under strongly reducing conditions, the iron oxides in the clay may be reduced to magnetite, the black iron oxide, and its presence can sometimes be detected with a magnet. Another method of obtaining a black colour on pottery is by coating with graphite (rare). Other colours were frequently obtained by coating a pot with pigments either before firing, or after firing. The most common colorants are red ochre, white clays, and white plasters (see pp. 182–5).

Thus, pottery can not only be made in a great variety of shapes, but it can also be decorated and embellished in many ways, either by taking advantage of the plastic properties of the clay itself, or by various methods of controlling the colour. In most cultures either plain or decorated pottery was the material used for household and storage vessels; but other pottery vessels were sometimes finely decorated and carefully made and used for ritual purposes or as luxury goods, either at the same time as, or instead of, other materials such as metal and stone.

Faience and Glass Vessels

Faience, and the blue or green glaze most commonly found on it, appear to be very early Near Eastern discoveries. Throughout Egyptian history faience was mostly used for small objects, beads, and figurines of various types (Pl. 19), but bowls and vases of faience were also commonly made. Vessels made from glazed faience are considerably less porous than clay vessels but more expensive and complex to manufacture, and their use can be largely explained in terms of aesthetic values. Thus, the small objects of faience include much jewellery and small (often amuletic) figures of deities. Occasionally faience was even used for the making of large ceremonial vessels with complex relief work, such as the Bocchoris vase (nearly 90 centimetres high) exported from Egypt to Tarquinia in Italy.

The earliest uses of glass were principally for small objects such as beads, amulets, and inlay work in historic Egypt. Small glass vases were also made at the time when the material was first discovered, but its use for this purpose only became really widespread in Roman times.

Faience is white, yellowish, or greyish paste. It is often fairly friable and may be quite soft, but some faience was made harder and less friable by partially fusing it with alkali or, less commonly, by mixing it with finely powdered glaze before fusing. This latter process also coloured the faience according to the glaze used, usually blue or bluish-green.

Faience is a paste of very finely powdered angular quartz. According to Lucas (1962) the quartz powder may have been mixed with natron, or a strong natron solution, to give the quartz sufficient cohesion to be worked more or less as clay, and to ensure cohesion after firing by causing partial fusion of the quartz grains. As more natron is added to the faience paste, the core becomes harder through fusion of the quartz grains and the faience grades into sodium glass. Faience objects were coated with powdered glaze, either before firing, or after firing, and then re-fired.

The blue glaze on faience objects is essentially a sodium silicate with some lime, coloured by copper silicate. The process of its manufacture is not known with certainty but it seems probable that a 'glass' was produced by fusing powdered quartz with alkali. The alkali used was most probably naturally occurring natron which contains some calcium carbonate as an impurity, or possibly plant ash which contains various salts of the alkalis sodium, potassium, and calcium. A copper salt, probably malachite, was added as a colorant. The glass was crushed, powdered, and applied either in powdered form or as a viscous liquid. The powdered glass is known as *frit*. On firing, the frit re-fuses and also partially attacks the surface of the faience core, thus adhering very firmly.

The difference between a glass and a glaze is essentially technological. Glazes are used as thin coats applied and fused on to a core, so that the essential properties of glazes are that they should not have a higher fusion temperature than the material to be glazed and that they should expand and shrink to the same extent as the core on heating and cooling. Glasses are used alone as the basis of the objects themselves, so that their shrinkage properties are not normally very important. However, since glasses were often worked by drawing or blowing (a rather late development), it is important that they should remain plastic over a reasonable range of temperature. Thus, although both glasses and glazes are prepared essentially by fusing quartz with alkali, there are usually minor differences in their composition. Both glasses and glazes are super-cooled silicate melts, i.e. silicates of sodium, potassium, or calcium which have solidified with random atomic structure and are therefore not crystalline. Their structure is analogous to that of obsidian, which is a glass formed by the rapid cooling of a natural silicate melt. The alkalis used to fuse quartz and alter it to a silicate melt are known as *fluxes*. They reduce the melting point of silica from 1,710°C to the range of 900°C to 1,400°C depending on the flux used. They also influence the properties of the glass.

In antiquity, the usual source of silica was quartz sand. When quartz sand contains iron, only a black opaque glass can be made so that when clear or coloured glasses were desired a non-ferruginous sand had to be used. In Northern and Western Europe where pure sand is rare, people had to use crushed flint as their silica.

The composition of ancient glasses shows that several different fluxes were used. The fluxes most commonly found are salts of potassium, sodium, calcium, and lead in variable quantities. Other elements sometimes occur in small quantities and these may have been impurities in ingredients used to make the glass. The choice of flux depended partly on the natural resources available, but by Roman times different fluxes were selected to produce glasses with different properties.

The possible sources of fluxes include naturally occurring natron, which is only found in arid regions – for example the Near East. Potassium may have been obtained from saltpetre, but it was more probably obtained from plant ash which is very rich in potassium salts. Plant ash also contains salts of sodium, calcium, and magnesium. Calcium salts are very widespread in the form of limestones and other calcareous rocks; dolomite consists of both calcium and magnesium salts. In addition calcium could have been obtained from gypsum, fluorite, or bone ash. Lead could have been obtained, from any of the lead ores.

The Egyptian glasses are sodium glasses with variable amounts of calcium. The sodium was probably obtained from natron, which occurs in the desert. Whether the calcium was deliberately added or not is uncertain, for many of the sands in Egypt are calcareous so that the calcium salts may have been added inadvertently. The presence of calcium, however, was essential to fuse the natron and quartz mixture, and the Egyptians considered that certain sands in Northern Egypt, which are calcareous, were much more suitable for glass-making than others.

For making vases and goblets, glasses were often made as pure and nearly transparent as possible (Pl. 17), but coloured translucent, or even opaque, glasses were also widely used, particularly in the earlier periods of glass-making (Pl. 18). The colour was obtained by including small quantities of the salt of a highly-coloured metal ion. Shades of blue were most commonly obtained from cobalt which gives a deep colour; and for lighter blues, as on many Egyptian glazes, copper was used in soda or potash glasses. When iron is also present in small quantities, a greenish blue is obtained. A purple colour like amethyst could be obtained with small amounts of manganese, but in large quantities, and especially in the presence of iron, an opaque black glass was produced. Red glasses have been found to contain the reduced red copper oxide and some green glasses were coloured by copper oxide in a lead glass. An opaque white glass was most commonly obtained with tin oxide.

Beads, Amulets, Jewellery, and Other Small Objects

Throughout antiquity the selection of materials for beads, jewellery, amulets, etc. or for inlay work was influenced by many considerations which were not functional and there seem to have been very few technological preferences. Stones were selected for their beauty and value and generally bright or clear colours were favoured, or stones with a good lustre and transparency were chosen. Quite often the magical properties of the stones were a major consideration in their use but for prehistory the knowledge of such properties is largely lost.

The many varieties of silica have been very widely employed for various forms of personal decoration in all regions. Quartz, as clear rock crystal and its coloured variants, particularly amethyst, as well as garnets and peridot, were among the hardest and most lustrous stones worked until the Roman period. In Egypt beryl was also worked from the Ptolemaic period on, but at first the stone could not be cut and was used in its natural hexagonal crystalline form and bored to make beads. There is no evidence that the hard minerals now called precious stones, such as ruby and sapphire, were known in the ancient world before classical Greek and Roman times. There is some doubt as to whether the Greeks knew and cut these hard stones, but by Roman times they were highly prized as gems and imported from India. It appears, however, that the diamond remained unknown until considerably later. Without diamond dust, the hard minerals could not be cut in the various faceted styles which are a rather late historical development in jewellery. The gems were polished in cabochon, using the impure form of corundum, emery, which is of the same hardness as ruby, or with finely ground dust of the minerals themselves. The lower face of the gem was sometimes hollowed to increase its brilliance and translucency.

Softer, transparent or translucent crystalline stones have sometimes been used, but less commonly than quartz. Among these the very clear variety of calcite, iceland spar, and fluorspar are the most common, including the green and amethyst coloured varieties of fluorspar.

In antiquity colour seems sometimes to have been more appreciated than translucency or brilliance as, for instance, when rock crystal was set in red cement to imitate carnelian in Eighteenth-Dynasty Egypt, or when stones such as quartz were glazed with blue frit. The earliest glazed stone objects are steatite beads of Badarian date. Later many other small objects, in particular scarabs and beads, were carved out of steatite and glazed.

It is not possible to enumerate all the stones used for beads, bangles, amulets, etc. throughout the various cultures of antiquity. They range from simple shale pebbles of dull colour and no lustre to rare bright and lustrous gems. Very frequently precious and semi-precious stones with localized occurrence, such as lapis lazuli or turquoise, were mined at great cost and transported over wide areas. Some stones seem to have been very generally favoured, especially the many non-crystalline forms of silica. Carnelian seems to have been particularly favoured in several cultures and the banded form of silica, agate, onyx, and sardonyx were also widely sought. Chalcedonic silica is virtually as hard as quartz and can be engraved, or given a very high polish with crushed quartz. These stones were made into finely engraved gems and cameos by Roman lapidaries.

Another hard, but less abundant, material which has been highly prized is jade, both nephrite and jadeite. These were especially valued in the Far East and in the New World where green was considered to symbolize the colour of life. Green stones therefore acquired magical properties and jade was worked into highly-skilled and elaborate carvings, jewellery and amulets. A less lustrous green stone, amazonstone, was also used, but it is frequently rather uneven in colour.

Among the softer stones, the bright-coloured turquoise and lapis lazuli seem to have been especially valued in Egypt, where their blue colours were also imitated in the vast quantities of glazed faience and stone beads, trinkets, and amulets. Steatite and serpentine were also easy to carve and pierce for beads or amulets and were much used, particularly in Egypt. Even coal beads have been reported from Chatal Huyuk in Anatolia and from the same site there are pendants made from mica and of various limestones.

Glass, which can be produced in a great variety and combinations of colours and patterns, became extensively used for most of the purposes for which decorative stones were employed. Pottery beads and pendants are also known.

Metals have been widely used for all forms of personal adornment. Among the earliest uses of copper and gold during the Chalcolithic was the manufacture of trinkets of various forms; copper was commonly drawn into a wire and then fashioned into pins, or spiral beads. As metals became more common, gold and silver became especially valued for making jewellery, but bronze continued to be very widely worked into pins, brooches, armlets, and similar small objects.

Many other small objects such as figurines, seals, ex-votos, and objects of ceremonial use were frequently made out of a great variety of materials. Minerals which normally only occur as very small crystals, pebbles, or concretions could not be used for many of these objects, and apart from seals, the very hard materials were less commonly used for small carvings than for jewellery. Clay seems to have been used more frequently for small figures, seals, etc. than for personal adornment. However, it is difficult to find any relationship between function of the objects and the material used. Already in the Palaeolithic, when the range of materials used for toolmaking was fairly limited, figurines were carved out of a variety of soft stones: limestone, stalagmite, steatite, serpentine, coal, hematite, and occasionally fire-hardened mud or mud and crushed bone paste. A recent survey of a homogenous group of small figurines from Neolithic Crete has shown the materials used to be predominantly clay, frequently marble, and rarely two forms of steatite, breccia, slate, shell, and bone. In later periods metals were also widely used for small figures, and since metals such as gold, silver, copper, and bronze could be cast, it became possible to standardize the forms of such small figures in a way previously impossible. This standardization is also clearly shown by the moulded faience figures of deities so common throughout ancient Egypt (cf. Pl. 19).

Pigments

Any mineral which has a *streak colour* can be powdered and used as a pigment. The pigment may be applied by using the mineral as a crayon, if the surface to be coloured is harder than the mineral in question, or the dry powder may be applied by rubbing or stencilling. To ensure that the colour would adhere well, pigments were commonly made into a paste with water or another medium. These media were organic materials such as fat, oil, blood, egg-white, etc. and they are not normally preserved. Some organic pigments and dyes were also used but since these fade and decay comparatively rapidly, very little is known about their use in antiquity. The mineral pigments, on the other hand, are normally well preserved and if they have not suffered from weathering processes or contamination, they retain their original colours fully.

There are many coloured minerals, however, which do not have a streak colour. This means that the colour is not sufficiently intense to show on the very fine powder particles which are transparent or white. Many of the mafic silicates, for example, are dark in colour but only give colourless, or very faintly tinted, powders. Minerals of this type can clearly not be used to make paints.

Ochres: Ochres feature prominently among the earliest colouring materials used and their use continued throughout prehistory and into later periods, even when much clearer reds, browns, and yellows could be obtained from other minerals. The earthy varieties of iron oxide were most commonly chosen, but kidney ore could also be powdered to give a dark, brownish-red colour. The colour of ochre depends on the degree of hydration of the iron oxide and also on the presence of impurities. The pure ochres have clear colours, the very hydrated oxide (limonite) is yellow, and the dehydrated oxide (hematite) is red. The colour of ochre, therefore, varies in different localities and some occurrences, with small amounts of black manganese dioxide, are known as *sienna* and *umber*. They have darker and less clear colours than ochres.

The colour of ochre can be altered by heating to dehydrate the oxide. The process is irreversible and hematite cannot be hydrated simply by heating in water. It is therefore possible to obtain redder shades of ochre by roasting yellow or brown ochre, but not to produce yellow ochre from the red or brown varieties.

Red: Ochre was the only source of red colour in prehistory. Another red pigment can be obtained from the rather rare mineral *cinnabar* (mercuric sulphide). This has a very brilliant shade known as vermilion, but it is doubtful whether it was much used in antiquity, at least before Roman times. A more common source of clear red in Greek and Roman times was from red lead

(lead oxide Pb_3O_4) or *minium*, which may have a more orange-red colour than vermilion. Red lead occurs naturally with other lead ores, but it was also prepared artificially from *calamine* (lead carbonate) by heating it moderately to about 400°C.

Yellow: A much clearer yellow than yellow ochre was obtained from the arsenic sulphide *orpiment*. Orpiment usually occurs with *realgar* from which it is derived through weathering, and the two minerals do not seem to have been clearly distinguished. Orpiment is clear yellow in colour, but the presence of much realgar may impart a distinct reddish or orange tint. Orpiment and realgar were never used in Palaeolithic times. Its earliest use in Egypt was probably in the Eighteenth Dynasty, but it may have been known earlier in regions where it occurs naturally, particularly in Asia Minor.

Blue: A blue pigment was obtained from the blue copper carbonate, *azurite*, which may have been used quite early in antiquity. It has a brilliant blue colour, but sometimes occurs mixed with malachite. An artificial blue pigment, *frit*, was first prepared in Egypt by fusing quartz sand or pebbles with copper ore, most probably malachite and lime. This forms a glass which, when finely powdered, can be used as a pigment or re-fused as a glaze. For use as a pigment, the frit had to be very finely powdered, but even so, blue frit paints often remained slightly granular.

A blue paint, ultramarine, can be made from the semi-precious brilliant blue stone, *lapis lazuli*. However, if lapis lazuli is simply powdered and used as a pigment it gives a faint, rather greyish blue colour and the preparation of clear blue ultramarine was probably not known before mediaeval times. Lapis lazuli generally occurs as an impure mineral of lazurite which also contains calcite and iron pyrite. To produce a clear blue pigment the lazurite is extracted with a weak alkali.

Green: Green was obtained at a very early period in Egypt from the green copper carbonate *malachite* and this remained the principal source of green pigment wherever it was available. Sometimes *chrysocolla* may have been powdered instead. A green frit was also prepared by making frit with a small quantity of iron, although the iron may not have been a deliberate addition, since many sands naturally contain some iron. Green frit has a more yellow-green colour than malachite, which is a very clear green. Some green pigments consist of mixtures of blue and yellow minerals, particularly blue frit and yellow ochre.

White: The most commonly used white pigments are *lime* and *gypsum*. These minerals occur abundantly, particularly lime. The pure and friable varieties may be used directly as a powder, for instance chalk, or they may be applied as very thin coats of plaster which ensures a much better adherence of the pigment. Other minerals which have been used as white pigments are white clays, particularly *kaolin*, and in some regions a white pigment was obtained from *diatomite*.

Black: Probably the most common sources of black pigments were charcoal and soot. Some black minerals have also been widely used since Palaeolithic times but they rarely give as black a colour as soot. *Graphite* is a very dark, steel-grey colour, but since it is soft it is easy to use as a pigment and can be made to adhere easily, even without preparation into paint. The earthy varieties of manganese oxide, *wad* and *psilomelane*, have been used as black pigments, but they often have a brownish tint, and occasionally a slightly bluish tint. *Stibnite* may occasionally have been used, particularly in the preparation of *kohl* (eye paint), but much kohl was prepared from *galena* or other black (or green) pigments.

CHAPTER SEVEN

Building Materials, Mining and Quarrying

Building Materials

A great variety of materials have been used throughout antiquity for building purposes, not only the inorganic materials considered here. However, it is the building stones, bricks, and tiles as well as the mortars and plasters of ancient buildings which are most commonly preserved. The use of organic materials such as wood, reeds, etc., has frequently had to be inferred from the architectural details, or from other indirect evidence such as post holes and the charred remains of wooden structures etc.

Building Stone

A rock used as building stone must be able to withstand the weight of the overlying structure. Thus, poorly consolidated sediments such as many mudstones, shales, and some sandstones, are unsuited to all but the simplest wall constructions. Chalk and many shelly limestones are also too friable to serve as durable building materials. Many compact sediments, however, such as sandstones and limestones, are among the most commonly-used building stones. Igneous rocks have also been used since they are compact, generally homogenous in structure, and have a high crushing strength. Igneous rocks are usually harder and more difficult to dress than sediments and when both are available in any locality, sediments are less laborious and therefore cheaper to use.

When a sandstone or limestone is very homogenous in structure, blocks can be dressed with equal ease in three directions, and the rock is often referred to as a 'free stone'. When the bedding or jointing, or both, are strongly developed this affects the manner in which a rock can be used. Bedded rocks laid with the bedding horizontal may be as strong and resistant as free stones. If the bedding is laid parallel to the wall it is easy to obtain a smooth flat surface, but with time the rock is liable to split along the bedding and to flake off.

The porosity of a rock affects its durability. A porous rock is liable to disintegrate more rapidly than one with low porosity, when exposed either to the action of frost or to salt infestation. This situation was appreciated by the Romans, for whom it was probably a more immediate problem than for earlier architects in warm and arid climates. Vitruvius, for example, recommended that stone should be quarried two years before the commencement of building, during the summer (dry) season, and by no means during the winter (i.e. when the moisture content of the stone is likely to be high). After two years' exposure to the weather, the blocks which remained sound are likely to continue to do so even if used for exposed outer walls. Those which show slight deterioration can be used in the foundations, where they remain protected from the extremes of weather.

For heavy monumental masonry, when strength is of especial importance, as for instance in the construction of the pyramids in Egypt, it was sometimes necessary to use hard granitic rocks or quartzite instead of the more easily worked sandstones and limestones. For overhanging features it is important that the blocks used should be homogenous and faultless, otherwise the unsupported part may fracture along any natural plane of weakness such as a bedding or joint plane. This is particularly important in the construction of lintels and similar features which span a gap and are supported only at two extremities. To span wide gaps of this type in massive pyramid constructions, the Egyptians had recourse to the use of good, unfissured granite, until the discovery of hard siliceous sandstone (quartzite) in the region of Silsila. When roofs were corbelled as in the Mycenean tholoi, or spanned by an arch, the problem of finding huge unfissured blocks of rock was overcome and less massive structures could be built. For those lighter structures the more easily worked sandstones and limestones were suitable. In fact, for vaulting, lightness of structure and hence lightness of material can be an advantage, and even very light rocks such as travertine were used by the Romans, and the earliest barrel vaults known from First-Dynasty Egypt at Saqqara are of mud brick.

In many ancient buildings the core of the walls are built up out of roughly dressed blocks of 'soft' building stone and the surfaces are faced with carefully cut or even sculptured slabs of rock to form a more decorative surface. Rocks used for facing and other decorative features are often those used also for other building purposes, but consideration of beauty as well as durability or cheapness may enter into their selection. Many rocks, including 'hard' building stone, have been used in this way in different regions. In Egypt granite and diorite were much used, as well as the more easily worked compact limestone. In Asia Minor, a black slightly vesicular basalt was used in much Hittite architecture, with the result that highly-polished surfaces could not be achieved.

The use of such hard crystalline rocks for sculpture and other decorative stone-work imposes limitations on the forms which can be achieved. Before the use of iron tools, the hard rocks were probably only worked by pounding, sawing, drilling, and grinding. Copper and even bronze chisels would be blunted very rapidly and could not cut the rock. This severely limits the possibility of cutting forms with narrow re-entrant angles. Even with iron or steel chisels, hard and/or brittle rocks such as granite and other acid igneous rocks do not lend themselves to slender projections or detail in deep and high relief. Under the impact of repeated hammering these rocks shatter easily, in narrow projections, or in fine free-standing detail, and forms have to be made compact with detail in low relief. From the study of some unfinished Egyptian statuary, Zuber (1956) has suggested that the choice of hard rocks, and the techniques of working such rock, has strongly influenced Egyptian monumental works. Since the rock could only be hammered, ground, or drilled, sculptures were designed as projections of two-dimensional designs in two perpendicular planes rather than 'in the round' (Pl. 20). However, even when using the softer rocks – such as limestone – the same style was used, although these rocks could be chiselled.

In Greece a variety of crystalline, compact marbles of different colours were used for facing buildings and for statuary. The very pure white Penthellic marble of Greece, and also the Italian marbles, were particularly valued both for their appearance and also for their homogenous quality and resilience. These crystalline marbles (hardness 4) can be chiselled into delicate forms with considerably less risk of shattering than the hard crystalline rocks (Pl. 21) (hardness ranging from 6 to 7). They can also be given a high polish and marbles have been used for some of the finest statuary both in antiquity and in later times.

Some of the very soft rocks, such as serpentine (hardness 2 to 5) and steatite (hardness 1 to 2), have also been used for decorative stone-work and for elaborate carving, but these rocks are too soft for most structural purposes.

When flat slabs of rock are required, as for paving stones or roofing slabs, the natural fissility of thinly-bedded rocks or of metamorphic rocks was sometimes exploited, but harder compact rocks were often preferred for pavings, particularly basalt, marble, and compact limestones.

Bricks and Tiles

In regions of unconsolidated sediments, such as the wide alluvial plain of ancient Mesopotamia, building stones were not easily available. In such regions, walls were either simply built up of mud pisé or artificial building blocks were manufactured out of clay and silt. These bricks were often sun-dried to hard blocks which do, however, distintegrate again if thoroughly wetted. Sun-dried bricks are therefore only suitable in arid or semi-arid regions. In wetter climates the bricks must be fired so that the clay is irreversibly dehydrated. They can then retain their shape and hardness, even in heavy rain storms.

To make bricks, natural clay deposits could be used and mixed with water to a suitable consistency for moulding. Frequently, however, chaff, sand, or other coarse material had to be added, for if a very pure clay is used the bricks shrink considerably on drying. This shrinkage and the irregular drying process in direct sun-heat causes cracks and distortion in the shape of the bricks. With sand or chaff a very plastic material can still be obtained which is shaped in moulds, and the shrinkage is much reduced.

The shape and size of bricks has varied greatly over time in different regions. Already in pre-pottery Jericho two distinct shapes of brick were made: the plano-convex and the 'cigar-shaped' bricks. The rounded, elongated shapes of these early bricks suggest that they may have been shaped by hand. Moulds for the standardization of shape and size became very widely used and varied according to fashions or needs. For instance, in Egypt where mud-brick structures were extremely common, small buildings such as private houses were made out of small highly standardized bricks, measuring about 22 × 11 × 17 centimetres; but for some of the massive temple structures larger bricks were made ranging from 30 to 40 centimetres long, and as much as 20 × 15 centimetres deep. Both in proto-literate Egypt and in Syria small standardized mud bricks were made for special features such as the recesses of temple walls. In Roman times, many different specially shaped fired bricks were prepared for cornices, columns, and other architectural features. Roofing tiles could equally easily be made out of clay and Roman tiles were very elaborately designed to form neatly-fitting and waterproof roofing, and were commonly used in conjunction with stone masonry.

Plaster and Mortar

Plaster and mortar were often necessary to consolidate stone or brick structures, although 'dry walling' structures (without binding material between the masonry) can be made extremely strong with large and accurately dressed blocks. Plasters have also been widely used as a finishing surface on walls, to conceal any irregularities of structure, as in the pre-pottery levels of Jericho, where both walls and floors were covered in a lime plaster which was highly burnished. Plasters were also used to make a smooth and white base for painted decoration, for example in the mud brick tomb at Hierakonpolis in Egypt, where the walls were covered with mud mortar and finished with a thin layer of whitewash or yellow ochre and then painted.

The simplest and perhaps the earliest plaster used is *mud plaster* or clay, which is simply applied very wet and allowed to dry. This was particularly used with wood, reed, or mud-brick structures, and with mud-brick walls the bricks and plaster may be of identical composition and extremely difficult to distinguish. Mud plaster is clearly only suitable in dry regions, or for internal wall facing. Since many clays in arid regions naturally contain lime or gypsum, or both, as impurities, mud plasters may superficially resemble an impure lime or gypsum plaster, but they differ radically from the latter. Both lime and gypsum plaster are prepared by burning the mineral to alter its chemical composition. The prepared plaster is then powdered and mixed with water for use. The setting process is only partly a drying process, but it also involves chemical changes which reconvert the plaster back to its original composition (lime or gypsum). The adhering properties of these plasters are largely due to the fact that they are made to crystallize on to the stone, brick, or other base used.

In arid or semi-arid regions gypsum plaster and gypsum mortar were widely used, particularly in Egypt, where the water-resistant lime plaster and mortar were only introduced in late dynastic times.

Gypsum plaster, better known as plaster of Paris, was prepared from naturally occurring deposits of gypsum. In many Near Eastern countries this occurs abundantly as desert crust on, or just below, the desert surface. Gypsum was also mined or quarried, principally in the form of alabaster. The gypsum is heated to at least 100°C, which converts it to the anhydrous form of calcium sulphate, anhydrite. On mixing with water the anhydrite reabsorbs water and is converted back into gypsum. Since the natural deposits of gypsum usually contain lime and sometimes also iron as impurities, these may occur fortuitously in the gypsum plasters used in antiquity. The presence of iron tends to impair the whiteness of the plaster and to give it ochreous tints. Ancient plasters are also often greyish in colour, due to contamination with charcoal and ash from the fires. When a smooth even wall surface was desired, the plaster could be applied very wet, and even in extremely thin coats, as a whitewash. When used as a binding medium, however, the plaster was generally mixed with sand before wetting. On setting, this forms a concreted 'sandstone-like' substance known as gypsum mortar. It is stronger and more binding than pure plaster, but its gritty consistency made it unsuitable for wall covering.

Since gypsum is soluble in water, gypsum plasters were not used in the more humid climates of Europe, where a binding material was made by burning lime. The chemistry of lime plaster and mortar is slightly more complex than that of gypsum. *Lime plaster* is prepared from naturally occurring calcium carbonate. This may be obtained from a great variety of pure calcareous rocks or from shell deposits. As with gypsum, such deposits are rarely quite pure, and the plasters and mortars of antiquity usually contain other minerals which are, however, not necessarily deliberate additions.

The lime is burnt or calcined to convert the calcium carbonate to calcium oxide or *quicklime* ($CaCO_3 \xrightarrow{\text{(heat)}} CaO + CO_2$). To calcine lime a temperature of around 900°C is required, considerably higher than for burning gypsum, so that any lime impurity in gypsum plaster is unlikely to have been converted to quicklime. The quicklime is mixed with water, or *slaked*, which converts it to calcium hydroxide, or *slaked lime* ($CaO + H_2O \rightarrow Ca(OH)_2$). The slaked lime sets partly by evaporation of water, and also by the absorption of carbon dioxide from the atmosphere, and is reconverted to calcium carbonate or *lime*. Lime plaster alone is not very strong and for building purposes it was normally strengthened by the addition of sand before *slaking*, thus converting it into a lime mortar. Sometimes the plaster was toughened by mixing it with some fibrous material such as straw.

Mining and Quarrying

Prospecting

As has been seen, already in prehistory people were fully aware of the varying properties of different rocks and deliberately selected suitable materials for special purposes. In the Lower Palaeolithic, suitable stone, often flint or other siliceous rock, was selected for toolmaking from among the pebbles and boulders of river gravels. However, opencast mining for flint may well have started as early as the Palaeolithic, for tools were sometimes made from flint nodules which had not been worn to pebbles. By Neolithic times people had not only appreciated the association between flint and chalk, but also the fact that flint nodules frequently occur in beds which can be followed underground for considerable distances. Thus, by sinking shafts from the chalk surface, they found that a bed of flint could be reached at depth.

There is very little definite evidence for the methods of prospecting employed in prehistoric times. The habit of searching for flint and chert in gravel deposits led to the discovery and use of other siliceous stones which could also be flaked into tools. Many of these, such as chalcedony and various forms of opaline silica, normally occur in small nodules and pebbles and were first exploited when very small stone tools were made in the various microlithic cultures throughout the world.

With the technological innovations of the Neolithic, a greater variety of stone tools were made serving very different purposes and consequently many new rock types were exploited. Some were regularly collected or quarried from remote areas and traded and transported over long distances, so that the beginnings of some degree of specialization in prospecting methods must already have existed at this period.

The native metals, gold and copper, were probably first discovered while exploring river gravels. Once the properties of metals were appreciated a deliberate search for them seems to have been made, for the number of metal objects found already in Chalcolithic times appears too great to be the result of chance finds only. The metallic sheen of native metals and the bright colours of the copper ores used must have given early miners considerable help in their search. In the region of Umm Hat in Egypt, for instance, virtually every blue stain on the rock had been tested by the Egyptians for copper ores. But many of the exploratory cuttings ended in barren rock and they were not extended deeper to try to meet the richer vein at depth (the copper of this region was worked largely for its silver content). However, surface indications of lodes are often indirect. The weathered outcrop of many copper lodes is a gossan cap of limonite which results from the weathering of the associated iron pyrites, while the copper ores are found in lower levels. Gold in Egypt, for instance, was known to be associated with quartz veins, so that a search for gold was in the first instance a search for quartz veins.

In ancient literate times descriptions of prospecting methods are few. Pliny refers to the frequent occurrence in the Spanish mines of the precious metals gold and silver in the oxidized zones of copper veins, whereas in Britain white pebbles in a stream bed, according to Pliny, were taken as an indication of gold placer deposits. The miners of Laurium in Attica (Greece) seem to have clearly observed certain associations of mineral deposit with geological structure, such as the occurrence of argentiferous lead deposits on the contact zones between strata of mica schist and marble. This enabled them to reach ore deposits for which there was no surface indication (see below). Such observations were extremely rare and, in every known case, lodes and other deposits were discovered either by direct or indirect surface indications. Special mining expeditions were sent out by the Egyptians, already in Old Kingdom times and perhaps earlier. Although much of the labour force was drawn from slaves or the armies, mining and prospecting had become a specialist profession. In classical Greece, also, specialists were employed to supervise mining and quarrying activities while Alexander the Great took mineral prospectors with him on his travels into Asia.

Whatever their methods, the ancient prospectors seem to have explored their region very thoroughly, for in the Egyptian desert the copper and gold deposits are now virtually exhausted and throughout the Mediterranean regions the oxidized copper ores, malachite and cuprite, were so extensively worked out by Middle Bronze Age times that the lower lying sulphides had to be exploited to supply the increasing demand for metal.

Alluvial Deposits

Pebbles and boulders in a river deposit have undergone frequent rolling and battering, so that the harder rocks which are also resistant to corrosion predominate, particularly the siliceous rocks, flint, chert, quartzite, and some of the tough metamorphic rocks such as schists. River gravels, therefore, are an excellent source for the hard homogenous rock fragments needed to make the stone tools used throughout the Stone Ages and later. Many ancient gravel deposits were exploited in the same way as active stream beds and in North America quite a number of 'mines' are known, where large pebbles and boulders were dug out of lightly consolidated ancient gravels by digging pits, and even small chambers, into the deposit. The tools were frequently roughed out on the spot.

River pebbles were also a source of many hard minerals which were used as semi-precious stones from Neolithic times onwards: the crystalline forms of silica (quartz) rock crystal, amethyst, and citrine and the colloidal forms of silica such as carnelian and agate, as well as less common hard minerals such as garnet, beryl, peridot, and others.

Alluvial deposits were an important source of some of the heavy minerals used in antiquity: the native metals, gold and copper, some metal ores, particularly cassiterite and magnetite, and a few other minerals such as zircon, emery, and garnet sands. It is generally believed that gold and native copper were first known as 'stones' from river sands and that subsequently it was found that they have unusual properties, in that they can be worked by beating and bending, rather than by flaking and grinding.

The simplest method of extracting the heavy minerals from sand or gravel is by panning. The gravel is swirled in a wide flat dish filled with water. The heavy particles settle, while the lighter quartz sand is carried by the swirling motion and can be allowed to flow off. This is a slow and tedious method and more sophisticated methods were devised, all based on the same principle that moving water carries away light sand and leaves an enriched deposit. To catch small particles of gold, the washings were passed over the hides of goat or cattle in Egypt, or bundles of cloth in Nubia. Gold was worked in this way in many rivers throughout prehistoric and historic times, but in regions where gold veins outcrop near the surface, gold was also mined. The mined gold was separated from the gangue by crushing, i.e. in effect reducing it to a fine sand and washing. In Egypt, the milled rock was washed on sloping tables over which a stream of water could be directed, and similar tables or troughs were used in many other mining processes.

In pre-Roman times cassiterite was obtained predominantly from placer deposits. The streams draining the granite masses of Cornwall and Brittany were worked extensively, as were those of Spain, Saxony, and Bohemia. In several stream valleys in Cornwall large stone blocks are found battered and lightly hollowed; they were used as anvils on which large lumps of ore were broken by hammering before smelting. At Carnon, a miner's horn pick and wooden shovel were found, believed to date from the Bronze Age. There is also evidence from stamped tin ingots in Cornwall that the Romans exploited the tin deposits on a commercial scale, although by the 4th or 3rd centuries B.C. the Cornish tin was being superseded by tin from the Spanish mines.

There is much less evidence for the extraction of other materials such as zircon and emery. Archaeological evidence for the use of loose sandy materials, such as emery or the 'red sand' garnet, would not easily be preserved except under very favourable conditions. However, Pliny refers to the use of sands from Naxos (emery) and from India (probably zircon) and other regions for working stone, so that by Roman times at least, emery and other hard sands were exploited as abrasives. Quartz, which is the most common and abundant component of sands, was also used for working stone.

Mining

Among the earliest known mines are the flint mines in western and central Europe, many of which are securely dated to the Neolithic period. At Grimes Graves in southern England, some of the shallow pits which are purely open workings of an outcrop of flint nodules are considered by some to be as early as late Palaeolithic in date. A few flint flakes of Palaeolithic type were found in these pit fillings but these might well be derived, so that the date of the chalk pits remains uncertain. There is indirect evidence for flint mining of some sort in the Palaeolithic, by the frequent use of flint nodules to manufacture implements. The shallow pits were excavated with picks of long bones, mostly of ox. They followed an outcrop of a bed of hard black flint nodules on the chalk slopes. The deeper mines at Grimes Graves are of Neolithic date. There are vertical shafts ranging from 10 to 14 metres deep, which open out into a wider bell-shaped chamber from which a number of short irregular galleries diverge in all directions. The shafts were cut with picks of deer antler. They are cut across beds of inferior grey flint and down to the bed of hard black flint which has excellent flaking properties. Similar mines are found at Spiennes in Belgium, and in other chalk regions of northern France, Belgium, and Scandinavia. In central Poland a brown banded variety of flint was widely traded throughout the late Palaeolithic. It seems probable that flint was already mined at this period, but definite mining evidence is first known from Swiderian (Mesolithic) times, and continues into the Neolithic.

In the Metal Ages metallic ores were mined extensively in all parts of the Old World where they could be found near the surface. Mines are essentially of two types: opencast works and subterranean gallery mines. Where opencast working was possible, this was generally preferred, and the increase in deep mining in the late Bronze Age and later periods is probably largely a result of the exhaustion of the surface deposits and the increasing demand for metal.

The opencast copper mines of Alderley Edge in Cheshire are the earliest known in Britain and are considered to be early

Bronze Age in date. The ore deposit has permeated a soft sandstone by the upward movement of copper-bearing solutions. In the surface rock, malachite and chrysocolla are the most common ores. The ore was obtained from irregular pits and trenches from 4 to 5 metres deep but no galleries were driven into the rock. There is no evidence for the use of metal tools, and sandstone was probably loosened by driving wooden wedges into joints and bedding fissures of the rock. Fire-setting (breaking up of the rock by fire and then cooling it with water) is not likely to have been necessary in as soft and porous a rock as the Keuper sandstone of Alderley Edge. The lumps of rock were broken with hammers of tough hard schist to separate the ore from the gangue and the ore was again pounded in the vicinity of the mine before smelting.

When necessary, gallery mines were driven far into the rock to follow the ore-bearing veins. Horizontal or slightly sloping passages (adits) were driven into the mountain side, for vertical shafts raise serious problems of haulage and ventilation and seem to have been avoided, particularly in the prehistoric periods. The Mitterberg mines in the Tyrol may serve as an example of deep horizontal mines for copper ore. Although a small outcrop of oxidized copper ores occurs in the vicinity of the mines the galleries follow an outcrop of copper pyrites in quartz, and the more easily smelted ores have apparently not been exploited. The Mitterberg mines were started as opencast workings in the mountains and the galleries follow the ore lode into the mountain side at a gentle slope for a depth of more than 100 metres. The mining techniques of Mitterberg have been reconstructed in detail by Pittioni (1951). The galleries are fairly high and it seems certain that fire-setting was used extensively to work the hard quartz vein. Considerable amounts of timber must have been required for the mining operations, for timber was also used very extensively in the galleries. Long wooden platforms were constructed on which the waste could be dumped, thus leaving a low passage for the miners below the platform. This technique greatly reduced the work of haulage of rock waste and it also ensured the thorough ventilation of the mine through the space left between the gallery roof and the dump. This ventilation was essential if fires had to be lit at the face.

The ore was pounded and sorted from the quartz gangue near the mines but most of the smelting was carried out in the valleys, possibly because all the available wood in the vicinity of the mine had to be reserved for the mining operations.

In later, more centralized societies, the inexhaustible supply of slave labour made deep mining operations feasible on a much larger scale. With the increasing demand for metals in the late Bronze and Iron Ages deeper ore bodies had to be exploited, particularly for copper, silver, and gold. Iron mines were also worked more extensively, but superficial deposits of iron ores are much more widespread than those of the other metals of antiquity. In the deep mines, haulage and ventilation problems are more complicated, and there is ample evidence from Greece and from Rome that mining became a highly organized and skilled industry, in which specialist 'engineers' were employed as well as large numbers of unskilled labour, mostly slaves.

The change from small opencast workings to complex deep mines is clearly seen in the Laurium region of Attica which became the principal source of silver for Athens. The ores are argentiferous galena, usually associated with hematite and pyrite, and also zinc blende and cerussite. The ore veins are of hydrothermal origin and have permeated an intensely metamorphosed sequence of deposits which are also crossed by minor folds and faults. The country rock consists of three beds of altered limestone, the lower two of crystalline marble, interstratified by mica schist. The ore has been deposited almost entirely along the contact zones between the marbles and the schists. Where the schist lies above marble, the iron ore has permeated the schist which has a fissile structure; but at the upper contact-zone of marble on schist the ore deposits are poorer, since the metalliferous water could be forced upwards through joints and fissures of the limestone into the upper schist (Figure 30).

On the mountain slopes, the contact-zones between the upper two limestones and the schists are exposed to various extent and many irregular opencast workings, probably of Middle or Early

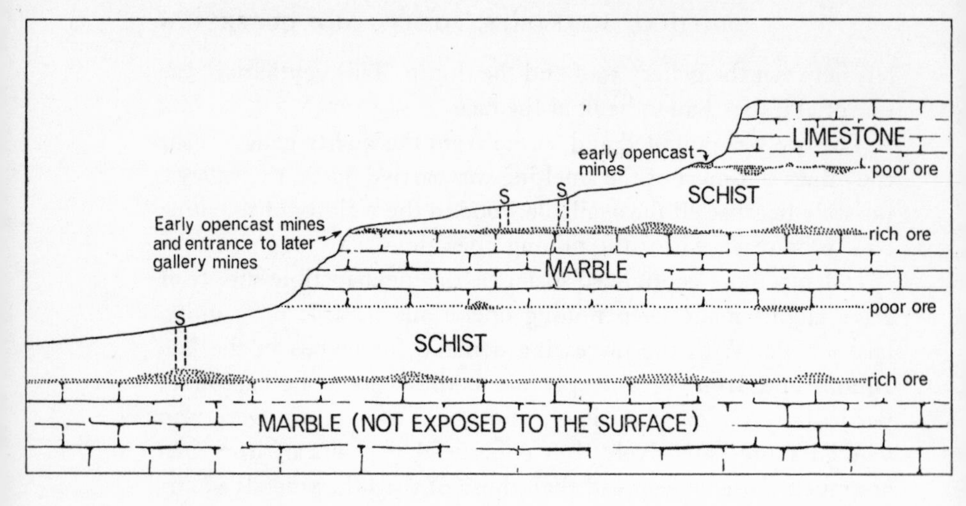

Figure 30 Diagrammatic section through the ore deposit at Laurium (after E. Ardaillon, 1897). S = shaft

Bronze Age times, are found in these lodes. The lower, and the richest, deposit between the lower schist and lowest marble is only exposed in one locality and was not known to the early miners of the region. In classical Greek times the mining operations were greatly extended and long, extremely narrow, galleries were cut into the mountain with iron tools (hammer, chisel, and pick). The galleries follow the irregular slope of the schist/limestone contact-zone until a rich ore deposit was encountered. Only then was the gallery enlarged to extract the concentrated ore, leaving pillars of poor ore where necessary, or building supports of rock rubble to support the roof of the chamber so excavated. Vertical shafts were sunk to meet the underground galleries, so that the ore could be hauled up on a rope and basket, and especially to ensure some ventilation. Elaborate systems of shafts and chimneys had to be cut into barren rock to ensure the air circulation in the mines. The vertical shafts also seem to have been used as entrances and exits into the mines, for ledges are left at regular intervals on which ladders could be rested.

It seems quite certain that the geological relationship between ore and country rock was fully appreciated by the miners, for although many exploratory galleries exist, none of these were driven randomly into solid rock, but they always follow the interface of schist and limestone. Further evidence for this lies in the exploitation of the lowest ore deposit, which they could not have followed from the surface. However, vertical exploratory shafts were sunk from the surface in both the upper and lower schist. In each case an interface with limestone was reached which could be explored for argentiferous galena and usually it yielded rich ore. It is unlikely that the miners realized the full complexity of the geological succession, or that they were aware that the two ore-bearing strata were not one and the same, for the nearby deposits of the Ocha mountains in Euboea which have a very similar geological structure were not tested in this way.

Quarrying

In mining operations the rock is broken up into irregular fragments of varying sizes in order to extract the ore or other minerals, such as precious stones. A variety of methods were employed to break up the rock, by taking full advantage of any weakness of structure such as faults, joints, and bedding, or by fire-setting. In quarrying, however, the manner in which the rock breaks must be carefully controlled if blocks of stone of the required size are to be obtained. Natural planes of weakness of the rock such as joints and other fissures cannot be used at random, and methods such as fire-setting in which the manner of fracture is completely controlled can be used only to a limited extent. When very large blocks are required for statuary or monumental masonry, the rock has to be cut out of the quarry face, and it is generally considered that large-scale quarrying for building purposes could not have been attempted without metal tools. Small-scale quarries to obtain blocks of rock suitable for the manufacture of stone tools such as axes and knives are known from a Neolithic context, for instance in Wales. Several prehistoric axe factories have been identified in Britain, and in most cases the axes were made from the loose scree blocks on the mountain slopes, but at one of the factories at least, at Mynydd

Rhiw in North Wales, the rock was quarried directly from its outcrop (a narrow zone of schist produced by the contact metamorphism of shale by intrusive dolerites). The method of extraction is similar to that of primitive opencast mining: by hammering and wedging out small blocks. The overburden of soft unaltered shale was removed to facilitate access to the seam as work progressed and where the thickness of shale became too great, the quarry was abandoned and a new working started near by.

Before the advent of metal tools, naturally occurring blocks and boulders were worked with stone tools and sand abrasives, not only for comparatively small objects such as vessels and statuettes and so on, but also for the earliest stone monuments. The European stone megaliths are built of naturally occurring blocks which are sometimes roughly dressed to the required shape.

The earliest stone masonry, and therefore systematic quarrying, is known from Egypt already in the Archaic period. Throughout Dynastic Egypt naturally occurring boulders, particularly of the hard rocks such as granite, were dressed and used in masonry but the building stones were mostly obtained by quarrying. Different methods were used for the soft sedimentary rocks, limestones and sandstone, and for the much harder and tougher igneous rocks, granite and basalt. Even the extremely hard quartzites of the Aswan region were quarried.

Some of the earliest and most extensively worked quarries are the limestone quarries at Tusa and Ma'sara. At Ma'sara the stratum of good building stone occurs at some depth underground and nearly horizontal tunnels have been cut into the cliff face to reach the required limestone bed. The tunnels rise slowly up to the quarry face, presumably to facilitate the transport of the blocks. The face was always kept perfectly vertical, and blocks of rock were removed first by cutting and hammering out a recess near the roof about half a metre high and of the same width as the blocks to be removed. On this shelf a man could squat to cut narrow trenches 10 to 12 cm wide along the three vertical sides of the block. The base of the block was then detached by inserting wedges, either metal wedges which were hammered in, or wooden wedges which could be made to exert pressure by wetting the wood. The next block could then be removed directly below the first in the same manner, until the ground level of the quarry was reached, when the whole process is repeated. In the Ma'sara quarries, faces up to 20 feet (6 metres) high were worked in this way. But in open-air quarries, where the surface of the rock was quarried, vertical faces of 40 feet (12 to 13 metres) or more are left, and the quarry floor shows a step-like structure from which the blocks have been removed. Sandstones were quarried in the same way and wherever possible, as at the famous site of Silsila, full advantage was taken of the natural horizontal bedding and vertical jointing of the rock.

The rock was cut with a copper chisel struck with a wooden mallet, and the chisels must have needed frequent resharpening. The tool marks left on the rock face show rows of sloping grooves, or commonly, as in the limestone quarry of Beni Hasan, distinctly curved lines. This has led to the supposition that picks must have been used to cut the narrow separating trenches, although there are no known examples of copper picks in the archaeological record.

Hard rocks, such as granite and especially quartzite, could not be quarried in the same way. It is still open to question whether copper tools were used on these hard rocks, but it seems unlikely since a copper chisel would quickly be blunted even if it could make any appreciable mark on the rock at all. It is certain that most of the work, if not all, was done with stone tools. By hitting the granite repeatedly with short sharp blows of a hammer made from a tougher rock, the granite surface is bruised and small flakes removed. In this way deep trenches can be cut simply by hammering with a tough stone, for instance of diorite, as used in the granite quarries at Aswan.

The methods of extracting blocks of hard rock are most clearly seen in some of the quarries where for one reason or another the work was abandoned before completion, as for instance the obelisk quarry of Aswan. The partially weathered surface rock was broken up by fire-setting, and the crumbly burnt granite removed and pounded until a flat surface of fresh sound rock was prepared. To obtain large flawless blocks, as for the Egyptian monuments, the surface rock had to be removed to a considerable depth. The outline of the block was then marked by shallow grooves and red and black paint, and any cracks or fissures in the rock were carefully explored by pounding out small trenches to ascertain how deep the fissures penetrated. At Aswan the original size of the proposed monument was modified at least three times to avoid dangerous fissures which would have caused the block to crack on lifting. A separating trench was cut all round the proposed obelisk, 70 to 75 cm wide, and at least twice as deep. This was done by pounding with dolerite balls, removing a thin layer of rock a few centimetres thick at a time. The work was done so regularly that the side of the trench shows a regular corrugated surface, each groove corresponding to the width of rock cut with a dolerite ball (Pl. 22). Very large blocks like the Aswan obelisk could not be undercut by wedging, for the differential stresses set up in the block would greatly increase the risk of cracking. The Aswan block seems to have been abandoned soon after the work of undercutting was begun, but it seems that this was also carried out by hammering tunnels underneath the monument, in what must have been exceedingly cramped positions. The undercut tunnels were probably filled with stacks of rubble to hold the block in position, while the intervening rock was also removed.

There is much less detailed information about quarrying procedures from other regions, although quarries are known from Greece, Italy, and other countries, particularly from the later Roman period. With the advent of iron tools, stone cutting became considerably less laborious. Hardened iron can be used on rocks to great advantage and from Roman quarry marks, and pictorial representations, it is clear that a variety of specialized iron tools were used by quarry men. In particular they used a heavy pick-axe with a broad cutting edge as well as hatchets, wedges, and presumably hammers. The rock was quarried in blocks of the approximate size and shape required, usually from open-air workings, but underground quarries are also known, for instance the tufa quarries of the Grotta Oscura near Rome.

From classical Greece, much less is known of the quarrying techniques, but from the marks left on abandoned quarries, it is clear that blocks were also removed in approximately the size and shape required. When large blocks were needed they were first separated from the living rock by a vertical trench on all sides and finally detached, probably by wedging.

Conclusions

The discussion in Chapters 6 and 7 of the various artefacts in antiquity shows that rocks and minerals have been used as raw materials in many different fields of human technology since the beginning of prehistory. 'Stones' of many types were used for the manufacture of tools, weapons, vessels, ornaments, etc. and for building purposes, and other minerals were used as raw materials for the preparation of new substances, such as metals, pottery, glass, etc. For certain purposes the materials used were often carefully selected to take advantage of the properties of different rocks, minerals or metals. To a certain extent the availability of rocks limited the choice of raw materials in any locality, but this limitation was frequently overcome by trade or travel.

In the Palaeolithic, when a comparatively limited variety of tool types were made, usually requiring hard and sharp edges, siliceous rocks were most commonly exploited; but for other purposes, such as for pigments, or for carving small figures, soft rocks were used. Since most of the materials used in the Palaeolithic are fairly widespread, they could generally be obtained locally, and when good flaking rocks were not available, others with similar properties were often substituted. However, already at this early period there is evidence for at least some trade or travel to obtain flint and shell.

During Neolithic times, the increased range of tools used led to new and more specialized requirements in raw materials, such as tough rocks for making celts, and clay and rocks for building. Many new rocks and minerals were sought and used, and the range of mineral materials found even on early sites such as Jericho in Palestine, or Nea Nikomedeia in Greece, exceeds that found at any Palaeolithic site. It is also during this period that the properties of many naturally occurring minerals were first deliberately altered to make new materials such as pottery and plaster. At the 'Neolithic' sites of Hacilar and Chatal Huyuk in central Anatolia, the range of rocks and minerals exploited is particularly wide for cultures of such early date. At these sites many of the 'new' rocks and minerals were used for ornament or small sculptures, and some of the 'old' materials were put to new uses, such as cones of obsidian with a polished base, which may have been the first mirrors. The exploration and exploitation of new materials led necessarily to the development of new techniques of working stone and to the development of mining and quarrying. The use of new materials, some of which are of fairly restricted occurrence may, in part, account for the increase in trade which took place during this period. Reliance on local mineral resources was often supplemented, or even superseded, by imports of more suitable rock as, for example, the spread of obsidian from localized sources throughout much of the Mediterranean region where previously flint or chert had been used.

The discovery of smelting processes, long after native metals had been known and used on a very small scale, made available an entirely new range of materials which could be applied to many of the varied uses of stone. The discovery of metals opened up an entirely new field of technology and in many instances, especially after the discovery of iron, metals entirely displaced the earlier stone tools and weapons. The new technological possibilities of metals were, perhaps, most dramatically displayed in the design and development of weapons, but indirectly the use of metal tools also affected the technology of earlier crafts, such as the working of wood and stone.

CHAPTER EIGHT

The Identification and Dating of Rocks and Minerals in Archaeology

THE study of rocks has two important uses in archaeology besides that of gaining a better understanding of ancient technology: one is the identification of imported materials and the other is the application of dating techniques to certain rocks and to pottery. The analysis of imported materials and the identification of their sources is one of the main forms of evidence for ancient trade and exploration.

The identification required, both for the application of dating techniques and for tracing the source of imported materials, is far more detailed than can be obtained by the macroscopic methods outlined in the previous chapters. However, unless archaeologists are able to assess the likelihood of various materials being either imports or locally obtained, they may not be able to select the most suitable samples to take full advantages of the possibilities offered by petrological techniques. With the knowledge necessary to identify the type of rocks found in archaeological contexts, and some knowledge of the geology of the region under investigation, suitable samples may be selected for detailed analysis. Similarly, an understanding of the principles involved in dating techniques will enable archaeologists to select suitable material for dating and also help to assess the significance of any date obtained.

Except for techniques which deal specifically with patina, such as the dating of obsidian artefacts, any detailed work on materials used in antiquity must be done on fresh material. The processes of patination alter the nature of the material to a greater or lesser extent and may affect both the composition and the structure of the material. Even to arrive at an accurate macroscopic identification of a rock, it is usually necessary to examine it on a fresh break. This however, is, often impracticable when dealing with ancient artefacts and preliminary identifications often have to be made from an examination of a patinated surface. With some knowledge of the types of patina which may form on different materials under different conditions, it is frequently possible to arrive at an approximate identification and in many instances such approximate identification is sufficient to assess the significance of the material in question. It is therefore important to consider some of the processes of weathering and corrosion on the various materials used in antiquity.

Patination and Corrosion

The type of corrosion, and the depth to which corrosion has penetrated, depends on the surroundings in which the object has been preserved. The processes of corrosion are the same as those which, in time, result in the decay of rocks and their conversion to sediments and soils. However, for many ancient artefacts the time elapsed since they were discarded is considerably shorter than the time involved in the formation of soils and sediments from fresh rock. Palaeolithic objects may be as much as 1 million years old and on these early objects patination may be very intense, even on resistant rocks.

The decay processes result from mechanical forces, chemical reactions, and the action of bacteria and other organisms. The effect of organisms is largely chemical, and usually results in corrosion through the liberation of acids. The penetration of vegetation, and particularly of plant and tree roots, also has considerable physical effects, particularly in the disintegration of buildings and other structures.

Monuments which do not become buried beneath soils, sediments, or habitation debris, are subjected to weathering by changes in temperature and humidity in the atmosphere and by the effects of wind erosion. Wind erosion is most marked in arid regions where the soil is not protected by a layer of vegetation.

Sand and silt particles of such desert soils are picked up by the wind and have a strong eroding effect. This is very characteristically seen on many of the Egyptian desert monuments. Wind erosion does, however, also occur in more humid regions, but there its effect may be partly or entirely masked by the effects of rain and/or frost.

In regions where the minimum winter temperatures fall below 0°C, frost weathering is likely to occur. The intensity of such weathering on ancient monuments depends on the porosity of the building materials and the moisture available, as well as on the frequency of alternate freezing and thawing.

Pure rain water does not have an appreciable eroding effect, but since all rain water is slightly acidified by solution of atmospheric carbon dioxide, it does have a very slight corrosive effect on building materials. Soluble minerals, such as sodium or potassium minerals and gypsum, are easily dissolved and rocks or mortars which contain these materials may be very corroded by the action of rain water. Calcareous rocks are also corroded by acidified rain water, but on compact and crystalline rocks the process only occurs on the exposed surfaces and is extremely slow. Calcareous sediments, such as sandstones, are more rapidly disintegrated by rain water than many pure limestones, since their porosity is often considerably higher. As the cementing medium of a calcareous sandstone is corroded, the sand particles are loosened and the rock becomes friable. In igneous and metamorphic rocks the mafic silicates may be slightly corroded by rain water but siliceous minerals, especially quartz, are extremely resistant to acid corrosion.

The principal disintegrating effect of rain water, however, is not directly through corrosion. The decay is largely caused by alternate periods of rain and drought. During a period of drought following rain, the moisture in the building materials evaporates from the exposed surface of the building stones. This causes the recrystallization of the salts formed through corrosion. Such recrystallization occurs mostly near the surface of the stones and results in the mechanical disintegration of the exposed surface of building stones or other material. Even non-calcareous rocks which are very resistant to corrosion may be affected by this type of decay, especially if they are used in conjunction with other calcareous rocks, or with mortar or plaster.[1]

Many ancient monuments have suffered much decay and collapse simply through structural faults or through the uneven, sinking of foundations, not due to the environmental effects of mechanical, chemical, or other decay.

Objects which are preserved in water, in a river, or on a beach, are rolled and abraded, depending on their size, hardness, and specific gravity, in the same way as any other pebble. On a beach the battering action is so strong that even hard rocks are rapidly rounded and abraded and all evidence of a stone being an artefact may be destroyed. In a river the process of abrasion is generally much slower. Projecting features are rounded, whereas re-entrant facets may remain quite fresh. If the river is rapid or turbulent, the abraded edges may be rough and battered (Pl. 23b); but in slow moving water the abrasion results principally from the movement of small sand grains or silt grains and the abraded edges may be highly polished.

Objects which are lost on the sea floor, as in the case of many shipwrecks in the Mediterranean sea, may be entirely protected from rolling and battering. Such objects may be deeply encrusted in marine organisms and some organisms have a slight corrosive action on rocks. The permeation by sea water, however, may have much more serious effects on the preservation of shipwrecked objects than corrosion by marine animals. Once the objects have been recovered from the sea floor and are dried out, the evaporation of sea water causes crystallization of the salts in the rock pores or in the pottery or other material, and this generally results in the mechanical disintegration of the material. Salt infestation of this type is particularly destructive on porous materials such as pottery, but it also affects materials of low porosity (cf. Plate 25).

When metals are corroded by salt water, some of the metal

[1] On buildings which are in or near present-day towns or industrial centres, the decay process, though basically similar, may be more complex; for in such areas rain water also contains sulphur compounds which are highly corrosive.

itself is attacked by the chloride ions of sodium chloride and other salts of sea water. The copper in copper and bronze objects becomes altered to copper chloride, silver to silver chloride, and iron to iron chloride. This chemical alteration normally starts from the surface and gradually penetrates deeper into the metal as the newly-formed salts flake off.

The corrosion of buried objects depends on the soil conditions, especially on soil humidity and acidity, and in tropical regions also on the high soil temperatures.

In temperate humid regions the decay of different materials varies largely with the soil acidity. All the soluble substances, such as sodium or potassium compounds, are rapidly dissolved and leached out. In acid soils (i.e. non-calcareous soils), calcareous substances may be very heavily corroded or even entirely decomposed and leached out. Mafic silicates are slowly disintegrated by soil acids and broken down into sodium, calcium, and magnesium salts, iron oxides and colloidal silica. The salts of sodium, potassium, and magnesium which are soluble are leached out of the corroding rock quite rapidly, and this may leave it enriched with iron oxides which generally impart a characteristic ochre coloration, yellow, brown, or red, depending on the soil humidity and temperature. Silica is relatively insoluble at normal soil temperatures and is leached out only very slowly.

In very acid soils, such as sandy heath soils and many peaty soils, the iron oxides may also be leached and only crystalline silica remains in a fresh condition.

In calcareous soils, corrosion is much less intense and objects buried in such soils are normally much better preserved than those buried in acid soils. Colloidal silica, however, is corroded by alkalis and substances such as flint or glass, which are well preserved in acid soils, may be heavily patinated under calcareous conditions.

Under tropical/humid conditions, soil temperatures may average as much as 40°C and chemical decay is much intensified. The relative solubilities of iron oxides and silica, however, become reversed. Thus, whereas under temperate conditions iron oxides are leached out in acid soils and silica is very slightly affected, at high temperatures silica becomes more soluble than iron oxide and is therefore leached out of rocks more rapidly. This results in the rapid decay even of siliceous rocks which may be left with a thick patina of iron oxide. At high soil temperatures during periods of drought, these often become dehydrated to the red hematitic form.

Under arid or semi-arid conditions, chemical disintegration is slow, even in hot deserts. The movement of ground water in the soil is mostly upwards through evaporation at the soil surface, so that soluble salts are not leached out of the soil, but reprecipitated near its surface. Any objects buried under such conditions are likely to be salt-infested in the same way as objects recovered from sea water (Pl. 25). The salts of desert soils, however, are principally carbonates and sulphates of sodium and calcium.

In very arid soils when potassium is available, even the very soluble salt saltpetre may be formed on the soil surface and also in porous buried antiquities.

Under exceptional conditions of complete aridity, as in the pyramids of the Egyptian desert, neither chemical nor bacterial decay can take place and the preservation of antiquities may be extremely good, so that even many organic materials are well preserved. In the waterlogged conditions of some peaty soils, as in many of the Danish bogs, bacterial activity may also be impeded and some organic remains may be exceptionally well preserved; even soft human tissues, parts of clothing and leather have often been found with burials.

Some Common Forms of Patina on Antiquities

The decay of stone objects, pottery, and similar materials normally begins from the surface and gradually penetrates into the body of the material. The rate at which this happens is extremely difficult to determine, since it depends on many independently variable factors. The depth of patination, therefore, cannot normally be used to estimate the age of an ancient artefact. However, when objects of the same or closely similar material, such as flint and chert, are found together in the same type of deposit and show *markedly* different depths of patination, it may sometimes be possible to conclude that objects from distinct periods have become mixed within a single deposit. The separation of groups of implements on the basis of their different degree of patination has sometimes been possible when dealing with Palaeolithic assemblages of different dates. With later assemblages, however, the differences in patination are rarely sufficiently great to be used in this way.

A striking example of differences in patina comes from the handaxe industries of Southern India. Quartzite handaxes of very similar type, with a deep red patina, a deep yellow patina, and a slight grey patina respectively, can easily be distinguished; they belong to three separate phases of the handaxe culture, during which climatic conditions changed considerably. A more classic example comes from the famous site of Chelles on the river Somme in northern France, where two early phases of the handaxe culture were first recognized (Pl. 23). By separating the rolled and abraded handaxes from the fresh, unabraded tools in the same gravel deposit, it became possible to isolate the early 'Chellean' phase from the later 'Acheulean' phase of the handaxe culture. This separation subsequently proved to be correct by the discovery of unabraded 'Chellean' tools in very early gravels at Abbeville on the same river.[2]

Flint, chert, and other siliceous rocks: Colloidal silica is more readily soluble than the crystalline form, so that in any rock which contains both, such as flint, chert, etc. weathering proceeds by the leaching of the colloidal silica, leaving a porous structure of cryptocrystalline silica. This layer of cryptocrystalline silica looks white, due to the reflection of light on numerous randomly orientated crystal facets. However, since it is porous, the patina of flint, chert, and similar rocks is easily stained by other substance in solution in the soil. When the layer of patination is thin, it may be partly transparent or translucent and the colour of the fresh flint beneath it may then impart a greyish or bluish tint to the patina.

[2] The Chellean phase is now more correctly referred to as Abbevillian, although it is, in fact, an early phase of the Acheulean.

Sandstones cemented with silica, or other silica-indurated rocks, weather in a similar manner; but if the silica is a cementing medium, its solution leaves the grains of the original sediment non-consolidated and the surface of the rock becomes friable. Quartzites are extremely resistant to weathering, but patination develops in the same manner as on other siliceous rocks.

Desert gloss is a highly lustrous patina which sometimes forms on flint, chert, or other siliceous implements in hot semi-arid regions. The gloss which forms on the surface of the implements is a thin coat of pure colloidal silica. It results from solution of the colloidal silica by hot water during the rare wet periods and its redeposition on the surface of the implement when the moisture evaporates. A similar patina forms on siliceous rocks in hot springs. The gloss from a hot spring can sometimes be distinguished from desert gloss, since in a spring the entire surface of the implement may be corroded through solution and the shape of the implement becomes less sharply distinguishable.

A narrow zone of glossy patina is commonly formed on the cutting edge of blades used as sickles. This not a true patina, but results from wear through use of the implement. Grasses have tough stalks which contain a higher amount of siliceous material than most plants. Through repeated cutting of such tough and hard material, the edge of the sickle blades becomes very highly polished. In fact this glossy surface on the cutting edge of blades has often been taken as proof that the blades were in fact used as sickles; but, of course, it gives no indication that the grasses cut were domesticated and not wild.

Another form of patina which is not uncommonly found on siliceous pebbles or stones is due to their use as pot boilers. By heating in a fire and throwing into cold liquid, the stones are subjected to sudden changes in temperature which results in a distinct crazing of the surface. If the stone contains even very small amounts of iron oxides as impurities, they become dehydrated during the heating process and such stones then acquire a deep red or red-brown coloration. In rare instances a thin, grey lustrous film is also formed on the surface of siliceous pot boilers. This probably results from the presence of alkalis in the fire, from plant ashes and lime, which partially fuse with silica and form a glaze.

Non-crystalline rocks, such as flint and chert, which are subjected to frost often fracture in distinctive ways known as *potlid fracture* and *starch fracture*.

Potlids are roughly circular fragments of flint which split off due to contraction and expansion of the material. The scar left by a potlid fracture is a shallow round depression. It can be distinguished from a flake scar on a flint artefact by the absence of distinguishing features such as the bulb of percussion, ripple marks, etc., and by the fact that the deepest part of the depression is not near a suitable edge from which a flake could have been struck. Starch fracture, also referred to as columnar fracture, is less common than potlid fracturing, but the process is very similar, except that the fragments are elongated. Starch fractured flint forms elongated fragments, on which the scars are roughly parallel to the length of the fragment. The occurrence of potlid fractures on flint, chert, or similar implements is evidence that they were subjected to severe frost or heat.

Igneous and metamorphic rocks: Differential weathering of the mineral grains in igneous and metamorphic rocks results in the formation of an uneven surface and, if weathering of the mafic minerals and felspars is intense, the rock surface may disintegrate and become friable. The patina formed on such rocks depends both on the composition of the rocks and the grain size. In general, an outer zone of patina forms which is enriched in the siliceous minerals and in the less soluble products of weathering of the mafic minerals. If the iron salts are not leached out, such a patina may be coloured brown or red-brown. On implements which have weathered in very acid soils, the iron salts are often leached out of the surface zone of patination, which is then generally white or greyish. In peaty soils rich in humus, this zone may be stained with organic matter which is generally very dark brown or black. Beneath the outer bleached zone of patina, there may be a second iron-coloured zone which grades into unaltered rock (Pl. 24). On implements which have weathered under tropical soil conditions, the layer of patina is enriched in dehydrated iron oxides and impoverished in silica, generally resulting in fairly friable and highly-coloured patination.

Glass and Glazes: Since glass and glazes are highly siliceous materials, their corrosion is more intense in alkali soils than in acid soils. The rate at which glasses and glazes decay depends to a certain extent on the flux used to fuse the silica: potassium and sodium are easily leached out and potash or sodium glasses are relatively unstable. Calcium and lead glasses also decay through the removal of the metal ions, leaving a surface layer of more or less pure amorphous silica. The patina on glass usually forms thin but distinct layers of silica which peel off easily. When these layers are slightly displaced, the patina appears iridescent through the multiple refraction of light; sometimes the patina is a dull silvery grey.

Metals: The corrosion of metal objects results in the formation of salts of the metal, which may be identical, both chemically and mineralogically to some of the ores from which the metals are smelted.

Gold is very resistant to corrosion and it is normally found unpatinated.

Silver commonly forms a thin film of black silver sulphide. In soils rich in chloride ions, a grey-brown layer of protective silver chloride is formed, which is dense and generally protects the underlying metal from further corrosion.

Copper corrosion products are very commonly carbonates, but copper oxide and chloride are also often formed. The copper oxide patina, Cu_2O, is the red oxide and this is often formed in a thin layer between the metal and the outer corrosion layer, or in narrow cracks and fissures, such as in welded joints. The green copper carbonate, malachite, is characteristic of many copper and bronze corrosion surfaces and under drier conditions, a blue copper carbonate, azurite, is formed. When chloride ions are present, copper and bronze may be very badly decayed, for chlorides react easily with copper. Copper chloride varies in colour from bright green to black, and on many copper and bronze objects both the carbonate and chloride corrosion are present. Chloride corrosion is known as 'bronze disease', for the presence of chloride on copper or bronze objects continues to be corrosive even out of the soil.

Tin was rarely used in its pure state in antiquity, but as a component of bronze it is fairly common. Tin is prone to corrosion into oxides and chlorides, and bronzes which are rich in tin may be covered in a patina of greyish tin oxide corrosion.

Lead corrosion forms the lead carbonate, cerussite, which is dark grey and forms a protective layer on the metal. Yellow, brown, and pink oxide patina is known and in the presence of chlorides, a complex chloride and carbonate salt is formed which is white and powdery.

Iron rust consists of various iron oxides and hydroxides which are identical in composition to limonitic forms of ochre. In less strongly oxidized soils the black oxide magnetite is also formed.

Rocks and Minerals as Evidence for Trade and Exploration

The identification of rocks and minerals in order to throw light on the foreign connections of ancient peoples is, perhaps, the most widely acknowledged use of petrology in archaeology. Most excavation reports contain a discussion of the possible contacts between the people concerned and neighbouring regions, and this is almost invariably based on two different procedures: influences in the style and techniques of manufacturing artefacts, and the occurrences of material imported into the locality. The petrological recognition of such imports is, therefore, an important aspect of archaeological work for, of the two approaches, it alone is not subjective. It requires both knowledge of the materials used in antiquity and of the mineral resources of the locality in question.

The study of imports may be considered in two stages: the first is the recognition of an object as an import, either on stylistic grounds or because of the material used (or both) – and this must usually be done by the archaeologist; the second stage is finding the source from which the material has been obtained – and this may require specialist analysis.

A macroscopic identification of any material used (as outlined in Chapters 1 to 5) is usually sufficient to assess whether it may have been obtained locally or not. Even in regions for which geological maps and memoirs are available, it is often necessary to be able to identify the locally occurring rock and mineral types, for details indicated on geological maps are insufficient for any but the most general work. In many areas, particularly outside Europe, detailed information on the local geology is not easily available in the form of maps and surveys. In such areas it is usually essential to carry out a brief survey of the local geology. A full survey of this sort requires the services of a geologist, but much valuable information can be obtained from less detailed and specialized work.

Clean outcrops of rock may be comparatively easy to find and identify macroscopically on a freshly-fractured sample. In many regions, however, the rocks are covered by a mantle of soil or by drift deposits, such as silt, sand, or gravel. When the drift deposit or soil is shallow, fragments of the underlying rock may be easy to find at small depth, particularly on slopes. When such deposits are very thick, and can be presumed to have been equally thick in the past, the underlying rock is not likely to have been available in antiquity. Although geological maps, particularly the drift maps, indicate the presence of deposits such as sands or gravels, the petrological nature of such deposits is not normally given. When looking for sources of materials, such as pebbles used for bead making or other small artefacts, it may be necessary to examine the contents of gravels closely. This should be done by splitting the pebbles, for the thick patina often found on pebbles in river gravels may completely mask both the colour and the texture. The examination of clays used for pottery cannot normally be done macroscopically, but the occurrence or absence of suitable clays can be determined.

In carrying out a survey of the type described above, it is important to examine topographical features; for these are sometimes, though by no means always, the result of differences in the underlying lithology. Hard rocks erode less rapidly than the softer rocks, so that marked differences of slope may arise at or near the contact between rocks of different type. Small igneous intrusions may stand out as isolated hills or ridges, and the rocks of sills or of lava flows are not uncommonly found capping flat-topped hills.

A knowledge of the most common occurrences of various rocks and minerals may save fruitless search for the source of certain materials. There is, for instance, no point in looking for flint in regions other than chalky country or deposits derived from chalk; obsidian, as shown on pp. 72 and 86, occurs only in regions of recent (Tertiary or Pleistocene) volcanic activity; amazonstone, which occurs most commonly in acid pegmatite veins, will not be found in basic rock formations, or in sediments other than those derived from acid rocks. However, it is impossible to give hard and fast rules for the occurrence of most rocks, for the local surface geology of any region is the result of geological history and, where old rocks are exposed, the geological structure may be extremely complex and the variety of surface rocks very great.

When an artefact is made out of a mineral or rock type which occurs locally, the archaeologist usually assumes that the material was obtained from the local source. Such an assumption may often be justified, unless the artefact can be shown on stylistic grounds to be imported. However, without petrological examination of both the material used and the presumed local source such an assumption cannot be verified. From Greek and Roman times it is known that the qualities of various rocks which are petrologically similar were closely considered. Thus when seeking materials such as marble, alabaster, or various forms of onyx, the nearest available sources were by no means always the ones exploited. Preferences for certain rock sources over others may well have existed in earlier times also, but only petrological examination could determine this. The common assumption that local sources were always the ones used presumes both that there were no preferences for specific sources, and that local resources were always known and exploited.

The identification of the exact source of an imported material usually requires much more detailed petrological work than that needed to recognize it as an import. It is not sufficient to determine macroscopically that an artefact has been made out of any one type of mineral or rock, for the same mineral and rock types occur in many widely separated regions. Some minerals, on the other hand, have a fairly restricted occurrence and for such minerals it may be comparatively easy to ascertain their source or origin. For example, lapis lazuli is only known to occur in few regions in western Asia. In early historic times the mineral was imported from these western Asiatic regions, so that it must be assumed that earlier imports of lapis lazuli were also from western Asia. In literate times, accounts of trading or travel expeditions often name or describe the source of imports: it is well known that the Egyptians sent special expeditions to Sinai to mine turquoise and copper ores. Sometimes, however, these literate sources are not very explicit, or the true interpretation of the rocks or localities referred to is not known. Stylistic analysis or literary allusion may often give the geographical area from which the materials may have been imported, but confirmation of this can only come from detailed scientific analysis.

For most rocks and minerals, analysis is carried out with the microscope to arrive at a fuller identification of the minerals and texture of the rock than can be achieved by macroscopic means. For some rocks, particularly glasses or very fine textured rocks in which minerals cannot be examined microscopically, it is usually necessary to determine the chemical composition when undertaking comparisons with possible source material. The examination of clays is also carried out either microscopically or by chemical means, depending largely on the coarseness of the clay. For metals however, microscopic analysis cannot yield any information with regard to the ores from which they were smelted. Work on the source of metals in antiquity is based very largely on chemical data.

The identification of the source of a rock is based on comparisons of the sample with examples of possible source material. Some rocks have more characteristic features for comparison than others. Igneous rocks can, theoretically, be matched with a high degree of accuracy from the comparison of mineral composition, including accessory minerals, texture and any alteration of the minerals. When dealing with very homogenous rocks such as quartzite or pure marbles, it may be much more difficult to find diagnostic differences between the same rock types from different sources. Sedimentary rocks such as pure sandstones or limestones may also be more difficult to match accurately than igneous rocks, but less pure sediments may have very characteristic mineral assemblages, texture, cementing medium, and other features.

The exact composition and structure of a rock is not always constant over large areas. For instance, the grain-size of igneous intrusions may be markedly coarser near the centre of such an intrusion than near its perimeter. The mineral composition of intrusions such as dykes has occasionally been found to vary with depth, for the first minerals to crystallize out, usually the mafic minerals, tend to sink in the unconsolidated magma, so that the lower portions of such structures may be more basic than their upper limits. Sedimentary rocks may also vary over quite small distances and over small thicknesses due to irregularities in the conditions of sedimentation. The identification of the source of single mineral artefacts may be much more difficult than for rocks. A pure quartz crystal from any particular locality cannot be distinguished from quartz from any other locality. Sometimes minor differences in composition of individual minerals may be diagnostic of any one source, but generally such material does not lend itself so well to source identification as whole rock samples.

For the microscopic examination of a rock used to make an artefact a small piece, generally of the order of $\frac{1}{2}$ cm thick and 1 sq. cm in area, has to be cut out. For fine-grained rocks it may be possible to work from smaller samples, but in very coarse-grained rocks larger samples may be necessary to obtain a representative piece. In all cases the thin section examined must include a representative sample of the unweathered part of the rock. By grinding a very thin slice mounted on a glass slide, the rock can be cut to a thickness of only 20 to 30 microns (1 micron = 0·001 cm) and on such a thin section the optical properties of the minerals are examined. In this way the identification of the rock can be extended beyond the identification obtained macroscopically.

For igneous rocks, the position of a rock within the types defined on pp. 70–6 can be determined from an accurate identification of the felspars and an estimation of the relative amounts of the essential minerals. Pyroxenes and hornblendes can easily be distinguished, and the accurate position of pyroxenes, hornblendes, and micas within their respective mineral classes can be determined. The identification of accessory minerals may help to distinguish two rocks which have the same composition of essential minerals and, therefore, have the same classificatory nomenclature. Accessory minerals may also distinguish different facies of the same rock. For instance, the presence of tourmaline in a rock identified as a granite from Dartmoor would suggest that the sample in question is more likely to have been obtained from near the periphery of the Dartmoor granite intrusion than from near its centre. The grain-size and habit of rock minerals may also distinguish different facies of the same rock. The possibility that differences of accessory minerals or grain-sizes might represent different facies of the same rock rather than different rocks can only be confirmed by closer inspection of the source rock. The degree to which minerals have been altered, such as the serpentinization of olivines, the alteration of felspars to sericite, etc. are useful criteria by which to distinguish rocks of the same nomenclature and grain-size.

In the microscopic examination of sedimentary rocks, the procedure of identification is similar to that used for igneous rocks. Both the grain-size and the mineral composition are considered in the nomenclature of these rocks. Differences between rocks of the same nomenclature occur in the shape of the rock grains and in the degree of cementation and of any alteration of the rock. The identification of minerals which occur in small quantities may then be useful in distinguishing rocks which are otherwise similar.

The potentialities of such rock analyses are, perhaps, best illustrated by the petrological survey of celts in Britain and Brittany, already discussed in Chapter 6. It will be seen that in several instances the sources of rocks of similar type and nomenclature have been identified in various parts of the country, but the large number of axes in the survey which are still ungrouped illustrates the difficulty of finding exact sources.

The technique for identifying the sources of clay used for making pottery is similar to that used for identifying rocks, since clay is in fact an unconsolidated sedimentary rock. A thin slice of the pottery can be prepared by impregnating a piece of pottery in a suitable resin before grinding. The samples used are generally of the same size as for rocks, but similar samples are often sufficient, unless the grit in the pottery is very coarse. The clay minerals are too small to be seen even under high power with a petrological microscope. For the purpose of source studies, microscopic analysis of the pottery is confined to the identification of particles of sand size. In some cases this coarse material has been deliberately added to the clay to facilitate firing (see p. 175). Deliberately added temper of crushed rock fragments can be distinguished from naturally weathered rock and mineral fragments by their much sharper outlines and uncorroded surfaces. If a natural sand has been added, it may be sharply differentiated, both in range of grain-sizes and in mineral composition, from small quantities of the silt and/or sand which occur naturally in the clay (Pl. 26). If the grit particles in the clay are unabraded, whether fresh or corroded, it may be assumed that the clay is the residual weathering product of a rock *in situ*. From the identification of the minerals and rock fragments it is often possible to judge the type of rock from which the minerals have weathered and this, in turn, may indicate possible sources for the clay, or at least exclude impossible sources. If the grit particles consist of abraded mineral and/or rock grains, the clay is likely to be a sediment, such as an alluvial deposit.

To examine very fine-textured pottery, it may be necessary to identify the type of clay minerals present. This can be done by

X-ray diffraction for the crystalline clays. A small, finely powdered sample of the clay is irradiated with X-rays and the diffraction of the rays is recorded photographically. The X-ray diffraction pattern obtained for any crystalline mineral is characteristic of the crystal form, and X-ray diffraction analysis has proved particularly useful for the identification of pure clays, as used in the preparation of slips on the finer Greek and Roman wares. When a composite clay is examined by X-ray diffraction, a composite pattern is obtained which includes patterns of all the different crystal forms present. The disentanglement of such patterns may prove extremely difficult unless good comparative data are available. In a composite clay, the relative intensities of the patterns for individual minerals give an approximate estimate of the amounts present. The exact quantitative analysis of clays cannot be carried out by X-ray diffraction, but for comparative purposes approximate quantitative results are valuable, at least in eliminating dissimilar materials.

Fine-textured pottery can also be examined chemically. A chemical analysis does not identify the minerals present, but for comparative purposes the identification of clays, or other materials, with the same chemical composition may be extremely useful. The chemical analyses are usually carried out spectrometrically, for 'wet' analysis can be extremely laborious and tedious. For spectrometric analysis a small, finely-ground sample of the clay is vaporized by passing a strong electric current through it, and the light emitted is analysed with a spectroscope (essentially a prism which splits the light into various colour components). Each element emits light of a characteristic colour. Thus, by analysing the light emitted by a sample its chemical composition may be deduced. The relative intensities of the light bands emitted are a measure of the quantities of the elements present. The accurate quantitative analysis of clays by spectrometry is a very tedious procedure. Approximate quantitative analysis in combination with other tests such as X-ray diffraction may often be sufficient for practical purposes.

The interpretation of comparisons between the chemical composition of clay artefacts and possible source material is often difficult. If the artefact is of fired clay, certain chemical changes which result from firing must be taken into account. Organic matter in clay may be burnt out or reduced to carbon during firing and other substances in the clay may be either oxidized or reduced during the firing. Comparisons are therefore made between samples of pottery and source clay fired under the same conditions (usually under strongly oxidizing conditions to eliminate organic matter). If the artefact is of baked or unbaked clay, contamination such as salt infestation may alter its chemical composition from that of the original clay and it is usually necessary to remove such contamination before comparisons can be made. Firing is often resorted to, even in the comparison of unbaked clays, to eliminate the organic matter.

Metal ores usually contain certain impurities and, during the smelting processes used in antiquity, some of these impurities may not be eliminated from the metal produced. For instance, copper ores commonly contain small quantities of one or more of the following metals: arsenic, antimony, manganese, iron, nickel, etc. Similarly, iron ores are rarely pure and may contain manganese, cobalt, nickel, or other metallic impurities. From a comparison of the spectrometric analyses of metal artefacts and ores it is theoretically possible to trace the source from which the metals were mined. The interpretation of the results of such spectrometric analyses, however, poses some serious problems.

During the smelting process, all the impurities may not be reduced, so that the relative amounts of impurities in the ore and the final metal produced from it may not be the same. Further, arsenic was sometimes deliberately added to copper or bronze to harden them, and it may not be possible to ascertain whether the arsenic in ancient metal artefacts results from deliberate addition or whether it occurs as an impurity derived from the ore.

When examining alloyed metals, such as bronze, spectrometric analysis is of very limited value for tracing the sources of the ores used, since it is generally impossible to ascertain to what extent the impurities in the alloy are derived from its various metal components. Further, since many ancient artefacts were remelted from earlier objects, metals from widely different sources may well become mixed in the same artefact.

Spectrometric analyses of metals have, however, proved very useful in distinguishing objects made from native metal sources and objects made of smelted metal. The composition of the native metal is not altered, unless it is melted and deliberately hardened or alloyed. Thus, since natural occurrences of native copper are usually very pure, it is generally assumed that artefacts of very pure copper were obtained from such native occurrences. Iron artefacts made from meteoric iron generally contain much higher proportions of nickel, and often also cobalt, than smelted iron.

Dating Methods

The Dating of Obsidian Artefacts

The technique of dating obsidian has been developed only very recently and it is still in an experimental stage. The method is based on the fact that when exposed to the atmosphere, obsidian slowly absorbs water. It has been assumed that the rate of absorption of water is constant in a given environment, so that the thickness of the hydration layer formed should be a direct measure of the time elapsed since the obsidian was flaked. Measurements of the hydrated layer on obsidian artefacts from deposits of known date show that from any one locality the rate of hydration is indeed fairly constant. The method also depends on the fact that the hydration rate of obsidian appears not to be affected by small differences in the composition of obsidian.

The process of hydration differs from patination since it only involves the diffusion of water into obsidian. Hydration of this type has not been observed on any other material. Patination, on the other hand, also results in the partial corrosion of the obsidian, especially in alkali surroundings, in tropical conditions, or near hot springs. The corrosion which results from weathering generally tends to speed up the hydration process, partly by the more rapid penetration of moisture in the presence of alkali and partly by increasing the porosity of the patinated surface.

Patinated obsidian artefacts, therefore, are not suitable for dating purposes.

Mechanical wear and abrasion on an obsidian artefact may cause the distortion, or even the removal, of the thin hydration layer so that measurements cannot be made on any abraded surfaces.

The effect of the structure and composition of the obsidian is more difficult to evaluate. Measurements of hydration layers on artefacts of the common acid obsidian and of a trachytic glass, both used in ancient Egypt, show that the rates of hydration do vary with differences in the chemical composition of the material. Most obsidian used in antiquity, however, is the acid kind, and differences in the composition of acid obsidian from various sources are usually small. The effect of such small differences on the rate of hydration does not appear to be great, but this is clearly one aspect of the technique which still requires research. The work on obsidian artefacts has not yet included an investigation of the effect of gas inclusions or spherulites in the obsidian. On a really homogenous glassy obsidian, the hydration layer formed is regular over its entire surface. Examination of obsidian with small percussion cracks has shown that hydration also proceeds along these cracks at the same rate as on exposed surfaces, and this suggests that structures such as small vesicles are not likely to interfere with the regular hydration process. The effect of crystalline spherulites is difficult to assess, but measurements would clearly have to be made on the glassy part of spherulitic obsidian artefacts.

The effects of the environment on the hydration rate of obsidian have been investigated on samples from very different climatic regions. Comparisons between artefacts from different localities indicate that temperature does strongly affect the rates of hydration, whereas the soil humidity has only a very slight effect. To explain the small effect of soil humidity it has been suggested that there is always sufficient moisture available, even in comparatively dry soils, to cover the obsidian with a molecular film of water. This aspect of the investigation also requires further study.

With the difficulties of the method in mind, obsidian artefacts can be used to calculate their date of manufacture. However, in order to do so the temperature at which the artefacts have been buried and preserved must be known. Thus the climatic history of the archaeological locality concerned must be understood. When dealing with comparatively recent material, such as for much New World prehistory, the environmental history of the artefacts can often be determined. Until now most of the work done on obsidian dating has been confined to such recent material. For older material, the environmental history of an archaeological region may prove to be a serious problem. In many regions environmental studies are not sufficiently advanced to determine fluctuations of temperature. In other regions environmental studies suggest that temperatures have been very variable, so that it becomes almost impossible to correlate rates of hydration with temperature fluctuations.

The technique of obsidian dating clearly requires more research before it can be confidently applied to date most archaeological obsidian. Even when the variables affecting hydration rates are better understood, the limitations inherent in this dating technique are likely to confine its use to problems concerned with comparatively recent material which comes from restricted areas.

Potassium-Argon Dating of Rocks

The potassium-argon method of dating rocks depends on the radioactive decay of naturally occurring potassium (K^{40}) in rock minerals into the gas argon (A^{40}). The rate of radioactive decay is known to be constant and to remain unaffected by any external influence. When a rock solidifies and its various minerals crystallize out, any contained potassium-40 slowly decays into argon (and also into calcium-40), and the gas is trapped within the crystal lattice where it accumulates. Thus by measuring the amounts of potassium and argon at any given time in a rock, and knowing the rate of decay of potassium-40 to argon, it is possible to calculate the time elapsed since the formation of the rock.

The half life of potassium-40 is $1{\cdot}30 \times 10^9$ years, which means that a given amount of potassium-40 decays to half its original amount in 1,300 million years. Naturally occurring potassium contains mostly potassium-39 and only 0·012 per cent radioactive potassium-40; further, when potassium-40 decays, 89 per cent of it decays to calcium-40 and only 11 per cent to the gas argon. The rate at which argon accumulates is, therefore, very slow, and when dealing with rocks of Pleistocene age not more than 2 million years old, the amounts of argon measured are minute. Special techniques have been devised for measuring such small quantities with a high degree of accuracy.

Theoretically, the potassium-argon method can be extended to bridge the time gap between the lower limits of the radiocarbon dating method and the upper limits of other radioactivity methods used for earlier geological periods. It is therefore a very important dating method for Pleistocene archaeology and rocks as young as 400,000 years have been dated by this technique. With such young rocks, however, some anomalous results have been obtained and these are not yet understood. The amounts of argon measured are very small and it is, therefore, extremely important that any rocks submitted for dating by potassium-argon estimations should be carefully selected to avoid any errors arising from unsuitable samples.

Since the date measured is the age at which the rock solidified, the method can be applied to Pleistocene problems when volcanic rocks are interstratified with other Pleistocene deposits. Potassic minerals of sedimentary origin are likely to be contaminated with older material in the sediments and are not generally suitable for this dating method. Implements made out of potassium-containing rocks cannot be dated by the potassium-argon method, since they were necessarily fashioned after the rock had fully solidified, often considerably later.

The rock minerals which contain potassium are biotite, muscovite, orthoclase felspar, microcline, sanidine (a potassic felspar commonly found in the more acid volcanic rocks), leucite, and some potassic minerals of sedimentary origin in saline residues. Other minerals such as pyroxenes and hornblendes also contain small amounts of potassium. Thus any rock which contains these minerals is potentially suitable for potassium dating.

Rocks which have been altered through any form of metamorphism, including hydrothermal alteration, are not suitable for potassium-argon dating, since the alteration of the minerals may involve the loss of the gas argon from the crystal lattices and changes in the content of potassium. Weathered rocks are clearly also unsuitable, since corrosion of rock minerals alters their composition. It is important, therefore, that any rock sample used for potassium dating should be fresh and this is usually ascertained through microscopic examination.

Another possible source of error which is more difficult to detect is the loss of argon from the minerals through diffusion of the gas from the crystal lattices. In unaltered biotite and sanidine, the retention of argon in large crystal grains has been shown to be good, but in very small crystals, losses occur through diffusion of the gas. In such cases the dates obtained may be too young. In other felspars, the losses through diffusion are generally too high even in large crystals for these minerals to be very reliable for dating purposes. Thus, in coarse-grained rocks it is preferable to isolate suitable crystals of biotite or sanidine for potassium dating purposes, rather than to use complete rock samples which also contain other potassic minerals. When using volcanic tuff, it may be relatively easy to isolate the minerals for dating; but with hard rocks the separation of individual mineral grains may be difficult and when relative ages only are required, comparisons of whole rock samples are adequate.

The argon which diffuses from the crystal lattices enters the rock matrix and moves along the rock pores between the crystal boundaries. Thus, in a coarse-grained rock or one which is fairly porous, the gas is rapidly lost. In very fine-textured rocks the gas may be retained within the rock for considerable periods, and experiments with very fine-textured basalts have shown that, although the potassic felspar grains in the rock contained only very small amounts of argon, most of the gas was concentrated in the fine groundmass between the felspars. Such very dense and fine-grained basalts can therefore be used as 'whole' rock samples for dating purposes, provided the rock matrix has remained fresh and completely unaltered.

Contamination of the rock samples by material trapped at the time of crystallization can also cause errors in the age estimation. The most serious forms of contamination from the point of view of potassium-argon dating are the inclusion of atmospheric argon, or of 'old' minerals. The possibility of contamination of this type is especially great when dealing with volcanic sediments such as tuff. Since atmospheric argon also contains two other isotopes of argon – argon 38 and argon 36 – in known constant proportions, it is possible to estimate the amount of contamination from atmospheric argon in a mineral. With young minerals which have a very low radiogenic argon content, the correction for atmospheric argon is proportionally much greater than for old rocks; and the errors arising from the calculations of atmospheric argon are correspondingly greater in younger samples and in minerals of low potassium content. It has been suggested, for example, that biotite crystals from tuffs less than 1 million years old generally contain a higher proportion of atmospheric argon than biotite in consolidated rocks.

The inclusion of 'old' minerals in tuffs arises either from fragments of rock torn from the volcanic neck during eruption of the ash, or from the addition of mineral grains to the tuff by normal sedimentary processes. If such 'old' mineral grains are included in the sample of tuff minerals, the age determined is likely to be unreliable, depending on the potassium and argon contents of these minerals.

The materials which have been used most successfully for potassium-argon dating are therefore of two main types: grains of individual minerals, usually either biotite or sanidine, which can be separated from the other rock constituents in tuffs and similar rocks; and whole rock samples of fine-textured unaltered rock such as basalt, obsidian and tektites (tektites are glassy nodules which may be meteorites, or are associated with meteoric phenomena).

Some of the youngest K-A dates measured are for sanidine crystals in tuff of the Eifel region in Germany. These tuffs are interstratified with river terraces of the Rhine and can be correlated with the first major glaciation in Europe. The dates, obtained from a large sanidine bomb and from samples of small sanidine crystals, are about 400,000 years; but some of the samples gave ages of 2 million years. It is interesting to note that some of the oldest dates obtained are from small crystals, whereas the large bomb yielded a date of 390,000 years. This unexplained discrepancy serves to show that a certain amount of caution is still necessary in interpreting potassium dates on young samples.

Other samples dated from minerals in tuff are biotite and felspar grains from tuff in Bed I at the famous site of Olduvai in Tanganyika. The samples date the fossil hominid *Zinjanthropus* to between 1·2 million years and 1·75 million years, considerably older than expected, and date back the beginnings of toolmaking to an even earlier period.

The early Olduvai deposits have also been dated from whole rock samples of the basalt which lies directly below Bed I. These dates should logically be older than the Bed I dates and give a latest possible date for the bed. The results obtained, however, are puzzling; for the dates yielded by basalt samples range from 1·3 million years to 2·25 million years. The reasons for the discrepancy between the tuff and basalt dates are not known, although it has been suggested that the tuff dates may be too old through inherited atmospheric argon or 'old' minerals, or that the basalt dates are too young through weathering or alteration of the fine-grained rock. Although two specially selected samples of basalt yielded dates of 1·7 to 4 million years old, which is in accordance with the tuff dates obtained, it must be noted that the Olduvai basalts show slight traces of alteration and are therefore not very reliable for dating purposes. The Olduvai dates serve to illustrate the importance of selecting fresh uncontaminated material for a dating technique which is extremely sensitive to even very slight sample faults.

More encouraging results of potassium-argon dating have been obtained from tektites and whole rock basalt samples from Java, which serve to date the fossil hominids *Pithecanthropus erectus*. The tektites, which are found in the same deposit (Trinil) as the fossil hominid, yielded dates of 610,000 years ±15 per cent, whereas the basalt which covers this deposit has been dated to 500,000 years. Both the dates obtained from the tektites and from the basalt are in accordance with other estimates of the age of these deposits.

Techniques for Dating Pottery

There are two methods for dating baked clay: one is based on the magnetism acquired by clay during firing; and another, which is still in an early stage of development, depends on the measurement of distortions caused by radioactive impurities in the clay.

The thermo-remanent magnetism method of dating pottery depends on the fact that on cooling, baked clay becomes lightly magnetized by the earth's magnetic field, and that the direction and intensity of the earth's magnetic field has changed over time. The changes in the earth's magnetic field can be determined from measurements on samples of ancient baked clay which have been dated by other means; but since these changes have not been uniform throughout the earth's surface, reference scales of this type must be established for each region in which the method is to be applied for dating purposes. It is known that the direction of magnetic north changes slowly at the rate of 0·2° longitude per year, and the angle of dip for any latitude has also changed over time.

Thermo-remanent magnetic dating can only be applied to baked clay which has remained in its original position and orientation since firing, and the method is therefore particularly useful in dating structures such as mud or brick kilns, or sometimes clay hearths.

If the place of origin of pottery is known within a radius of a few hundred miles, and the position in which the pot was fired can be ascertained, it is possible to date the ware from measurements of intensity and angle of dip only. This has been found useful in dating some heavily glazed wares, whose origin was known, and which must have been fired in an upright position. However, the nature of this method restricts its use to limited archaeological material.

The other method of absolute dating baked clay is based on the measurements of thermoluminescence, but the development of the technical procedure is still in an early stage of development. If this technique proves practicable, thermoluminescence dating will be extremely important, since it should theoretically be applicable to all baked clay.

This method of dating is based on the presence of very small amounts of radioactive materials in all clay (and also in other rocks). The radiations emitted by these radioactive impurities cause distortions in the lattice structure of the minerals, possibly through the displacement of electrons; but the mechanism of thermoluminescence is not yet fully understood. The strain caused by lattice distortions can be released by heating the clay to temperatures of a few hundred degrees centigrade. Thus when clay is heated, as in firing pottery, any lattice distortions which exist are released. After cooling, the destructive process of the radioactive impurities commences anew and distortions slowly accumulate. The amount of strain caused depends on three factors: the amount of radioactive impurities; the susceptibility of the pottery to radioactive emissions; and the time elapsed since heating.

The amount of strain is measured by reheating the pottery so that the energy locked up in lattice distortions, or electron displacements, is released. This energy is released in the form of visible light, so that it can be measured with a suitably designed photo-multiplier. The radioactivity of the clay and its susceptibility to irradiation can be measured, and from these factors the time since firing can be calculated.

Some of the most pressing problems of the technique of thermoluminescent dating lie in finding the appropriate methods of handling and preparing the sample before and during heating. The effects of long exposure to daylight or of the addition of radioactive material from the soil will also have to be assessed before the technique can be universally applied to the dating of ancient pottery.

Appendix

THE Table[1] below is a useful guide to the identification of some of the most common minerals. It is based on the physical properties of the minerals which can be observed with a hand lens, penknife, and streak plate. It may sometimes be necessary to fracture the mineral or rock sample to observe the cleavage.

An identification obtained with the aid of this Table should always be checked by reference to the fuller descriptions of minerals given in Chapters 2, 4 and 5.

Table of Mineral Identification

The mineral has a fine cleavage in one direction; is micaceous and can be split into thin leaves by the use of the knife point. Section 1.

Has a good cleavage in two directions. Section 2.

Has a good cleavage in three directions forming cubes or rhombs. Section 3.

Has a fine fibrous structure and cleavage. Section 4.

No apparent good cleavage. Section 5.

Section 1. Cleavage in one direction

A. Micaceous. Cleavage leaves flexible, elastic, tough (i.e. without brittleness). Occurs in crystals, shreds, flakes. Black, brown, grey or white. Transparent to translucent. *Mica*, p. 51.

[1] This table is reproduced in abridged form from Pirsson and Knopf, (1958), pp. 96–8, by kind permission of Professor A. Knopf. For a more detailed table using simple chemical tests see Pirsson and Knopf (1958), pp. 98–102.

B. Micaceous. Cleavage leaves tough, flexible, non-elastic. In crystals, shreds, masses. Generally green to dark green. *Chlorite*, p. 64.

C. Micaceous as a rule. Leaves flexible but non-elastic. Greasy feel, very soft. Marks cloth. White, greenish, grey. Generally in foliated masses. Translucent. *Talc*, p. 65.

D. Leaves somewhat flexible but showing cross-cleavage cracks when bent; in one direction fibrous, in the other brittle, forming rhombs. Soft; scratched by finger-nail, but not greasy in feel. Generally colourless, white or reddish; transparent to translucent. In crystals, masses, seams. *Gypsum*, p. 115.

E. Leaves a brilliant metallic lustre, like polished steel. *Hematite* (micaceous variety, rare), p. 144.

Section 2. Cleavage in two directions

A. Two cleavages at, or very nearly at, 90°. Brittle; hard, scratched by quartz but not by a knife. Generally of a light colour, white, pink to red, or grey; translucent or opaque. In crystals, grains, masses. *Felspar*, p. 45.

B. Generally of a dark colour, greenish to black; in grains or short prisms; may be light-coloured in metamorphic rocks and there generally elongated columnar in the cleavage direction. Cleavage good but not eminent; prismatic. Cleavage angles 87° and 93°. As a rule can be scratched by felspar. *Pyroxene*, p. 52.

C. Generally of a dark colour, greenish to black. Commonly in crystals, elongated or bladed in cleavage direction. Light-coloured in many metamorphic rocks. Cleavage very good with shining surface. Cleavage angles 55° and 125°. As a rule scratched by felspar. *Amphibole*, p. 54.

Section 3. Cleavage in three directions

A. Cleavage not at right angles, forming rhombs. Easily scratched by the knife. Usually white, sometimes tinted various shades to black; transparent to translucent. In crystals, masses, veins, etc. *Calcite*, p. 106 or *Dolomite*, p. 111 (if rhombic surfaces of crystals are curved, probably dolomite).

B. Cleavages at right angles forming cubes; soluble, strong saline taste. Transparent; colourless or white, rarely tinted. In crystalline masses. *Halite*, rock salt, p. 119.

C. Cleavage apparently cubic. No perceptible taste. Easily scratched by the knife. White, bluish. In crystalline masses. *Anhydrite*, p. 116.

D. Apparent cleavages forming rhombs, some seemingly cubic. Very hard, scratches quartz easily. In hexagonal crystals, grains, or lumps of dark smoky or bluish grey; more or less translucent. *Corundum*, p. 66.

Section 4. Fibrous or columnar structure

A. In opaque brown to black masses. Streak yellow brown. *Limonite*, p. 146.

B. In opaque red-brown to black masses. Streak brownish red. *Hematite*, p. 145.

C. Shreds easily into fine, flexible fibres like cotton or silk. *a.* White or light grey. *Amphibole asbestos*, p. 55. *b.* White to yellowish brown, silky; generally in veins in or associated with serpentine. *Serpentine asbestos*, p. 64.

D. White or pale colours. Translucent. Brittle, easily scratched by knife but not by finger-nail. In masses. *Calcite*, p. 106.

E. White to pale red. Silky lustre; translucent. Brittle; soft, scratched by finger-nail. In masses and seams. *Gypsum*, p. 115.

Section 5. Without good or apparent cleavage

A. Opaque brass yellow crystals with metallic lustre. Not scratched by the knife. *Pyrite*, p. 114.

B. Opaque, earthy, brown to black masses. Streak yellow brown. Scratched by the knife. *Limonite*, p. 146.

C. Opaque, reddish brown to brown-black masses, or crystals

and grains, iron black with metallic lustre. Streak brownish red. Scratched by the knife. *Hematite*, p. 145.

D. Opaque, iron black masses, grains or octahedrons with metallic lustre. Streak black, Magnetic. Not scratched by the knife. *Magnetite*, p. 145.

E. In garnet shaped crystals or spherical. Usually dark red to black and translucent. Brittle. Not scratched by the knife, or felspar. *Garnet*, p. 59.

F. In garnet shaped crystals. Colourless or white to grey-white, translucent. Scratched by felspar but not by the knife. *Leucite*, p. 50.

G. In transparent to translucent crystals of grains of a light yellowish green or bottle green colour. Not scratched by felspar. *Olivine*, p. 56.

H. In prismatic crystals, generally slender, shiny and black with triangular cross-section. Not scratched by quartz. *Tourmaline*, p. 56.

I. In grains, masses, or hexagonal pyramidal crystals. Conchoidal fracture. Greasy to glassy lustre. Colourless, white, smoky, dark; transparent to translucent. Not scratched by felspar. *Quartz*, p. 43.

J. In grains or masses, rarely in crystals having rectangular or hexagonal sections. Conchoidal fracture. Greasy, oily lustre. White, grey, or reddish translucent. Scratched by felspar. *Nepheline*, p. 51.

K. In masses. Dark or yellowish green. Easily scratched or cut by the knife. *Serpentine*, p. 64.

L. In masses, generally somewhat foliated. Greasy feel; very soft, marks cloth. White, greenish, grey. *Talc*, p. 65.

M. In hexagonal crystals, grains or lumps. Dark smoky or bluish grey; translucent. Very hard, not scratched by quartz, garnet, or tourmaline. *Corundum*, p. 66.

N. In masses, compact chalky. Friable, very soft, easily cut by finger-nail. Rubbed between the fingers, has a soft soapy feel. *Kaolinite*, p. 63.

Works referred to in the Text and Selected Further Reading

Chapters 1 – 4

HARKER, A., *Petrology for Students* (8th edition) (Cambridge 1956).

HOLDEN, A. and SINGER, P., *Crystals and Crystal Growing* (London 1961).

KIRKALDY, J. P., *Minerals and Rocks in Colour* (London 1963).

PIRSSON, L. V. (revised by A. KNOPF), *Rocks and Rock Minerals* (3rd edition) (New York 1958).

READ, H. H., *Rutley's Elements of Mineralogy* (24th edition) (London 1947).

READ, H. H. and WATSON, J., *Introduction to Geology. Vol. I. Principles* (London 1962).

Chapter 5

AITCHISON, L., *A History of Metals* (London 1960).

COGHLAN, H. H., *Notes on the Prehistoric Metallurgy of Copper and Bronze in the Old World* (Oxford 1951).

COGHLAN, H. H., *Notes on Prehistoric and Early Iron in the Old World* (Oxford 1956).

FORBES, R. J., *Metallurgy in Antiquity* (London 1950).

IVES, D. J. G., *Principles of the Extraction of Metals*, Royal Institute of Chemistry Monographs for Teachers, III (Cambridge 1962).

Chapters 6 *and* 7

ARDAILLON, E., *Les Mines du Laurion dans l'Antiquité* (Paris 1897).

BLAKE, M. E., *Ancient Roman Construction in Italy from the Prehistoric Period to Augustus*, Carnegie Institution of Washington, Publication **570** (Washington 1947).

CLARKE, S. and ENGLEBACH, R., *Ancient Egyptian Masonry* (London 1930).

EVENS, E. D., GRINSELL, L. V., PIGGOTT, S., and WALLIS, F. S., Fourth Report of the Sub-Committee of the South-Western Group of Museums and Art Galleries on the Petrological Identification of Stone Axes, *Proc. prehist. Soc.*, **28** (1962) pp. 209–266.

FORBES, R. J., *Studies in Ancient Technology*. Vol. III (Paints and Pigments) (Leiden 1955); Vol. V (Glass) (Leiden 1957); Vol. VII (Mining and Quarrying) (Leiden 1963).

HOULDER, C. H., The Excavation of a Neolithic Stone Implement Factory on Mynydd Rhiw in Caernarvonshire, *Proc. prehist. Soc.*, **27** (1961) pp. 108–143.

KING, C. W., *The Natural History of Gems or Decorative Stones* (London 1867).

LUCAS, A., *Ancient Egyptian Materials and Industries* (3rd edition) (London 1948); (4th edition, revised Harris) (London 1962).

PITTIONI, R., Prehistoric Copper Mining in Austria; problems and facts. *Institute of Archaeology, 7th Annual Report* (London 1951).

SMITH, G. F. H., *Gemstones* (13th edition, revised by F. Coles Phillips) (London 1962).

VITRUVIUS, *The Ten Books on Architecture* (Translated by H. M. Morgan) (New York 1960).

ZUBER, A., Techniques du travail des pierres dures dans l'Ancienne Egypte, *Techniques et Civilisations*, **5** (5 and 6) (1956), pp. 161–180, 195–215.

Chapter 8

AITKEN, M. J., *Physics and Archaeology* (New York 1961).

BROTHWELL, D. R. and HIGGS, E. S. (Editors), *Science and Archaeology* (London 1963).

HODGES, H., *Artifacts* (London 1963).

Index

Abbeville, 213
Abrasive, 161, 164–5
Adze, 157, 161–3, 168
Agate, *123*, 181, 195
Agglomerate, 87
Alabaster, 109, *116*, 173, 191, 219
Albite, *45–6*, 49
Alderley Edge, 197, 198
Aluminium, 23, 151, Table 1
Amazonstone, *50*, 78, 181, 219
Amber, *127*,
Amethyst, *45*, 68, 180, 195
Amphiboles, *54–6*, 73, 91, 93
Anglesite, *139–41*, 147
Andesite, *85*, Table 6
Anhydrite, 104–5, *116–17*, 191
Anorthite, *45–6*, 49
Antimonite, *153–4* (*see also* stibnite)
Antimony, 153–4, 165
Apatite, 40, 106, *117–18*, 139
Aphanite, 72, 84
Aquamarine, *60*
Aragonite, 106, *110–11*
Armant, 165
Arrow, 171
Arsenic, 153–4, 165, 225
Asbestos, 35, *54–5*, 65
Aswan, 78, 170, 202–4, Plate 22
Atom, 6, 19
  structure of, 14–17, Figure 2
Augite, 30, *53*, 87, Figure 12
Axe, 157, 161–3, 167–8, 201–2, Plate 14
Azurite, *136*, 184, 216

Barytes, 43, 68, 91, Figures 11, 17
Basalt, 11, 50, 54, 75, *86–7*, 160, 162, 172, 189, 230–3 (*see also* vesicular basalt)
Batholith, 9–10, 42, 58, 79
Bead, 165, 179–82
Beni Hasan, 203
Beryl, 43, *60*, 164, 180, 195
Biotite, *51–2*, 73, 229–30
Bitumen, 126
Blende, 140, *141–2*
Bloodstone, 123
Bornite, 134, *136–7*
Boulder, 99
Brass, 141
Breccia, *100*, 173, Plate 10
Brick, 189–91, 233
Bronze, 130, 165–8, 181–2, 188, 211, 225–6
  disease, 217
Building stone, 186–9, 209–10

Calamine, *141–2*, 184
Calcite, 31–2, 38, 40, 68, 100–1, *106–11*, 173, 180, Figures 24, 25, Plate 12
Calcium, 23, 25–6, 46, Table 1
  carbonate, 18, 105ff, 192, Table 2
  chloride, 17
  phosphate, 106, 117
  salts, 105ff, Plate 25
  sulphate, 106, 115, Table 2
Calcrete, 105
Carnelian, *123*, 160, 181, 195
Carnon, 196
Cassiterite, *138–9*, 148, 195–6
Celt, 157, 162
Cerussite, *139–41*, 147
Chalcedony, *122–3*, 159, 193

Chalcocite, 133, *137*
Chalcopyrite, 133, 134, *136*, 147
Chalk, *113*, 193, 197
Chalybite, *143–4*
Chatal Huyuk, 181, 205
Chelles, 213
Chert, 32, *123–4*, 159–60, 193, 195, 213–15
China clay, 63
Chlorite, 12, 43, 61, *63–4*, 94
Choukoutien, 160
Chrysocolla, *138*, 184, 198
Chrysoprase, 123
Cinnabar, *142–3*, 183
Citrine, *45*, 195
Clay, *61–4*, 91, 99, 101, 168–9, 174, 189–91, 218, 220, 223–5, 234, Plate 26
Cleavage, 14, 18–19, 23, 25, *32–5*
  of slate, 103
Coal, *125*, 181
Collophane, 117, *119*
Conglomerate, *99*, Plate 5
Copal, *127*
Copper, *133–8*, 147, 165–8, 179, 181, 188, 193–5, 197–200, 216–217, 220, 225
  glance, 137
  pyrites, 29, *38*, 68, 136, 198, 211 (*see also* chalcopyrite)
Corrosion, 208ff, 226–7
Cortex, 124
Corundum, 40, 43, *66–7*, 80, 98, 164
Covelline, *see* covellite
Covellite, 133–4, *137–8*
Cuprite, *135*, 147, 194
Crystal, 6, 26ff

Dacite, *85*, Plate 6
Dagger, 171–2, Plate 15
Diabase, *83*, Table 6
Diamond, *6–7*, 40, 180
Diatomite, *122*, 185
Diorite, 50, 74, *81*, 162, 188, Table 6, Plates 5, 14a
Dolerite, *83*, 162, 170, 202, 204, Table 6
Dolomite, *111*, *113*
Drill, 164–5
Dyke, 10, 42, 70, 221

Electrum, 132, 148
Emerald, *60*
Emery, *67*, 81, 164, 195–6

Faience, 176–9, 182, Plate 19
Felsite, 85
Felspar, 25, 42, *45–50*, 72–3, 76, 98, Table 4, Figure 22, Plates 1, 2, 4
  orthoclase, 30, 40, *45–50*, 229–33, Figure 21, Plate 4
  plagioclase, 30–1, *45–50*, Table 4
Felspathoids, *50–1*
Ferricrete, 105
Ferromagnesian minerals, 26, 38, 82–3
Flint, 32, *123–4*, 158–65, 171, 178, 193, 195, 197, 211, 213–15, 219
Fluorite, 43, *67–8*, 91, 139 (*see also* fluorspar)
Fluorspar, 32, 33, 40, 67, 180, Figure 16
Fossil wood, 122, 160
Frit, 177, 184

Gabbro, 54, *82–3*, Tables 5, 6
Galena, 33, 68, 132, *139–40*, 147, 150, 185, 199–201, Figure 15
Garnet, 43, *59*, 91, 94, 98, 180, 195–6, Figure 9, Plate 1c
Gerzeh, 148
Glass, 32, 38, *72*, 85–7, *176–9*, 181, 211, 216, 220, Plates 7, 17, 18
Glauconite, 101
Glaze, *177–9*, 216, 233
Gneiss, 50, 52, 92, *93–4*, Plate 9
Gold, 98, *131–2*, 148, 174, 181, 193, 196, 199, 216
Granite, 10, 43, 50, 52, 63, *76–8*, 80, 139, 163, 187–8, 202–4, Tables 5, 6, Plates 2, 4, 20

Granodiorite, *78–9*, 80, Tables 5, 6, Plate 1
Graphite, 6–7, 94, *126*, 176, 185
Gravel, 99
Graywacke, *101*, 163
Greenstone, 83, 93, 95–6, 162
Grimes Graves, 197
Grossularite, 59
Grotta Oscura, 204
Guano, *117–18*
Gypsum, 35, 40, 105, *115–17*, 185, 191–2, 209, Figures 12, 18, 26

Hacilar, 206
Halite, *119–20* (*see also* rock salt)
Halloysite, 62
Hammer stone, 169–70
Hardness, 6, 40
Hematite, 36, 45, 143, *145–6*, 183, Figure 19
Hierakonpolis, 164, 190
Hornblende, 23, 42, *54*, 83–4, 95, 162, 230
Hornblendite, *83–4*, Table 5
Hyacinth, 60

Igneous rocks, 9ff, 11, 13, 71ff, 161, 215–16, 221, Plate 1
Ilmenite, *83*
Ion, 17
  size of, 19
Iron, 17, 26, 38, 148–52, 165–8, 188, 199, 217, 225
  ores, 143–7
  oxide, 49, 100, 101, 211–12
  pyrites, 26, *144*, Figure 9 (*see also* pyrite)
Ironstone, 145

Jade, *see* Jadeite and Nephrite
Jadeite, *53–4*, 163, 181
Jasper, *123–4*, 159–60
Jericho, 172, 190, 205
Jet, *125*
Joint, 10, 12, 78, 87, 100, 112, 187, 201

Kaolinite, 43, 62, *63–4*, 93, 185
Kidney ore, 146, 183, Figure 19
Knife, 158–60

Labradorite, *50*, 82, 87
Lapis lazuli, *51*, 181, 184, 220 (*see also* lazurite)
Laurium, 194, 199–201, Figure 30
Lava, 10, 70, 87
Lazurite, 51 (*see also* lapis lazuli)
Lead, *139–41*, 147, 216
Leucite, *50*, 229
Lignite, 125
Lime, 177, 185, 191–2 (*see also* calcium carbonate)
Limestone, *111–15*, 181, 186–9, 209, 221
Limonite, 133, 143, *146–7*, 183, 217
Lode, 131, 194, Figure 27
Lodestone, 145

Macehead, 170–1, Plate 6
Magma, 9, 12–13, 42–3, 72
Magnesian limestone, 114
Magnesium, 20, 26, 111, Table 1
Magnetism, 233
Magnetite, 83, 143, *145*, 195, 217
Malachite, 37, *135–6*, 147, 177, 184, 194, 198, 216
Manganese, 38, *155–6*, 179
Marble, 92, *114–15*, 163, 189, 219, 221, Plate 21
Marl, 113
Ma'sara, 202–3
Melaconite, 135
Mercury, *142–3*, 148–52
Metal, *129–30*, 165–8, 210–11, 216–17, 225
Metamorphic rocks, 10, 12–13, 61, 90ff, 102, 215–16, Plate 1
Metasomatism, 91
Meteoric iron, 144, 148, 226
Mica, 18–19, 23, 35, 42, 51–2, 91, 94, Plate 1c
Microcline, *50*, 78, 229
Millstone, 170
Minium, *141*, 184
Mitterberg, 198–9

Montmorillonite, 62
Mortar, 190–2, 210
Mudbrick, 188
Mudstone, 102
Muscovite, *51–2*, 78, 229
Mynydd Rhiw, 201–2

Natron, *119–20*, 177–9
Naxos, 169, 196
Nea Nikomedeia, 159, 163, 205
Nepheline, *51*, 80
Nephrite, *54*, 163, 181
Nickle, 8, 152
Nitre, 121

Obsidian, 32, *86*, 158–9, 167, 206, 219, 226, 231, Plate 7
Ochre, *146–7*, 176, 183–5
Olduvai, 89, 160, 232
Olivine, 20–1, 25, 39, 42, *56*, 65, 82–3, 87, 93, Table 4, Figure 11
Onyx, 109, *123*, 181, 219
Oolite, 113
Opal, 122, 159, 193
Ore, 10, 13, 43, 66, 129ff, 194, Figure 27
Orthoclase, *see* felspar
Orpiment, *154*, 184

Patination, 207, 208ff, 226–7, Plate 24
Peat, 125
Pebble, 98, 169, 180, 193, 218, Plate 5
Pegmatite, 42, 78
Peridot, *56*, 84, 180, 195
Peridotite, *84*, Table 5
Pewter, 139, 141
Phenocryst, 71–2, 76, Plates 3, 4, 13
Phosphorite, 117–18
Phyllite, 103
Pigment, 182–5
Pitch, 126
Pitchstone, 86
Plagioclase, *see* felspar
Plaster, 190–2, 210
Porphyritic rock, 71–2, 77, 80, 85, 87
Porphyry, 72, 85, Plates 3, 4, 13
Potassium, 23, 121, 229
-argon, 228ff
Pot boiler, 214
Potlid fracture, 215
Pottery, 210–11, 223–5, 233–4, Plates, 5, 6 (*see also* clay)
Prase, 123
Psilomelane, *155*, 185
Pumice, 86–7
Pyrites, 96, 133, *143–4*, 148 (*see also* iron pyrites)
Pyroclastic rocks, 87–90
Pyrolusite, *154–5*
Pyroxene, 21, 42, *52–4*, 55, 83, 93, 230, Table 4
Pyroxenite, 84, Table 5

Quartz, 11, 32, 35, 36, 40, 42, *43–5*, 50, 91, 98, 100, 121, 160–1, 180, 209, 221, Tables 4, 5, Figures 13, 20, Plates 1, 2, 3
Quartzite, 92, *103–4*, 160, 169, 187–8, 195, 202, 213–15, 221
Querns, 170

Realgar, *154*, 184
Rhyolite, 85, Table, 6
Rock crystal, *see* quartz
Rock salt, 28, 105, 119 (*see also* halite)
Ruby, *67*, 180

Saltpetre, *121*, 178, 212
Sand, 12, *99*, 161, 164, 192
Sandstone, *101*, 170, 186–7, 221, Plate 1b
calcareous, 112, 209
Sanidine, 229–30
Sapphire, 67
Saqqara, 168, 188
Sard, 123
Saw, 163–4, 168
Schist, 52, 64, 92, *94–6*, 195, Plate 1c
Sediments, 11–13, 98ff, 221–3, Plate 1
Selenite, 116

Serpentine, 43, 56, 61, *64–5*, 82, *96*, 163, 173, 181, 189
Shale, 12, *101–2*, 160
Sickle, 159, 168–9, 214, Plate 14
Siderite, *143–4*
Silcrete, 105, 160
Silica, 25, 42–3, 100, 101, 121–4, 181, 211, 213–15
Silicate, 7, 13–14, 20ff, 45ff, Figures 6, 7, 8
Silicon, 20, Tables 1, 3
Sill, 10, 42
Silsila, 187, 203
Silt, 99
Silver, *132–3*, 140, 148, 174, 181, 194, 199–201, 216
Slate, 12, 64, *92*, 102–3, Plate 11
Smelting, 147–52
Smithsonite, *142*
Soapstone, 66, *95*
Sodium, 17, 23, 25, 46
  chloride, 25–7, Table 2
  salts, 119ff
Specific gravity, 6, 38ff
Spiennes, 197
Stalagmite, 109
Starch fracture, 215
Steatite, 23, 66, *95*, 173, 180–1, 189
Steel, 165–7, 171, 188
Stibnite, *153–4*, 185 (*see also* antimonite)
Succinite, 127
Sword, 171–2, Plate 16
Syenite, 50, *79*, Tables 5, 6

Talc, 23, 40, 43, 61, *65–6*, 91, 95
Tektite, 231–3
Tenorite, *135*
Thermoluminescence, 234
Tile, 189–90
Tin, *138–9*, 147, 166, 196, 217
Tinstone, 98, *138–9* (*see also* cassiterite)
Topaz, 40, 43, *58–9*, 78
Tourmaline, 37, 43, *56–8*, 78, 139, 222, Figure 23
Trachyte, *85*, Table 6
Travertine, 109, 188
Trona, *119–20*
Tufa, 109, 204
Tuff, *88–9*, 160, 162, 230–2
Turquoise, 43, *69*, 181, 220
Twinning, 48–9, 82, Figure 22, Plate 4

Ultrabasic rocks, *73*, 83ff, Tables 5, 6
Ur, 148

Vesicular basalt, *87*, 170, 188
Vessels, 172–9
  clay, 174–6
  faience, 176–9
  glass, 176–9
  metal, 174
  stone, 165, 172–3, Plates 10, 13
Volcanic rock, 10, 70, 229, 233

Wad, 155–6, 185
Weapons, 170–2

Zinc, *141–2*, 151–2
Zircon, 43, *59–60*, 98, 164, 195–6